INFORMATION THEORY OF
CHOICE-REACTION TIMES

INFORMATION THEORY OF CHOICE-REACTION TIMES

D. R. J. LAMING

Psychological Laboratory, University of Cambridge, England

ACADEMIC PRESS

London and New York

1968

ACADEMIC PRESS INC. (LONDON) LTD.

Berkeley Square House

Berkeley Square

London W.1.

U.S. Edition published by

ACADEMIC PRESS INC.

111 Fifth Avenue

New York, New York 10003

Library of Congress Catalog Card Number: 68–19259

PRINTED IN GREAT BRITAIN BY

W. Heffer & Sons Ltd, Cambridge, England

PREFACE

The research in this monograph had its beginnings in a series of experiments conducted in the autumn of 1959 and the spring of 1960 with the object of distinguishing between discriminability of the signals and signal entropy as determinants of choice-reaction time. They were inspired by a paper by Crossman (1955), in which it appeared that these two factors interact rather than summate in their joint effect upon reaction time. The experiments compared pairs of stimuli of different difficulties of discrimination and in their design assumed that reaction time was related to signal entropy by a relation of the form

$$\text{R.T.} = a - b \sum_i p_i \log p_i,$$

where a and b are positive constants, p_i is the probability that signal i will be presented and the summation runs over all the alternative signals. As the series of experiments progressed, increasing doubt was cast on this assumption. The final two experiments were published (Laming, 1962), not because they demonstrated anything new about the role of signal discriminability, but because they provided evidence contrary to the then generally accepted theory of choice-reaction times.

About that time I became acquainted with the work of Tanner and Swets (1954) and Stone (1960) and explored the possibilities of accounting for my results in terms of both fixed-sample and sequential statistical models. A sequential model seemed the more promising alternative and in the summer of 1960 I elaborated the proposal of Stone (1960, pp. 252–4). The next three years were spent in an empirical examination of this model. In the light of seven experiments the model suffered certain modifications, but the essential idea remained unchanged, and the research was written up in my Ph.D. thesis in the autumn of 1963. This monograph is a revised and condensed version of that thesis, incorporating certain theoretical afterthoughts. The theory has been further developed and recast in information-theoretic terms; nonetheless an examination of Appendix A will reveal the extent of my indebtedness to both Stone (1960) and Wald (1947).

To many psychologists choice-reaction times must seem a small and insignificant topic, and therefore some justification is needed, why so large a monograph should be devoted entirely to this subject. The choice-reaction experiment, more than any other psychological experiment, affords an opportunity for establishing an exact quantitative theory. There are two dependent variables, the response and the reaction time, and these must both be accounted for by a single intervening process. Perhaps this makes the problem difficult—certainly it restricts the range of admissible models—but in one sense it makes the problem easier to solve, because quite a small experiment is usually sufficient to discriminate between alternative hypotheses. Putting this another way, the yield of information from a choice-reaction experiment is high relative to the effort involved. By way of contrast there are some studies of choice behaviour for which there exist two or more quite disparate models giving nearly identical predictions, and a very large experiment would be required to discriminate between the alternative hypotheses already proposed.

The difficulty of arriving at an understanding of choice behaviour would be eased if the experiment were redesigned so that a response time could be measured and, more important, if psychologists knew what to do with response times when they had recorded them. The yield of information from each experiment would then be much increased. It can be seen, therefore, that the research reported in this monograph has wider implications than the solution of a narrowly defined problem posed by a certain generic type of experiment. For the solution of this problem will lead to experimental and analytical techniques of greater efficiency than those at present in use and valid over a much wider area of psychological research than that considered here.

This monograph contains a detailed exposition of a mathematical theory and a definitive account of seven experiments, hitherto unpublished. It has been written primarily for those engaged in research on choice-reaction times and related topics. But both the theoretical ideas and the empirical results will arouse a wider interest than this, contributing to our collective understanding of choice-behaviour in general. Some parts of the book will also be useful in teaching at an advanced level.

In the course of the research and in the preparation of this monograph I have received help from many different people. Dr. D. E. Broadbent and Mr. D. G. Champernowne jointly supervised my work as a research student, and in the first place I wish to thank them for the invaluable advice, criticism and encouragement which they both gave me.

Dr. A. R. Jonckheere acted somewhat as an advisory editor in the preparation of the manuscript. I am deeply grateful to him for the long hours he has spent reading, criticizing and discussing every part of the text.

The research reported here was begun in Cambridge at the Psychological Laboratory and completed at University College London. In Cambridge I held a research Scholarship at Trinity College and a research studentship awarded by the then Department of Scientific and Industrial Research (now the Science Research Council). The D.S.I.R. also made a grant towards the cost of apparatus. Mr. R. L. Gregory and Dr. A. Carpenter made certain suggestions regarding the apparatus and these are acknowledged specifically in the text. The analysis of the data was carried out on the EDSAC II and I am grateful to the Director and staff of the Mathematical Laboratory, Cambridge, for the facilities they provided and their frequent advice and assistance. I also wish to thank about 200 others, mostly undergraduates of Trinity College, who acted as subjects for the experiments.

The preparation of this monograph was begun at University College London and completed after my return to Cambridge. In addition to Dr. Jonckheere's help, certain parts of the manuscript were read by Prof. R. J. Audley, Prof. G. H. Bower, Dr. T. Shallice, Mr. I. B. Stilitz, Mr. H. P. F. Swinnerton-Dyer and Dr. A. T. Welford; I am grateful to them for their comments. I also wish to thank Miss M. Simpson, who prepared the figures, and Miss K. Watts, who helped in the arduous task of seeing the monograph through the press. The Science Research Council have continued to support this work both while I was at University College London and here in Cambridge, and the analysis of the data was in part assisted by a grant from Trinity College, Cambridge. Finally I would like to thank Professors O. L. Zangwill and G. C. Drew for the encouragement and the continued opportunity to pursue my interests.

The Psychological Laboratory,   D. R. J. LAMING.
University of Cambridge
September, 1967

CONTENTS

APPENDIX A.   THE TWO-CHOICE THEORY.

APPENDIX B.   THE MULTI-CHOICE THEORY.

APPENDIX C.   TWO METHODS OF ANALYSIS.

CHAPTER 1

THE EXPLANATION OF CHOICE-REACTION TIMES
IN TERMS OF COMMUNICATION THEORY

1.1. Introduction.

A choice-reaction experiment consists of a series of trials, on each of which the subject is presented with a signal, chosen from a finite set of signals, and makes a response as soon as possible after the signal appears. There is a different response for each alternative signal and the subject must make that response which corresponds to the signal presented. Although the subject knows roughly when the signal will come, he does not know which signal it will be and is therefore uncertain about which response he will have to make. In a typical experiment the signals might be represented by a set of pea-bulbs and the responses by a set of morse keys. When one of the pea-bulbs lights up the subject presses the corresponding morse key as quickly as possible. The time taken to do this includes not only the time to notice one of a certain set of changes in the environment, but also the time to decide which key should be pressed. A "choice-reaction time" therefore includes a "decision time".

The few basic qualitative facts about choice-reaction time were discovered early. Donders (1868) distinguished three types of reaction:

A: 1 signal, 1 response;

B: n signals, n responses;

C: n signals, respond to only one of them;

and found that the C-reaction took longer than the A-reaction, but was faster than the B-reaction. Donders interpreted the difference between the C- and A-reaction times as the time occupied in discriminating the signal, and the difference between the B- and C-reaction times as the time taken to choose the correct response. Merkel (1885) found that reaction time increased as the number of alternative signals was increased from one to ten; Blank (1934) noted that this relation was approximately logarithmic, but no theoretical interpretation was put on this result until 1950 (Hick, 1950; see below). Henmon (1906) showed that reaction time also increased with the difficulty of the discrimination, but again there was no theoretical treatment of this result until Crossman (1955).

There were relatively few choice-reaction experiments prior to 1950. For the most part they had no theoretical orientation and the data were not published in sufficient detail to be of use in discriminating between present day theories. These experiments are therefore not important to the argument here and will not be described further; there is a comprehensive review of them by Woodworth (1938, pp. 298–339).

Before presenting any new theory of choice-reaction times, it is necessary to examine those theories that have been proposed hitherto. The work of Hick (1952), Hyman

1

(1953) and Crossman (1953) led to a theory in which human performance is compared to that of an ideal communications system. Mean reaction time is related linearly to the average entropy of the signals because the system contains a communication channel of limited capacity through which all signals must pass. This will be referred to as the Communication Theory of choice reaction times.[1] This theory, and the experiments that gave rise to it, will be described in this chapter and will be followed by theoretical and empirical criticisms. But this will not by any means be a review of work on choice-reaction times done in the context of Communication Theory. Reference will be made only to those experiments and theoretical ideas that are essential to the argument. This chapter will argue that the attempt to explain choice-reaction times in terms of Communication Theory should now be abandoned; it will not attempt to survey all the experiments that have been done or all of the theoretical ideas that have been put forward.

There are two ways in which the Communication Theory can be criticized. First, at a theoretical level, the analogy with a communications system has not been whole-hearted; rather, certain convenient aspects only of the analogy have been selected. If the analogy is followed consistently, its use in the context of a choice-reaction experiment appears *a priori* unreasonable. Moreover it leads to certain predictions about human performance that are so far from the truth that Communication Theory cannot be reconciled with the experimental results by any set of amendments. The analogy with an ideal communications system therefore fails to justify a theory of choice-reaction times, although those predictions that have commonly been associated with it might find empirical validation.

A second level of criticism examines empirically those predictions that have usually been accepted on the basis of Communication Theory; recently they have been faced with contrary evidence. There have been conflicting determinations of the limiting channel capacity, effects due to discriminability and stimulus-response compatibility without any obvious way of incorporating these factors into the theory, and more recently doubt has been cast on the fundamental relation between reaction time and signal entropy. The choice-reaction problem appears more complicated than the Communication Theory will allow and there is need for a new theory.

Several writers have already responded to this need. Apart from the interest in choice-point behaviour in general, several models have been published which have been developed for and applied specifically to choice-reaction times. These will be examined critically in Chapter 2. Some of these models have already been developed to a point at which they can be tested against the experiments to be described later in this monograph; certain implications of the other models will be developed here so that they too can be tested. The empirical tests of these models will be reported in Chapter 7 after the experiments have been described.

1.2. The Communication Model.

That which has hitherto been called "Information Theory" in the psychological literature will here be referred to as "Communication Theory", and this change in terminology requires some explanation. In Chapter 3 a new theory will be presented, which is an *information theory*. It uses a certain statistical measure of *information*, which is not the same as that used in Communication Theory. In order to prevent confusion between these two theories the term "Information Theory" will always

---

[1] See below for the reasons for this terminology.

refer to the theory of Chapter 3 and "information" is reserved for a concept to be introduced on p. 31, except possibly where these terms appear within quotation marks. Since the essence of Communication Theory is an analogy between the human subject and an ideal communications system, the new label is appropriate. The measure which is used in Communication Theory, $- \sum_i p_i \log p_i$ (where p_i stands for the probability that signal i is presented), and has hitherto been called "information", will here be called "entropy" because of its formal similarity to the measure of entropy in thermodynamics (cf. Weaver, 1949, p. 103).

In the Communication Theory of choice-reaction times human performance is compared to that of an ideal communications system. Figure 1.1 shows a schematic

FIGURE 1.1

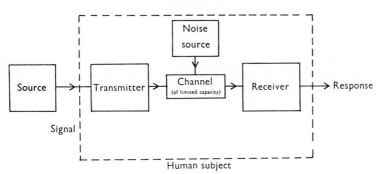

Schematic diagram of an ideal communications system (after Weaver, 1949, p. 98).

representation of an ideal communications system. The *source* selects a *message* from a set of alternative messages. The *message* is transformed by the *transmitter* into the *signal* which is actually sent through the *channel*. The *receiver* performs the inverse transformation on the *signal* when it has been received to recover the original *message*. The output of the *noise source* is added to the *signal* in the *channel*, thereby distorting the *signal*, so that the message received is sometimes other than the message sent.

The series of signals shown to the subject in a choice-reaction experiment is identified with the output of the source. (Unfortunately the term "signal" is habitually used in one sense in a choice-reaction experiment and in a different, though related, sense in Communication Theory.) The series of responses made by the subject is identified with the message received at the other end of the system. The speed of transmission of a message is limited by the capacity of the channel, so that in practice mean reaction time is proportional to the average entropy of a signal; that is,

$$\text{R.T.} = - b \sum_i p_i \log p_i, \qquad (1.1)$$

where p_i is the probability of signal i being presented, the summation runs over all the alternative signals and b is the reciprocal of the channel capacity, assumed constant. The capacity of the channel is defined as the number of units of entropy ("bits") it can transmit in one second; so the time taken to transmit a message of a given entropy is inversely related to the capacity of the channel.

When there are n alternative signals, all of them equally probable, $p_i = 1/n$ in equation (1.1) and the right hand side becomes $b \log n$. A result similar to this was demonstrated by Hick (1952). Hick used ten pea lamps arranged in a "somewhat irregular circle" and ten corresponding Morse keys. He measured the mean reaction times to several series of equiprobable signals with numbers of alternatives from two to ten. He fitted both his own and Merkel's (1885) data to the equation

$$t(n) = b \log(n+1), \tag{1.2}$$

where $t(n)$ is the mean reaction time to one of n equiprobable signals. Equation (1.2) provided a slightly better fit than the equation

$$t(n) = a+b \log n,$$

where a is a constant, and Hick interpreted the factor $(n+1)$ as follows: Beside the uncertainty of which response will be required, there is also uncertainty about when it will be required, and this temporal uncertainty is equivalent in its effect upon mean reaction time to one extra signal. Thus $log \ (n+1)$ becomes the corrected entropy of an equiprobable n-choice task. The conclusion was "that the amount of information extracted is proportional to the time taken to extract it, on the average".

Hick tested this conclusion in a second experiment in which two subjects were trained to perform a 10-choice task making up to 70 per cent errors. Using Shannon's (1949, p. 38) correction for equivocation in a noisy channel he showed that a similar channel capacity was effective in a well practised subject at different error rates.

Hick's paper has had a profound influence on subsequent research into choice-reaction times. He replaced a rank-order type of lawfulness with a quantitative equation (1.2). The very accuracy of this equation in a graphical sense (see Hick's Figure 1) has commended Shannon's measure of entropy to psychologists' attention. He also showed that choice-reaction time was determined not so much by the stimulus presented as by those stimuli which were not presented, but which might have been. The study of choice-reaction times appeared ripe for a probabilistic theory.

Hick did not himself advance the Communication Model described above as an interpretation of his result. But his work soon led to this as a popular model for choice-reaction times: "A human subject making a sequence of choice-responses is considered as a channel transmitting information. Earlier work suggests that the rate of transmission is limited, and so that response time is proportional to the 'entropy' of the source of signals". (Crossman, 1953, p. 41). Crossman showed that this hypothesis was also valid when the signals were not equally probable. His subjects sorted playing cards and by changing the number of categories into which they were sorted and the number in each category (e.g. black/red, suits, pictures/plain) the entropy of the task was varied. His results conformed approximately to the equation

$$t = a-b \sum_i p_i \log p_i, \tag{1.3}$$

where p_i is the probability of signal i being presented and a and b are constants.

Other more accurate evidence in support of equation (1.3) came from Hyman (1953). Hyman's subjects responded to a light by uttering a nonsense syllable; the light appeared in one of several positions and a different nonsense syllable corresponded to each position. In common with Bricker (1955) Hyman considered that the uncertainty of when a signal would appear was a factor quite separate from that of choice, and should be represented by a constant, the constant a, in equation (1.3). Hyman tested this equation in three different ways: He varied (i) the number of equiprobable alternative signals, (ii) the relative frequencies of occurrence of the signals while the number of alternatives remained the same, and (iii) the first order conditional probabilities of occurrence of the signals while the unconditional probabilities remained equal. He obtained similar regression lines of mean reaction time on entropy under each condition for each of four subjects.

Thus far equations (1.2) and (1.3) appear to provide accurate formulae for mean reaction times, and the form of these equations makes the interpretation in terms of Communication Theory immediately attractive. But there is much to be said in criticism, and Rapoport (1959) and Laming (1966) have looked for alternative interpretations of these equations. The interpretation in terms of an analogy with an ideal communications system will be criticised at a theoretical level in §1.3, and empirical evidence undermining the apparent accuracy of the reaction-time equations will be presented in §1.4.

1.3. Theoretical critiques of the Communication Model.

The question which exposes the theoretical weakness of the Communication Model is: How are the elements of the model shown in Figure 1.1 identified in the experimental situation? For the most part this question has been carefully evaded. Hyman (1953, p. 188) is the only writer to suggest an explicit identification:

"The choice-reaction experiment can be looked upon as a model of a communication system. The display represents a transmitter of information. Each alternative stimulus or *signal* represents a *message*; more information can be transmitted the greater the number of messages from which one can be chosen. The *channel* over which the signal is transmitted can be considered as the air space between the light and the subject, and might also include part of the subject's visual afferent system. The subject also acts as a *receiver* or decoder in that at some point he decodes the signal into its message and reacts with the appropriate response."

In this identification the *signal* transmitted through the communication channel is identified with the stimulus presented to the subject and is therefore not only observable but at the experimenter's disposal. For this reason the performance of the subject and the apparatus, considered jointly as a communication system, should be wholly non-ideal.

The derivations of equations (1.1–3) depend on Shannon's Theorem 11 (1949, p. 39):

Let a discrete channel have capacity C and a discrete source the entropy per second H. If $H \leqslant C$ there exists a coding system such that the output of the source can be transmitted over the channel with an arbitrary small frequency of errors (or an arbitrarily small equivocation). If $H > C$ it is possible to encode the source so that the equivocation is less than $H-C+\epsilon$ where ϵ is arbitrarily small. There is no method of encoding which gives an equivocation less than $H-C$.

This is a limiting theorem and it gives equation (1.1) as a lower limit to the mean reaction time, by considering in how short a message (in terms of number of channel symbols) each alternative signal can be specified. Its proof considers messages of infinite length and all possible ways of encoding these into sequences of channel symbols. There must be at least one way which achieves the theoretical maximum efficiency, and this way of encoding transforms the statistical structure of the message so that it matches the characteristics of the channel. In general such an encoding can only be achieved at the cost of an infinite coding delay; the entire message must be emitted by the source and stored in the transmitter before any part of it is sent through the channel. But it is probably true in practice that tolerably efficient transmission can be achieved with but small coding delays.

It is also essential to Shannon's theorem that the system of coding chosen shall be matched to the statistical structure of the message source. Maximum transmission rate, which is assumed in equation (1.1), is approached as the statistical structure of the messages in their encoded form approaches a certain optimum, which is determined by the channel characteristics. If the statistical structure of the message source is changed—as, for example, when the probability structure of the sequence of signals in a choice-reaction experiment is changed—then the encoding system must also be changed to maintain the efficiency of transmission. The encoding system is embodied in the performance of the transmitter. But in Hyman's analogy the *transmitter* is represented by the display, a part of the physical apparatus, and its performance is therefore fixed. So the encoding system is invariant and is not capable of adjustment to match the statistical structure of the signal sequence. Under these conditions there can be no maximisation of the transmission rate.

This criticism can be expressed in another way: In Hyman's analogy the experimenter selecting the signals by the operation of a switch corresponds to the *source*. Each message thus emitted is transformed by the *transmitter* (the display) into a light signal, which is then passed through the *channel*. This transformation is invariant in that a given position of the experimenter's switch always causes the same light to be shown to the subject, irrespective of what other positions of the switch might have been selected. Now the time taken to transmit a given sequence of symbols through the channel (i.e. a message specified in its encoded form) depends only on the channel characteristics. So in Hyman's experiment, if his identification of the elements of the ideal communications systems in Figure 1.1 is followed, each position of the experimenter's switch is always transformed into the same light signal, which must always take the same (average) time in transmission, irrespective of whatever other signals might have been presented in its place. The reaction time to a given signal should therefore be independent of the sequence of signals in which it appears: this was not Hyman's finding.

1.3.1. The irrational use of Shannon's measure in choice-reaction experiments.

A communications system can only take advantage of the statistical structure of the messages it carries in so far as the encoding system can be adjusted to match. Shannon's Theorem 11, from which equation (1.1) is derived, supposes that the encoding system is infinitely flexible. Hyman's interpretation of his experimental result was invalid because he identified the symbols passed through the communication channel in such a way as to render the encoding system invariant. It is clear that any successful analogy must identify the experimental signals with the output of the *message source* and embody the *transmitter*, the *channel* and the *receiver* in the subject. This interpretation is indicated in Figure 1.1. The channel symbols and the system of encoding are then unobservable intervening variables. But this interpretation also has its difficulties.

The simple manner in which Shannon's measure of entropy has usually been applied in psychology has already been criticised by Cronbach (1955). This measure applies only to ideal channels, in which messages are infinitely long, in which an infinite coding delay is acceptable (though not always necessary), and where complete and accurate knowledge of the probability structure of the signal series is stored in the system. In a choice-reaction experiment the messages are, of necessity, very short. The very design of the experiment requires that each signal must be passed completely through the system, encoded, transmitted and decoded and the response registered, before the next signal is emitted from the source. Reaction time must therefore include not only transmission time, but also the time required to encode and decode the message and to execute the response. These last three components have been assumed constant, since, except for studies of discriminability and stimulus-response compatibility (see pp. 10–15), variation in mean reaction time has consistently been equated with variation in average message length (in terms of the minimum number of channel symbols required per signal) alone.

The effect of having only very short messages to pass may be illustrated by considering the performance of a noiseless discrete ideal communications system passing binary symbols at a uniform rate in Hick's (1952) experiment. This is a problem of straightforward binary coding and the optimal solution is represented by the tree in Hick's Figure 3 (a and b). Hick obtained this performance characteristic from each of two conceptual models, one a progressive classification process in which the identification of the signal was progressively sharpened by a series of dichotomous decisions, and the other in which copies of the signal were generated by a self-replication process and compared simultaneously with a fixed set of templates.

All of these three models, the binary Communication Model and the two suggested by Hick, yield the same set of predictions and are subject to the same criticisms, some of which have already been made by Hick (1952) and Welford (1960, §2.3.1B). These models do not yield equation (1.2) exactly unless $(n+1)$ is restricted to integral powers of 2. Although they give an approximation to equation (1.2) that probably lies within the limits of error in Hick's experiment, they also lead to some unacceptable predictions when $n = 1$ or 2. If Hick's interpretation of the factor $(n+1)$ is correct, so that a simple reaction involves a single binary choice, then it follows from all of these models that mean simple reaction time should be independent of the temporal uncertainty of the stimulus! Alternatively, if equation (1.3) and Hyman's treatment of temporal uncertainty is preferred, it follows that the mean reaction time in a two-choice experiment should be independent of the relative signal probabilities. These unpalatable predictions follow from these models because mean reaction time is permitted to take only a discrete set of values, although signal probabilities may (in theory) be varied continuously. It also follows that apart from a random component individual reaction times should be integral multiples of the simple reaction time. Hick looked for and failed to find any corresponding periodicity in his data. Welford (1960, pp. 200–204) has considered several elaborations of the models described above, which reconcile them in part to the experimental results. But Welford's search models have hardly been developed far enough to afford an empirical test and they do not overcome the fundamental criticism that mean reaction time must be discrete-valued and that individual reaction times must be integral multiples of a basic unit.

1.3.2. Continuous responding tasks.

Each signal in a choice-reaction experiment corresponds to a separate message transmitted through the system. Usually there is only a small number of alternative signals, and the number of ways in which the corresponding messages might be encoded for transmission through the channel is limited. Under these conditions it is not in general possible to approach the maximum transmission rate. But there are experiments in which the signals have been presented at a uniform rate irrespective of the subject's responses. The responses tend to lag behind the signals, so that a greater variety of coding systems is available. Each message transmitted through the channel might carry partial information about two or more successive signals. In these circumstances the maximum transmission rate may be more nearly approached.

The study of Alluisi, Muller and Fitts (1957) will serve as a typical example. The subjects watched a random sequence of Arabic numerals projected on to a screen at a uniform rate. Under some conditions they repeated the numerals aloud, under others they pressed a corresponding key. By changing the number of alternative numerals used and the rate at which they were presented, the experimenters could select different presentation rates (stimulus entropy/second) and measure the resultant trans-

FIGURE 1.2

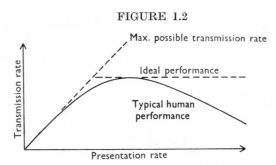

Typical relation between presentation and transmission rates (bits/second) in a paced serial task, compared with the performance of an ideal communication channel (cf. Alluisi, Muller and Fitts, 1957).

mission rate (stimulus entropy/second, response unknown—stimulus entropy/second, given the response. Shannon, 1949, p. 38). The typical relation between these two factors for a human subject is shown by the continuous curve of Figure 1.2. At low presentation rates performance is nearly faultless. At higher presentation rates errors begin to appear and the transmission rate is a little less than the presentation rate. As the presentation rate is increased still further, the transmission rate rises to a maximum and then decreases. For comparison the performance characteristic of an ideal communication system under these conditions is shown by the dotted lines in Figure 1.2; there is little similarity between the human and the ideal. Alluisi, Muller and Fitts found other evidence besides, that there is a difference in function between a human subject and an ideal communications system. There were two ways of changing the presentation rate, by changing the number of stimuli per second, and by changing the number of alternative stimuli used; these two ways were not at all equivalent in their effects upon human performance.

Under the conditions of a paced serial responding task such as this a coding delay becomes possible with a consequent increase in the number of available coding systems. The performance of an ideal communications system will be more nearly optimal, and the relation between transmission time and entropy implied by equation (1.1) will be more exact. But the typical performance of a human subject shows less similarity with that of the Communication Model here than under the less ideal conditions of Hick's experiment. Indeed, Figure 1.2 considered by itself does *not* suggest any analogy between a human subject and an ideal communications system.

1.3.3. Delayed serial responding tasks.

Other experimental evidence demonstrates quite categorically that human subjects are not capable of encoding messages after the manner of an ideal communications system. For an enforced response delay is not only no advantage, but a positive hindrance to efficient human performance.

The evidence comes from an experiment by Kirchner (1958), which was originally intended to study the effects of ageing. He showed his subjects one of twelve lights, and they responded by pressing a corresponding key. The lights appeared in random order at a slow uniform rate, one at a time, and the subjects were instructed to respond zero, one, two or three signals in arrear. Such an enforced response delay makes a greater number of encoding systems available in an ideal communications system, with a consequent improvement in performance, albeit a marginal one. But human subjects make progressively more errors as the response delay is increased. Under the conditions of Kirchner's experiment a delay of three signals seemed to be the maximum that could be tolerated.

It cannot now be disputed that there is a fundamental difference of function between a human subject engaged in a serial responding task and an ideal communications system. The dramatic qualitative difference between ideal and human performance in Kirchner's experiment was due, of course, to a failure of human retention. The point here is that in any appeal to Shannon's Theorem 11 (and hence in the derivation of equations 1.1–3) there is implicit the assumption that the system can retain sequences of signals more or less indefinitely, if need be. For dealing with continuous messages the transmitter requires a double-ended memory store like a shift register. Each group of channel symbols is generated from a string of signals held in the memory store. As each group of symbols is transmitted a signal is dropped off one end of the store and the next signal from the source added on at the other end. Although human subjects are able to recall events in the serial order of their occurrence, immediate memory is at best "single-ended".

Human subjects are not able to encode messages in the sense envisaged in Shannon's Theorem 11. This undermines whatever rationale there was for interpreting equations (1.2) and (1.3) in terms of Communication Theory. The statistic $H = - \sum_i p_i \log p_i$ may be meaningful in some psychological contexts, but there is no theoretical justification for relating it to the time taken to perform any task. Although the comparison between a human subject in a choice-reaction experiment and a communications system can obviously still be made, the Mathematical Theory of Communication cannot provide a basis for any theory of human performance.

The true interpretation of equations (1.2) and (1.3) is thus not at all obvious. The most reasonable of the models suggested by Hick (1952) have been criticized above. Before this question is considered any further, the empirical accuracy and validity of equations (1.2) and (1.3) should be examined.

1.4. Experimental critiques of the Communication Model.

For the most part the equation

$$t = a - b \sum_i p_i \log p_i \tag{1.3}$$

has been looked upon as the fundamental reaction time equation. p_i is the probability of signal i and the summation runs over all the alternative signals. a and b are constants: a represents an apparatus constant and the effect of temporal uncertainty about the signal; b has usually been interpreted as the reciprocal of the channel capacity. If this equation is correct, then b at least should take similar values from one experiment to the next, and reaction time should be a function of the signal probabilities only. Here are two points at which an empirical attack might be directed, and the particular form of equation (1.3) is a third.

The initial discoveries of Hick (1952) and Hyman (1953) encouraged a great deal of research into choice-reaction times and related topics organized in the context of the Communication Model. Welford (1960) has made a comprehensive review of this research up to that time, and his conclusions will be examined here.

1.4.1. The relation between reaction time and entropy.

Some doubt was cast on the validity of equation (1.3) even in Hyman's original paper (1953). The entropy of signal i is $- \log p_i$, so that the mean reaction time to signal i should be

$$t_i = a - b \log p_i. \tag{1.4}$$

Hyman found that equation (1.3) gave a good account of the mean reaction time when averaged over all the signals in the series, but if the p_i were not all equal, the mean reaction time to signal i was not so different from the series mean as equation (1.4) required. Thus although the looked for relation between reaction time and entropy was found when the mean reaction time was averaged over *all* the signals in the series, it was not found when the mean reaction time to a particular component signal was considered.

In some circumstances equation (1.3) fails even to account adequately for the series mean reaction times. Laming (1962) had his subjects sort cards according to the length of a black stripe placed somewhere along the centre-line. Only two lengths of stripe were used in a pack of cards and the entropy of the pack was varied by changing their relative frequencies. The time taken to sort the pack was significantly non-linear as a function of entropy. There was further evidence that the form of the reaction time equation changed after only a little practice, indicating that reaction time is a function of more than the signal probabilities.

Both of these criticisms have been based on the form of the reaction time equation favoured by Hyman, (1.3). Welford (1960, §2.3), on the other hand, has argued at length for the form (1.2) in preference to (1.3), but only in experiments involving some temporal uncertainty, such as Hyman's experiment. In Laming's experiment equation (1.3) *must* be used. Following Hick (1952, Appendix 1) it is possible to derive an equation for the mean reaction time to a given signal, analogous to (1.4)

$$t_i = b\{\log(1/p_i) + \log(n_e + 1/n_e)\}, \tag{1.5}$$

where n_e is the effective degree of choice (i.e. $\log n_e = - \sum_i p_i \log p_i$). But equation (1.2) is very similar to (1.3) when used as a regression equation for reaction time data, and because of the size of Hyman's effect (see the example given on p. 194 of Hyman's paper), it is not to be expected that the substitution of equation (1.5) for (1.4) would alter the qualitative nature of his result.

1.4.2. Discrimination experiments.

The reaction time equation (1.3) contains no variable representing the ease of distinguishing between the several alternative signals. But it was clear from the work of Crossman (1953) that the perceptual nature of the signals influenced the reaction time. Different sets of signals having the same entropy nonetheless give different mean reaction times. In particular, if the red pictures and black plain in a pack of cards were sorted from the black pictures and red plain the average time per card was comparable to most four-choice reaction times.

Welford (1960, §2.3.1A and §2.5) has reviewed the evidence on discriminability available at that time and reached the following conclusions: A choice-reaction involves both the *perceptual identification* of the signal and the *selection* of the response. Most choice-reaction experiments are dominated by the time spent in choosing the response, which is given by equation (1.3). But in some experiments the difficulty of perceptual identification exercises a demonstrable influence upon the response time and these are therefore called *discrimination experiments*. It is uncertain whether the two component processes, perceptual identification of the signal and choice of response, follow one another in time or whether they overlap. There is some evidence that they can overlap (Crossman, 1955) and in commenting upon the results of Birren and Botwinick (1955: shown in Welford's Figure 10) Welford writes: "It looks as if discrimination of which line was longer and choice of response proceeded simultaneously, and that the recorded reaction time was either the choice time or the discrimination time, whichever was longer."

These conclusions depend upon a particular interpretation of several sets of experimental results. The first of these came from Crossman (1955), who investigated the ease of discriminating between cards bearing different numbers of randomly arranged spots and between different weights. In a series of two-choice experiments Crossman examined three theoretical functions:

$$t = k \log_2\{x_1/(x_1-x_2)\}, \tag{1.6}$$

$$t = k \{\tfrac{1}{2}(x_1+x_2)/(x_1-x_2)\}^2, \tag{1.7}$$

$$t = k/(\log x_1 - \log x_2), \tag{1.8}$$

where x_1 and x_2 are the physical magnitudes of the two signals (numbers of spots, weights, etc.) and $x_1 > x_2$. Equation (1.6) was allegedly derived from Wiener's (1948, p. 75) formulation of the entropy of a measurement;[2] equation (1.7) depends upon an analogy between the subject's decision process and a parametric fixed-sample statistical test; equation (1.8), which Crossman called a confusion function, is related to the Weber-Fechner Law. Crossman considered that equation (1.8) fitted his data the best.

For his fourth experiment Crossman made a hypothetical generalisation of his confusion function (1.8) to multiple discriminations. His subjects sorted cards into two, three, four or five piles according to the number of spots they bore, and the confusion-value of each pack seemed of itself to be a sufficient determinant of sorting time independent of the entropy. I write "seemed" because the one set of data which Crossman presents graphically shows considerable scatter. It is to this

---

[2] Wiener (1948, equation 3.03) gives the entropy of a measurement of an unknown quantity, x, where the measurement is subject to error, as

$$H = -\log_2 \frac{\text{(measure of } X \text{ after measurement)}}{\text{(measure of } X \text{ before measurement)}}.$$

In Crossman's experiments X takes either the value x_1 or x_2, never any intermediate value. So the entropy contained in the identification of the signal is always unity, independent of x_1 and x_2. This result becomes obvious when it is asked in how few binary symbols the signal can be specified.

experiment that Welford referred as evidence that perceptual identification and choice of response might overlap.

It may be that Crossman's generalisation of his confusion function was not valid. So Laming (1962) set out to re-examine the relative roles of signal discriminability and entropy in choice-reaction experiments. He failed to discover anything further about discriminability, but showed that equation (1.3) was not correct under the conditions of his experiment. In these circumstances it is not clear how Crossman's (1955) Experiment IV should be interpreted.

In his review Welford examines equations (1.6–8) and two other formulations as well. He seems to prefer equation (1.6) to (1.8) and exhibits the data of Henmon (1906), Birren and Botwinick (1955) and Botwinick, Brinley and Robbin (1958) plotted against the function $\log_2\{x_1/(x_1-x_2)\}$. These data all fit equation (1.6) better than (1.8);[3] Crossman's data do not.

This matter has been investigated further by Shallice and Vickers (1964). These authors distinguish two types of discrimination experiment; one type yields results conforming to equation (1.6), the other to equation (1.8). In the light of their experimental results they consider the crucial difference between the two types of experiment to be a matter of design. If the subject is presented with a series of discriminations varying randomly in difficulty, then the results conform to equation (1.6), provided that successive trials are not too close together in time. But if the subject is presented with a series of discriminations of constant difficulty, the mean discrimination times from several such series conform to equation (1.8).

The critical experiment leading to Shallice and Vickers' conclusion is their third. But when the data from this experiment are plotted against equation (1.6) two interesting comparisons can be made. First, although the curve is positively accelerated, if only those points falling in any one of the ranges of discriminability studied by Henmon are considered (Henmon studied relatively narrow ranges of discriminability; see Welford, Figure 9), a linear function is adequate. Secondly, Shallice and Vickers' results are very similar to those from the younger age group of Birren and Botwinick (1955) when due allowance is made for the time occupied in manipulating the cards (about 0·5 sec./card) in the Shallice and Vickers experiment: this is to be expected. So on the evidence at present available equations (1.6) and (1.8) might well represent the difference between simultaneous and successive discriminations.

It is interesting that in all those experiments where Welford has found equation (1.6) to fit, and also in Shallice and Vickers' third experiment, the longer of the two lines, x_1, has been kept constant. So that in these experiments equation (1.6) is equivalent to

$$t = -k\log(x_1-x_2). \tag{1.9}$$

Indeed, when the lines are presented side by side in a simultaneous discrimination, their difference in length is a more natural measure of their discriminability than the ratio of their lengths, and some other function of (x_1-x_2) (e.g. $(x_1-x_2)^{-1}$) may give a better fit to the data.

The interpretation of these experiments in terms of Wiener's theory of the entropy of a measurement therefore fails on several counts, not least because Crossman's original derivation of equation (1.6) is spurious.[2] And there is no empirical

---

[2] See footnote overleaf on p. 11.
[3] Welford actually compared these sets of data with the equation
$$t = \tfrac{1}{2}k(x_1+x_2)/(x_1-x_2),$$
which is an approximation to equation (1.8).

justification for distinguishing between the roles of perceptual identification and choice of response. In the theory to be presented in Chapter 3 this distinction is abandoned. There "choice-reaction" experiments and "discrimination" experiments are regarded as of the same generic kind, involving a single unitary decision process.

1.4.3. Channel capacity.

The limiting capacity of the channel in the Communication Model of Figure 1.1 is an invariant of the system. Although this capacity may vary from one subject to another, it should be independent of the experimental situation. The constant b in equation (1.3) is the reciprocal of the channel capacity, which can therefore be determined from the experimental data.

Similar values of the channel capacity have been obtained from many experiments, but there are a few important exceptions. Merkel (1885), Hick (1952), Hyman (1953), Crossman (1953) and Hilgendorf (1966) all obtained results yielding transmission rates around 6 bits per second. But Klemmer and Muller (1953) with a more complex task achieved 12 bits per second, and Quastler and Wulff (1955) obtained rates of 24 bits per second for playing random music and typing random text. Bricker (1955) reviewing these results suggested that channel capacity determined a lower limit to the response time, which may be exceeded by a lower limit due to some other factor. If equation (1.3) is to remain valid in these circumstances, then the limit due to the "other factor" must have the form of a maximum transmission rate. What the "other factor" might be and why its limit on reaction time should take this particular form have yet to be explained.

However there are some experiments published after Bricker's review in which the channel capacity appeared to be infinite. These experiments failed to show an increase in reaction time when the number of alternative signals was increased.

Leonard's (1959) subjects rested their finger tips on a set of relay armatures. When one of the armatures vibrated the subject depressed that armature with the finger thus stimulated. There was no difference in the mean reaction times for two, four or eight alternative stimuli, though the reaction time was a little shorter when the same finger was stimulated every time (A-reaction).

Mowbray and Rhoades (1959) used signal lights and response keys in similar configurations. Their one subject practised over a long period with both two and four alternative signals. There was a progressive decrease in reaction time with practice down to an apparently asymptotic level, which was the same with both two and four alternatives. Mowbray and Rhoades considered that after sufficient practice choice-reaction time would become independent of the number of alternative signals and that the early results purporting to show a relation between mean reaction time and signal entropy had been obtained solely because the subjects had not overlearned their experimental tasks.

The published results from both of these experiments were obtained from the data from one finger only, an index finger. This would be a reasonable procedure if all the signal-response combinations used in such experiments were equivalent, except for differences in muscular response latency. But this seems not to be so.

Hick (1952) published a signal-response matrix for one subject in his second experiment showing the number of occurrences of each signal-response combination and the corresponding mean reaction time (Hick's Table I). The mean reaction times corresponding to responses 1 and 2 were by far the shortest, and these responses were made by the little and ring fingers of the left hand. It is unreasonable to suppose that these two fingers responded nearly one tenth of a second faster than any other finger solely because of differences in muscular response latencies. Hick also assumed that the several signal-response combinations he used were equivalent, since the data he fitted to equation (1.2) were obtained from these two fingers only; (these two fingers were used under every condition from two to ten alternatives.) It is not certain that Hick's results would have fitted equation (1.2) so well had he included the data from all the responses used. Crossman (1956) also found in his non-symbolic task that differences between reaction times for different responses far exceeded those between reaction times for different numbers of alternatives. Consequently the results of Leonard (1959) and Mowbray and Rhoades (1959) are open to more than one interpretation.

Yet a third interpretation is possible of the first experiment by Mowbray (1960), which also failed to show an increase in reaction time with increasing numbers of alternatives. Mowbray showed his subjects Arabic numerals and asked them to repeat the number aloud—a task which is thoroughly overlearned by most literate people. There was no increase in response time to the digit 8 as the number of alternative stimuli varied from two to ten. It seems likely that Mowbray's subjects responded throughout as if any of the ten numerals might have appeared, even in the two-choice condition. After all these numerals appear with approximately equal frequencies in every-day life and it is here that the overlearning occurs. 0·461 seconds is long for a mean two-choice reaction time (Hick's mean was about 0·26 seconds) and may be expected to decrease with practice.[4] Mowbray's (1960) second experiment does but confirm this interpretation. The subjects in that experiment were instructed to respond to only one of the alternative numerals, the 8. Their mean reaction time was less than in the first experiment for two, four, and six alternatives and greater for eight and ten. If the speed of reaction in the first experiment had been reduced to an ultimate minimum by excessive practice (cf. Mowbray & Rhoades, 1959), then it would not have been possible to obtain reactions any faster by omitting some of the responses. So in Mowbray's first experiment the reaction time to ten alternatives has not been reduced by practice to that to two, but rather the reaction time to two alternatives has somehow been increased to that to ten[5] (see also Mowbray, 1964).

These experiments, which have failed to show an increase in reaction time with increase in the number of alternatives, may carry interpretations other than that there is no fundamental relation between reaction time and signal entropy. But they nonetheless present evidence that under certain conditions, particularly after long practice, choice-reaction time becomes independent of the number of alternative signals. These results imply that the channel of Figure 1.1 has infinite capacity—or rather that there is no channel at all.

1.4.4. Stimulus-response compatability.

The concept of stimulus-response compatibility seems to have been formed out of the many human engineering studies undertaken during and after the 1939–45

---

[4] Mowbray was aware of this comparison. He quoted Woodworth (1938, p. 329) to the effect that voice reaction times are slower than finger reaction times. Brainard, Irby, Fitts and Alluisi (1962) found such a difference between vocal and finger responses to a set of lights, where it might have been accounted for by differences in compatability, but failed to find it in comparing responses to Arabic numerals, which is the task Mowbray used.

[5] The results of Leonard (1959) and Mowbray and Rhoades (1959) cannot be interpreted in this way, since their mean reaction times are all of the order of a two-choice reaction time or even faster.

War. It was used by Fitts and Seeger (1953), who showed that choice-reaction time was a function of the *matching* of the stimulus and response sets rather than of any independent features of either set. Just as in a communications system optimum performance is obtained when the message is so encoded that its probability structure in its encoded form matches the channel characteristics, so efficient performance is obtained in a choice-reaction experiment when the stimuli are presented to the subject in such a way that they "match" the corresponding responses. The exact meaning of "match" has yet to be defined. But if the signal is the lighting of a pea-bulb adjacent to its response key, the task is compatible; if the pea-bulb is adjacent to some other response key, the task is incompatible.

This concept of compatibility gained increased currency when it was discovered that the slope of the regression line of reaction time on stimulus entropy (the constant b in equation 1.3) was different for different stimulus-response sets. Deininger and Fitts (1955) conceived of a choice-reaction as a series of recoding operations transforming the signal into the response; in a compatible task fewer recoding operations are required. Recent developments of this idea have been reviewed by Sanders (1967). Leonard (1961) has proposed a slightly different concept of "coding uncertainty", which comprehends the ideas of discriminability and stimulus-response compatibility and the effects of practice, and is distinguished from stimulus uncertainty or entropy. It is a new interpretation of b in equation (1.3), which thus becomes a variable. But if these concepts are attempts to preserve the analogy with an ideal communications system as a basis for equation (1.3), they disregard the fact that in Communication Theory a coding delay is additive with transmission time, not multiplicative.

Stimulus-response compatibility and Leonard's coding uncertainty might alternatively be regarded as reinterpretations of equation (1.3) which abandon the traditional Communication Theory model, reinterpretations which are made necessary by those experimental results which seem to indicate different transmission rates. But evidence cited earlier in this chapter implies that the form of equation (1.3) is in error, even when considered purely as an empirical equation, and so the time is ripe for a yet more radical reappraisal of choice-reaction time theory.

1.5. Conclusions.

The attempt to explain choice-reaction times in terms of Communication Theory must now be abandoned. Such an explanation depends ultimately on an analogy between the human subject in a choice-reaction experiment and an ideal communications system, and it has been shown in this chapter that this analogy cannot be maintained. If it is pursued rigorously it leads to models such as Hick's progressive classification model, which do not fit the results particularly well. It is worthy of note that except for the review by Welford (1960), this and similar ideas have not been followed up. On the other hand equation (1.3) has been gladly accepted as a choice-reaction time equation. It has lasted as long as this only because its theoretical antecedents have not been rigorously examined.

Hick's (1952) paper set the theoretical course and had a shaping influence on things to come. It lead to a concentration on certain aspects of choice-reaction time—the relation between reaction time and signal entropy—to the exclusion of others—the differences in latency between different responses, for example. This emphasis influenced the design, perhaps even prejudiced the conclusions, of future experiments. All sorts of experiments were cast into a Communication Theory mould and some directly contrary evidence was not appreciated. Even the discordant results reported by Hyman (1953) seem not to have been accorded their fair weight.

It has always been possible to regard the Communication Theory of choice-reaction times as a set of empirical results bearing a superficial resemblance to the theory of communication systems, but without any particular theoretical justification. But in this chapter even a superficial resemblance has been shown illusory. The very form of equation (1.3) seems to be wrong. The discriminability of the signals influences the reaction time, but it is not obvious how to incorporate this factor into the reaction time equation, and the evidence that discrimination should be regarded as a process separate from the choice of the response evaporates when it is critically examined. The "channel capacity" is by no means invariant and may even be infinite. And the concept of stimulus-response compatibility, as a means of salvage, is inadequate. The theoretical anomalies and the empirical weaknesses of the Communication Model are now seen to be such that the Mathematical Theory of Communication cannot provide any basis for a theory of choice-reaction times.

CHAPTER 2

ALTERNATIVE MODELS FOR CHOICE-REACTION TIMES

2.1. Introduction.

This chapter contains a review of choice-reaction time models alternative to Communication Theory on the one hand and the random walk theory of Chapter 3 on the other. The selection of models for this review is not obvious and some justification is necessary why some models are included and others not. A few models have been explicitly developed for and applied to choice-reaction time problems, and these obviously ought to be reviewed. There are other models concerned with simple reaction times or with choice-point behaviour in general (such models are usually compared with the behaviour of a rat in a maze or on a jumping stand) which are capable of development and application to choice-reaction times, but which have not been so developed by their authors. The probabilistic mechanisms commonly used in these models will be described briefly for the sake of completeness. But it would be ridiculous to develop them here as models for choice-reaction time solely to demonstrate their unsuitability.

The ultimate purpose of this review is to see whether any of these models presents a tenable alternative to the random walk model of Chapter 3 when compared with the experimental data of Chapter 5. Sometimes additional predictions are derived from the author's original axioms to facilitate this. But I do not consider it my responsibility, when a model is found to fail, to discuss ways in which it might be modified to make it acceptable once more; this is left to the author of the model when he replies to my criticisms. Several of the models will appear unable to account for the results of Experiments 6 and 7 (pp. 68–78) because they (the models) do not take into account the perceptual relations between the signals in those experiments. These relations will be seen to dominate the experimental results. It is not obvious how these models might be modified and, indeed, a successful modification might be so far-reaching that a virtually new model is created. It ought to be emphasised that the data with which comparisons are to be made were all obtained from a particular type of experiment. Some of the models were intended to apply to much broader classes of decision processes, and the criticisms to be made in this chapter are valid only with respect to choice-reaction experiments that are qualitatively similar to those reported in Chapter 5.

Besides models for choice-reactions that have already been proposed there are certain schemes used in quality control methods (particularly moving averages) which seem at first sight to be potential bases for such models. It has not yet been possible to investigate these schemes systematically, so the discussion of them will be brief;

but it will appear later (§7.6) that they lead to an issue of fundamental importance in the study of choice-reaction times.

Some of the material discussed here has already been reviewed by Atkinson, Bower and Crothers (1965, pp. 155–184) and by McGill (1963, §2.3), who criticized the neural series hypothesis favoured by Restle (1961). But McGill was primarily concerned with matching the distributions of reaction time typically found in an experiment. Since it is likely that the distribution of reaction time is much affected by sequential relations in the date, which are as yet poorly understood (see Chapter 8), this particular comparison between theory and experiment is outside the scope of this monograph.

The following models will be reviewed here:

§2.2 An alternative derivation by Luce (1960) of predictions usually obtained from Communication Theory.

§2.3 The Markov model for sequential effects due to Falmagne (1965).

§2.4 Models analogous to a fixed sample-size statistical test.

§2.5 Probabilistic mechanisms used in models for choice-point behaviour, and the models of Audley (1960) and La Berge (1962).

§2.6 Models based on quality control statistics.

Finally in §2.7 certain uses of the sequential probability ratio test as a psychological model (not necessarily for choice-reaction times) will be enumerated.

The experimental results pertaining to these models will not be presented until Chapter 7 after the experiments themselves have been described. But the relevant predictions will be stated and, if necessary, developed here, and the outcome of the comparison with the experimental data will be mentioned briefly with a reference to the corresponding section of Chapter 7.

2.2. An alternative derivation of the relation between reaction time and entropy.

In the Communication Theory of choice-reaction times the use of the statistic $H = - \sum_i p_i \log p_i$ depends upon the consideration of the economical recoding of messages into sequences of binary digits (cf. Fano, 1949); this rationale was criticized in Chapter 1 on theoretical grounds. An alternative justification is possible by means of an axiom which leads to the additive decomposition property of H (cf. Shannon and Weaver, 1949, p. 19 and Appendix 2). This axiom is stated by Luce (1959) as his Axiom 1[1] and may be approximately characterized as follows:

(i) *The relative probabilities of an organism choosing each of the alternatives $A_1...A_n$ are independent of whether the organism is free or not to choose some other alternative, A_{n+1}.*

[1] "*Let T be a finite subset of U such that, for every $S \subset T$, P_S is defined.*
(i) *If $P(x,y) \neq 0, 1$ for all $x,y \in T$, then for $R \subset S \subset T$*
$$P_T(R) = P_S(R)P_T(S);$$
(ii) *If $P(x,y) = 0$ for some $x,y \in T$, then for every $S \subset T$*
$$P_T(S) = P_{T-\{x\}}(S - \{x\})."$$
Here R, S, T, U are sets and x, y etc. elements of them. If an element is to be selected from T, then $P_T(S)$ denotes the probability that the selected element belongs to the subset S. $P(x, y)$ is the probability of choosing x from the set $\{x, y\}$.

(ii) *If A_2 is always preferred to A_1, A_1 will never be chosen from any set of alternatives containing A_2.*

Luce shows that this axiom, if true, has far reaching implications for choice-behaviour. In particular, together with certain lesser assumptions, it leads (Luce 1960) to an equation for mean reaction time conditional on a given response, R_i,

$$E\{t|R_i\} = A(R) - B(R) \log P(R_i), \tag{2.1}$$

where $E\{\ \}$ indicates an expectation, $A(R)$ and $B(R)$ are functions of the response set $R \equiv \{R_i\}$, and $B(R) > 0$. The unconditional mean reaction time is then

$$E\{t\} = A(R) + B(R)H_R, \tag{2.2}$$

where $H_R = -\sum_i P(R_i)\log P(R_i)$, the response entropy.[2]

Reaction time is now related to response entropy rather than signal entropy as in equation (1.3). But in an experiment in which few errors are made these two equations will generate nearly identical predictions. The early Communication Theory results (Hick, 1952; Hyman, 1953; Crossman, 1953) therefore lend support to Luce's model. But not so Hyman's remark (1953, p. 194), that the mean reaction time conditional on a given signal, $E\{t|S_j\}$, is not so different from the series mean as equation (1.4) (cf. equation 2.1) requires. Further graphical evidence will be presented in §7.2 to show that the relation between mean reaction time and response entropy is not linear.

At this point it becomes pertinent to inquire whether Luce's choice axiom, which is the most important of the assumptions underlying equation (2.1), holds for choice-reaction experiments. By means of part (i) of that axiom it is possible to predict from the response frequencies occurring in an equiprobable n-choice reaction experiment what the response frequencies should be when one of the n signals is omitted from the set. This is done in §7.2.1 and the axiom is found not to hold.

2.3. The studies of sequential relations by Bertelson and Falmagne.

Bertelson (1961) varied the transition probabilities in a two-choice experiment, in which two signals appeared equally often. He found that a sequence with 75 per cent repetitions of signals did not take so long as a sequence with 75 per cent alternations, and this effect was enhanced when the intertrial interval was reduced to 1/20 second. In a random sequence of signals the response to a repeated signal was faster than that to an alternated signal and was influenced by more than the one signal immediately preceding in a sequence of repetitions or alternations. Bertelson concluded "that choice processes involve a transitory residual effect favouring repetitions". After each response the subject prepares for the next signal, usually with a bias towards that signal most likely to occur. But preparation for a repetition of the choice that has just been made is quicker than preparation for any other choice, so that with a short intertrial interval (0·05 seconds) repeated signals are heavily favoured; but as the intertrial interval is increased (e.g. 0·50 seconds) this asymmetry tends to disappear.

---

[2] In fact the assumptions of Luce's Theorem 4 (1960) imply that $B(R) = constant$. On the other hand they are not strong enough to determine the form of equation (2.1) uniquely. The additional assumption "$\mu(Q_R, x)$ is a function of R, x and a continuous function of $P_R(x)$ only" (see Luce, 1960, for the meaning of the symbols) would be sufficient to establish the result

$$E\{t|R_i\} = A(R) - B \log P(R_i).$$

Bertelson called this the "repetition effect"; he conceived of it as a first-order inter-action between stimulus-response cycles.

In a second paper Bertelson (1963) compared three different stimulus-response relationships in his two-choice responding task to study the interaction of stimulus-response compatibility with the repetition effect. In particular, he conjectured that either

(a) reactions to repeated and new signals involve different mechanisms, or

(b) the repetition effect is due to some facilitative after-effect favouring repetitions of the previous response.

Bertelson found that reaction times to both repeated and new signals were affected by changes in stimulus-response compatibility, but a larger effect was produced in reaction times to new signals. This result was not entirely consistent with either of Bertelson's hypotheses, as originally conceived, and he found it necessary to suggest a compromise. But there is another possible interpretation of these results: it is clear from Bertelson's Table 1 that stimulus-response compatibility acts here as a multiplicative factor in the reaction time equation (i.e. b in equation 1.3) with a constant term (a in 1.3) of 260 milliseconds (see also Broadbent and Gregory, 1965). The "repetition" effect is therefore comparable to the effect of bias in the signal sequence.

Falmagne (1965) has constructed a Markov model to account for the sequential phenomena demonstrated by Bertelson (1961) and Hyman (1953, Figure 2). He considers a "state of preparation". If a particular signal in an experiment, say S_A has recently appeared several times, the subject is likely to be prepared for it and will respond quickly when S_A appears again. But if some other signal, say S_B, has not appeared for a little while, the subject is likely not to be prepared for it and will respond but slowly when S_B is at last presented. So the reaction time to a given signal is in part a function of the preceding signals. The subject will respond more quickly to those signals occurring more frequently and in this way will match his performance to the objective signal frequencies.

For the sake of simplicity Falmagne postulates an "all or nothing" state of pre-paration. The total level of preparation is not constant; preparation for S_A does not necessarily imply a lack of preparation for S_B. The reaction time has a distribution function $K(t)$ if the subject is prepared for the signal that is presented, and $\overline{K}(t)$ other-wise; $E\{t|K\} < E\{t|\overline{K}\}$. $P_{A,n+1}$ denotes the probability that the subject is prepared for S_A at the start of trial $n+1$ and is related to $P_{A,n}$ by a linear operator:

If S_A is presented at trial n,

$$P_{A,n+1} = (1-c)P_{A,n}+c, \quad 0 < c < 1; \tag{2.3}$$

if some signal other than S_A is presented at trial n,

$$P_{A,n+1} = (1-c')P_{A,n}, \quad 0 < c' < 1. \tag{2.4}$$

If S_A is presented at trial n, the distribution of reaction time is given by

$$J_{A,n}(t) = P_{A,n} K(t)+(1-P_{A,n})\overline{K}(t). \tag{2.5}$$

It follows that $J_{A,n+1}(t)$ is related to $J_{A,n}(t)$ by a linear operator and is bounded by $K(t)$ and $\overline{K}(t)$.

If p_A is the probability of S_A appearing, $P_{A,n}$ has asymptotic value

$$p_A c/\{p_A c+(1-p_A)c'\},$$

and the mean reaction time conditional on S_A is

$$E\{t|S_A\} = \{p_A c\mu+(1-p_A)c'\overline{\mu}\}/\{p_A c+(1-p_A)c'\}, \tag{2.6}$$

where μ and $\bar{\mu}$ are the means of $K(t)$ and $\overline{K}(t)$ respectively.

In support of this model Falmagne reports one six-choice experiment. The signals were the digits 1 to 6 and they appeared with relative frequencies 0·01, 0·03, 0·06, 0·10, 0·24 and 0·56. Responses were made with the fingers pressing on relay armatures. In general the experimental results accorded well with the theoretical asymptotic mean reaction time equations, but the predictions of variances and third moments were less successful.

Although equation (2.6) gave a reasonable fit to the mean reaction times in Falmagne's experiment, it will appear quite inadequate when compared in §7.3 with the means from a five-choice experiment to be reported in Chapter 5. A further difficulty concerns the relative magnitudes of c and c'. Falmagne variously estimates the ratio c'/c as 0·210 and 0·231. Since Falmagne's starting point (p. 79) is an attempt to explain certain effects, notably those due to the number of alternative signals and unequal signal frequencies, in terms of sequential interactions, it seems natural that c and c' should be invariant under a wide range of experimental conditions. However, Falmagne is prepared to see them vary, although the invariant he suggests implies (equation 72, p. 121)

$$c/c' = (\bar{\mu}-t)/(\mu-t),$$

where t is a constant such that $\bar{\mu} > \mu > t > 0$. It follows that $c > c'$. But it will appear during the analysis of sequential relations in Chapter 8 that the two-choice experiments here require $c' > c$ (see p. 111).

In a second paper Falmagne (1963) has introduced three additional axioms concerning the production of errors. Let $\tilde{S}_A'$ and $\tilde{R}_A'$ here denote some signal and response respectively other than S_A and R_A:

(i) If the subject is prepared for S_A, he will make R_A with probability β when some other signal is presented;

i.e. $P(R_A|\tilde{S}_A \,.\, subject\ prepared\ for\ S_A) = \beta,$
   $P(R_A|\tilde{S}_A \,.\, subject\ not\ prepared\ for\ S_A) = 0.$

(ii) If the subject is not prepared for S_A when S_A is presented, he will make some response other than R_A with probability β';

i.e. $P(\tilde{R}_A|S_A \,.\, subject\ not\ prepared\ for\ S_A) = \beta',$
   $P(\tilde{R}_A|S_A \,.\, subject\ prepared\ for\ S_A) = 0.$

(iii) When an error is made the reaction time has a fixed distribution function $K'(t)$.

Now the first two of these axioms are not consistent. If the subject happens to be prepared for every signal and S_A is presented, axiom (i) gives the probability of some response other than R_A, say R_B, as β, while axiom (ii) gives this probability as 0. Consistency can be achieved at a price. It is necessary to suppose first that the subject is at each trial prepared for one and only one signal (on **p.** 165 Falmagne implicitly remarks that this condition is not imposed) and secondly that $\beta = \beta'$.

In his development Falmagne considers only one signal **or** one response at a time and so does not encounter these inconsistencies. He shows that

$$P_n(R_A|\tilde{S}_A) = \beta P_{A,n},$$
$$P_n(\tilde{R}_A|S_A) = \beta'(1-P_{A,n}),$$

and, by substituting in equations (2.3) and (2.4) and taking asymptotic values,

$$P(R_A|\tilde{S}_A)/P(\tilde{R}_A|S_A) = L\,p_A/(1-p_A), \tag{2.7}$$

where $L = \beta c/\beta'c'$.

Now there are certain implications of equation (2.7) which Falmagne does not develop. In an experiment every error may be classified both by its signal and by its response. Hence

$$\sum_i \{1 - P(S_i)\} P(R_i|\tilde{S}_i) = \sum_j P(S_j)\, P(\tilde{R}_j|S_j); \qquad (2.8)$$

so
$$L = 1,$$

and consistency of axioms (i) and (ii) also implies $c = c'$.[3]

In his paper Falmagne also reports a further experiment similar to that described above. Four signals were used, the numerals 0, 3, 7 and 9, and they appeared with relative frequencies 0·05, 0·10, 0·25 and 0·60. The experimental instructions laid great emphasis on speed and 47 per cent of the responses were errors. Falmagne quotes the error scores from a single subject, which conform well to the asymptotic predictions with $\beta = \beta' = 0.90$. But it will be shown in §7.3 that equation (2.7) fails in the experiments reported here.

2.4. Fixed sample-size models.

It has been suggested that the decision process used by a subject in a choice-reaction experiment may be analogous to a fixed sample-size statistical test (e.g. Crossman, 1955; Stone, 1960; cf. Swets, Tanner and Birdsall, 1961). Stone (1960) considers two such models, one for two-choice decisions, one for more than two alternatives. In both models the response with the greatest posterior probability is selected.

Stone supposes that a stream of information flows at a uniform rate from the signal to the subject. There is some uncertainty about the signal presented in that some patterns of information, at least, might arise from more than one signal. The stream of information may be represented by a sequence of independent random variables, regularly spaced in time, having a stationary distribution dependent on the signal presented. After a certain time, during which a corresponding length of the series is examined, a response is made. Choice-reaction time might therefore be split into three components: T_i, the time required for the information to reach that part of the brain where it is processed; T_d, the time required to collect enough information to make a response; and T_m, the time to execute a response. The essence of a fixed sample-size model is that, although T_d may vary from one series of signals to another, it is constant *within* any one experimental series.

Evidence is already available inconsistent with such a model. It is known (e.g. from Hyman, 1953) that in a two-choice experiment, if $P(S_A) > P(S_B)$, then $t_A < t_B$, where t_A, t_B are the mean reaction times to S_A, S_B respectively. Since T_d is constant, the difference between t_A and t_B must be due to differences in T_i or T_m. So one at least of T_i and T_m must be a function of *a priori* signal probability! This matter will be further examined in §7.4. It will be shown there that in the two-choice experiments of Chapter 5 T_i and T_m are the same for both signals; yet the above relation between the *a priori* signal probabilities and the mean reaction times holds nonetheless.

2.5. Models for choice-point behaviour.

Several models for choice-point behaviour have been published in the last few years, mostly in the context of statistical learning theory. They have certain features in common and it will be helpful to consider them together in order to exhibit their interrelations.

---

[3] In fact Falmagne assumes $\beta = \beta'$ and $c = c'$ in the evaluation of his experimental data in the 1963 paper.

These models share the fundamental idea of a chain of intervening events, which have been given various names ("orientation and approach responses", Bower, 1959; "implicit responses", Audley, 1960; sampling of stimulus elements, La Berge, 1962 and a set of criteria, which determines when a sequence of intervening events shall terminate in the making of a response. The decision process may be represented as a Markov chain in which the absorbing states correspond to the response criteria. In some models the intervening events occur uniformly in time, in others the temporal interval between two successive events is exponentially distributed. The intervening events usually fall into classes, one class corresponding to each response, and the behaviour of these models is for the most part determined by the response criteria. The following criteria have been studied:

(a) two successive events of the same class (Bower, 1959, Model B; Estes, 1960)

(b) K successive events of the same class (Audley, 1960)

(c) a difference of two between the numbers of events in each of two classes (Bower, 1959, Model A)

(d) a total of k events in any class (La Berge, 1962).

Bower and Estes are concerned with the choice-behaviour of a rat. They interpret the intervening events as observable orientation and approach responses on the part of the rat, so that the transition probabilities of the Markov chain may be estimated directly. These authors are principally interested in the probability distribution of the ultimate response in terms of the transition probabilities and they are not really concerned with response latency. However Bower shows that the number of steps to absorbtion in his Model A has a geometric distribution and that his Model B yields a similar result. Kintsch (1963) has added latency predictions to these models by supposing that the time duration of each step in the Markov chain is exponentially distributed. In the simplest case the time to absorbtion in the resultant Markov process is the sum of two exponential random variables with unequal parameters.

Audley (1960) is less specific about the identification of the intervening events, which are not necessarily observable. They form a Poisson process and if the response criterion is *two* successive events of the same class, Audley's model is closely related to those above. It is not certain whether this model is intended to apply to the sort of experiments described later in this monograph. But it is representative of a complex of ideas which has led to several different models and could easily be applied here, and so it is worth a closer investigation.

Audley considers two kinds of implicit responses, a and b, corresponding to two overt responses. These implicit responses occur with relative probabilities p and q respectively. $(p+q = 1)$. Each decision may be represented by a sequence of implicit responses, which terminates as soon as two a's or two b's occur in succession. The length of the sequence, n, is a random variable with generating function

$$g(s) = \{(p^2+q^2)s^2+pqs^3\}/(1-pqs^2).$$ (2.9)

As $p,q \rightarrow \frac{1}{2}$, $g(s) \rightarrow s/(2-s)$. Since the implicit responses occur in a Poisson process, the total response latency is then the sum of two exponential random variables (see Kintsch, 1963; McGill, 1963, §2.2).

In those experiments in which Vicarious Trial and Error can be observed, this is identified with an alternation in the sequence of implicit responses. Audley shows (p. 5) that on the average there would be fewer VTE's preceding the dominant response (i.e. the more likely response to occur). In the context of the experiments to be described later, the dominant response is the correct response, so that for a given signal errors should take longer than correct responses. It will appear in §6.4 that this is not the case.

In a subsequent paper (Audley and Pike, 1965) Audley has presented generating functions for $K > 2$. In this case the decision process is equivalent to a moving average over a sequence of independent random variables and will be discussed in §2.6. This does not exhaust the possible development of the model; K might take different values for different responses and the effects of signal probability, for example, might be represented in this way.

La Berge (1962) has investigated a rather different response criterion. In his model the intervening events are the sampling of a series of stimulus elements. Each element may be conditioned to any of the alternative responses or it may be neutral. Response R_i is initiated as soon as r_i elements conditioned to R_i have been sampled, provided of course that no other response has previously been made. The decision process may therefore be represented by a series of independent multinomial trials in each of which a ball is thrown at random into one of several boxes, not necessarily of equal size, or may be the ball misses the boxes altogether; a reponse is made as soon as any of the boxes is full.

If there is only one available response (simple reaction) the response latency is the rth waiting time in a series of independent binomial trials. This has a negative binomial distribution, which is positively skewed. The counterpart in continuous time is the rth waiting time in a Poisson process which has a gamma distribution. This idea has been used by Bush and Mosteller (1955, §14.3, 14.4) for the latency of a rat in a runway, by Restle (1961, pp. 165–172) for simple reaction time, and it is one of two special cases considered by Christie and Luce (1956). Restle's treatment of Chocolle's (1940) data has been criticized by McGill (1963, pp. 327–8), who finds the general gamma distribution a more plausible model (McGill and Gibbon, 1965; see also Snodgrass, Luce and Galanter, 1967). Some of the estimation problems have been considered by Taylor (1965).

For two alternative signals LaBerge derives predictions for response probability and mean latency in terms of incomplete beta ratios. But this treatment is not sufficient to afford a simple comparison between the model and the experiments in this monograph and one further prediction (not derived by La Berge) will be obtained here.

Let S_A and S_B be the only two alternative signals and suppose R_A is made after exactly m elements have been sampled. Exactly r_A of these elements will be conditioned to R_A and a variable number $x < r_B$ will be conditioned to R_B. Clearly $E\{x\}$ increases monotonically with m. Now $(r_A - x)$ is a sufficient statistic for the *a posteriori* Bayes probability of S_B, and the expectation of this probability therefore increases monotonically with m. But this is the probability of error conditional on m, so that for a given response the distribution of reaction time is stochastically greater when the response is an error than when it is correct. It will be shown in §7.5 that in the two-choice experiments here the contrary relation holds.

The treatment of choice-reaction times by Christie and Luce (1956) is somewhat different to the foregoing in that the authors do not consider response probabilities at all. They treat a choice reaction as composed of a number of elementary decisions which have to be made, some in series, some in parallel, according to a directed graph. They offer solutions for two special cases where the elementary decision latency has an exponential distribution:

(i) a *serial decision process* in which n elementary decisions have to be made in series leading to a gamma distribution of response latency (see above);

(ii) a *parallel decision process* in which n elementary decisions have to be completed in parallel. The response latency is then the largest of a sample of n variates drawn from a common exponential distribution. The resultant distribution of reaction time may also be represented as the outcome of a pure death process (cf. McGill, 1963, §4.3; see also Rapoport, 1959; Laming, 1966, and Lindsay and Lindsay, 1966).

2.6. Models based on quality control statistics.

Samples from the output of a manufacturing process may be checked at frequent intervals to ensure that the product continues to conform to a certain specification. The result of checking the rth sample may be specified by a random variable X_r and the problem of quality control is that of detecting a change in the distribution of the X_r, indicating that some adjustment is required in the manufacturing process, without too great a number of false alarms. A quality control statistic is some function of the X_r, frequently a moving average, which discriminates well and therefore quickly between the desired output, for which the X_r have a stationary distribution, and the sort of changes in output that are likely to occur. Since the subject in a choice-reaction experiment is required to detect as quickly as possible one of a number of possible changes in his environment, a quality control statistic might be expected *prima facie* to lead to a useful reaction time model.

Shallice (1964) has compared the perceptual moment hypothesis and certain models based on quality control statistics as explanations of psychophysical threshold phenomena and the perception of causality. He discusses four models for the detection of change, each of which operates on a series of independent and identically distributed random variables, $x_1 x_2 \ldots$ The $\{x_r\}$ may be regarded as a hypothetical series of observations or subjective measurements of the perceptual input.

(i) The *perceptual moment hypothesis*. Sensory input is integrated over discrete moments of time. x_n is the input during the nth moment; any detection at the end of the nth moment depends on x_n alone. The length of a moment has been variously reported in the interval 40 to 100 milliseconds.

(ii) An *arithmetic moving average*, $y_n = \sum_{r=0}^{k-1} x_{n-r}$. A detection is reported after the nth observation if y_n satisfies some criterion, say $y_n \geqslant$ constant.

(iii) A *geometric moving average*, $y_n = \sum_{r=0}^{\infty} \lambda^r x_{n-r}$, $0 < \lambda < 1$.

(iv) A sequential sampling method suggested by Page (1954). Let $S_n = \sum_{i=1}^{n} (x_i - \mu)$, where μ represents the limit of tolerable quality. The x_r are so arranged that S_n is decreasing while the quality is acceptable and increasing if the quality is poor. A change in output is detected if $S_n - \min_{0 \leqslant i \leqslant n} S_i \geqslant h$, a constant.

These models have in common that they select the most recent information as a basis for decision. Herein lies their suitability as detectors of change, and herein, it seems, lies an important characteristic of their behaviour as choice-reaction models.

(i) The idea of a perceptual moment leads to a reaction time model analogous to a Cartesian sequential test on the variables $\{x_r\}$. A response is made after the nth moment if $x_n \leqslant A$, (response R_A) or $x_n \geqslant B$ (response R_B); otherwise the output of the $(n+1)$th moment is examined. This decision process may be represented as a series of independent multinomial trials and it can be shown (e.g. Wilks, 1962, §15.3) that the distribution of reaction time conditional on a given signal is geometric and is the same whichever response is made.

This provides a means of discriminating between the perceptual moment model and the ideal random walk model to be discussed in §3.2. It is shown in Theorem B.6 (p. 152) that if the excess over the boundaries in the latter is ignored (cf. Wald, 1947, p. 47), the distribution of reaction time for a given *response* in a two-choice experiment is the same whichever *signal* is presented. It is clear from Theorem B.6 that this result follows essentially because all the information implicit in the "interim decisions" following the observations $x_1 \ldots x_{n-1}$ is used in making a decision after the nth observation. On the other hand the distribution of reaction time for a given *signal* in the perceptual moment model is independent of the *response*; this follows essentially because the information available for each "interim decision" has a stationary distribution and is independent of that available for any other "interim decision". These two models might therefore be characterized as "complete memory" and "zero memory" respectively. It will be found in §7.6 that choice-reaction experiments do not in practice conform to either of these simple predictions, but the distinction between them will nonetheless prove to be important.

(ii) A reaction time model may be developed from the arithmetic moving average as follows:

Let
$$y_n = \sum_{r=0}^{k-1} x_{n-r}; \qquad (2.10)$$

a response is then made after the observation x_n if $y_n \leqslant A$ or $y_n \geqslant B$; otherwise another observation is made.

In principle the behaviour of moving average schemes may be investigated by means of the theory of recurrent events (see Feller, 1957, Chapter XIII), but only certain special cases yield explicit solutions. Audley's (1960) decision model is formally a moving average over a series of independent binomial variables and may be treated in this way.

The implicit responses occur in a Poisson process with parameter λ and are of types a and b with relative probabilities p and q. Response R_A is made as soon as a run of K a's occur; R_B as soon as a run of K b's. Disregarding the time relations for the present, let

$$f_n = P(R_A \text{ after exactly } n \text{ implicit responses}),$$
$$g_n = P(R_B \text{ after exactly } n \text{ implicit responses}).$$

It can be shown by an argument following closely that of Feller (1957, Chapter XIII, §7 and 8) that the generating functions, $F(s) = \sum_{n=1}^{\infty} f_n s^n$, $G(s) = \sum_{n=1}^{\infty} g_n s^n$ are given by

$$F(s) = s^K p^K (1-q^K s^K)(1-ps)/(1-s+qp^K s^{K+1}+pq^K s^{K+1}-p^K q^K s^{2K}), \qquad (2.11)$$
$$G(s) = s^K q^K (1-p^K s^K)(1-qs)/(1-s+qp^{K+1}s^K+pq^K s^{K+1}-p^K q^K s^{2K}). \qquad (2.12)$$

The denominator may be written $(1-ps)(1-qs)H(s)$, where

$$H(s) = 1-(ps+p^2s^2+\ldots+p^{K-1}s^{K-1})(qs+q^2s^2+\ldots+q^{K-1}s^{K-1}),$$

and for $K \geqslant 3$ has a single positive real root, $s = x > 1$, which is smaller in modulus than any other root of $H(s)$. (cf. Feller, 1957, p. 301).

Hence
$$f_n \sim p^K (1-q^K x^K) x^{-(n-K+1)}/(1-qx)H'(x), \qquad (2.13)$$

where $H'(x)$ is the derivative of $H(s)$ at $s = x$, and

$$f_n/g_n \to p^K (1-q^K x^K)(1-px)/q^K (1-p^K x^K)(1-qx) \quad \text{as } n \to \infty. \qquad (2.14)$$

Relations (2.13) and (2.14) imply that the distributions of $(n\,|\,R_A)$ and $(n\,|\,R_B)$ are asymptotically geometric with the same parameter. Since the time distribution of n implicit responses is a gamma distribution with parameter n, the frequency function of $(t\,|\,R_A)$

$$f(t) \sim x^{K-2}p^K(1-q^Kx^K)\lambda e^{\lambda t(1/x-1)}/(1-qx)F(1)H'(x), \tag{2.15}$$

and $\quad f(t)/g(t) \to G(1)p^K(1-q^Kx^K)(1-px)/F(1)q^K(1-p^Kx^K)(1-qx) \quad$ as $t \to \infty$. (2.16)

If $K = 2$, $H(s) = 1-pqs^2$, which has two roots of equal modulus $\pm\sqrt{pq}$, and the partial fraction approximation implicit in (2.13) is no longer adequate. Explicit expansions of $F(s)$ and $G(s)$ are now obtainable,

e.g.
$$F(s) = \sum_{r=1}^{\infty} (p/q+ps)(pqs^2)^r, \tag{2.17}$$

and exhibit a certain periodicity. However, inserting the time relation of the implicit responses gives

$$f(t) = \frac{1-pq}{2p^2(1+q)}\left\{ \left(\sqrt{\frac{p}{q}}+\frac{p}{q}\right)\lambda\sqrt{pq}\ (e^{\lambda t\sqrt{pq}}-1)\ + \right.$$
$$\left. +\ \left(\sqrt{\frac{p}{q}}-\frac{p}{q}\right)\lambda\sqrt{pq}\,(e^{-\lambda\sqrt{pq}t}-1)\right\}e^{-\lambda t} \tag{2.18}$$

with a similar expression for $g(t)$. $f(t)$ and $g(t)$ are thus asymptotically exponential and as $t \to \infty$

$$f(t)/g(t) \to (1+p)(q\sqrt{pq}+pq)/(1+q)(p\sqrt{pq}+pq). \tag{2.19}$$

Relations (2.15) and (2.16) imply that Audley's model is asymptotically equivalent to a Cartesian sequential test over a series of independent and indentically distributed random variables, with the property that the distribution of response time for a given signal is independent of the response. Initially the criterion "k successive implicit responses of the same type" is approximately a difference count criterion (as in a sequential probability ratio test on the same variables) so that in practice the distribution of reaction time when an error is made should be intermediate between the distribution for the same response made correctly and that for a correct response to the same signal. But some evidence will be quoted in §7.6 to show that this relation does not hold in the experimental data here.

It seems reasonable that the prediction above should be true of any arithmetic moving average model. If $K = 1$ in equation (2.12) the model reduces to a Cartesian sequential test as in (i) above. As $K \to \infty$ on the other hand the model tends to the random walk model of §3.2. But this conjectured result has not yet been proved.

(iii) The same result may be reasonably conjectured of a geometric moving average. This may be expressed in the form

$$y_n = \sum_{r=0}^{\infty} \lambda^r x_{n-r}, \qquad 0 \leqslant \lambda \leqslant 1, \tag{2.20}$$

where $x_i = 0$ for $i \leqslant 0$. If $\lambda = 1$ this gives the random walk model of §3.2. As $\lambda \to 0$ on the other hand, $y_n \to x_n$, leading to the Cartesian model above. Again the suggested result cannot yet be proved. However Roberts (1959) has found that a geometric moving average is comparable in practice to an arithmetic moving average of similar total variance.

(iv) The sequential sampling method suggested by Page (1954) is equivalent to a sequential probability ratio test with starting point at 0 and boundaries at 0 and h.

Whenever the random walk crosses the boundary at 0, the test begins again from 0, and a detection is reported as soon as the walk reaches the boundary at h. So the test might be regarded as a series of independent trials of variable duration.

In a two-choice reaction experiment there are two possible ways in which the environment might change and so a decision model would include two tests of the type suggested by Page carried out simultaneously. The performance of this combined test is complicated and will not be investigated here. It is sufficient to remark that because this decision procedure is a compromise between a series of independent trials on the one hand and a sequential probability ratio test on the other, it is reasonable to expect that the distribution of reaction time when an error is made will show the same characteristic as in the examples above, namely, that it will be intermediate between the distribution for the same response made correctly and that for a correct response to the same signal.

This qualitative result is important for two reasons: firstly, in the absence of any decisive argument, it seems likely that it holds for a wide variety of potential choice-reaction models which have only a partial memory for information available at earlier stages of the decision process (i.e. moving average schemes in general); secondly, there is a little evidence from Experiments 1 and 2 of Chapter 5 suggesting that the result does not hold in practice. The foregoing argument therefore bears on the way in which a human subject collects and stores information in a choice-reaction experiment and hence on the sort of theory that should be constructed. This question will be discussed further in §7.6 in the light of the experimental evidence to be presented there.

2.7. The sequential probability ratio test in psychology.

Stone (1960) was the first to suggest the use of the sequential probability ratio test as a model for choice-reaction times. Wald and Wolfowitz (1948) have shown that this test is optimal among all statistical tests in the sense of requiring the smallest average size of sample for any given pair of error probabilities. Stone derived two results suitable for experimental test. Firstly, in a two-choice experiment the distribution of reaction time is the same whether the response is correct or an error. Secondly, assuming a condition of symmetry nearly equivalent to that of p. 127, he derived equations relating the mean reaction times and variances conditional on each signal to the probabilities of each sort of error. Finally, under the optimality condition of p. 128 Stone derived equation (A.12) for the unconditional mean reaction time. The sequential probability ratio test is the backbone of the model presented in Chapter 3, and I am indebted to Stone for the idea.

Fitts, Peterson and Wolpe (1963) and Fitts (1966) have made an intuitive empirical use of Stone's model and Laming (1962), McGill (1963), Edwards (1965), Audley and Pike (1965) and Casterette (1966) have added to the theoretical discussion. Edwards' contribution is the most distinctive. He has developed a normative Bayesian model for information processing, taking explicit account of costs, pay-offs and prior probabilities, which is applied, among other things, to choice-reaction times. It is necessary that costs and pay-offs are exactly controlled in the experiment and that the subject maximises his expected reward. For such an experiment some very specific predictions were derived. Edwards treatment of Stone's suggestion is quite different in spirit from the information-theoretic treatment here. The experiments of Chapter 5 are not suitable to test Edwards' normative model and a formal consideration of costs and pay-offs is outside the scope of this monograph.

McGill (1963) has reformulated Stone's model in terms of neural impulse counts. One counter is connected only to a source of "neural noise", while another counter registers impulses derived from the signal with noise superimposed. The critical variable is the difference between the two counters and Carterette (1966) has treated this formally as a random walk. Audley and Pike (1965) have discussed the same formal model, considering multiple choices as well, in terms of implicit responses (Audley, 1960). These models are related to the general information model developed here with Poisson-distributed random variables (p. 134).

There are two other ways in which the sequential probability ratio test has been used in psychology. One of them is the treatment of response latency in psychophysical tasks. Carterette, Friedman and Cosmides (1965) and Wolfendale (1967) studied signal detection tasks and Pickett (1967) a pattern perception task, and all three compared their response times with the sequential probability ratio model, among other stochastic models. In these experiments the stimuli were exposed continuously until the subject made his response, so that, in principle, sampling time was unlimited. On the other hand the subjects appear to have striven for maximum accuracy without consideration of the time taken. Carterette *et al.* reported that their subjects did not even know that response times were being recorded; the other two writers are not specific on this point. When the subject is not instructed to respond quickly, the sequential probability ratio test does not obviously represent the best strategy and the significance of response latencies is uncertain.

The other use of the sequential probability ratio test concerns the integration of information over a series of discrete stimulus presentations; it is exemplified by Becker (1958), Swets and Green (1961) and Sanders and Ter Linden (1967). Becker studied a sequential sampling problem in which the subjects had to distinguish between two binomial populations. Successive samples were experimentally discrete and identifiable, and Becker found that, although the sequential model represented the subjects' behaviour to a first order, there remained some discrepancies not accounted for. Sanders and Ter Linden conducted a similar experiment to that of Becker and found that their subjects were prepared to make increasingly risky decisions as the sample increased in length. Swets and Green allowed their subjects to make a series of discrete observations, as many as they liked, of the same signal in an auditory detection task. In general their subjects did not integrate information over successive observations and, even under special experimental instructions, did not approximate a sequential probability ratio procedure. These experiments might reasonably be compared with Edwards' normative Bayesian model, but they are not within the field of application of the choice-reaction model presented in Chapter 3.

CHAPTER 3

THE RANDOM WALK MODEL

3.1. Introduction.

In this chapter a new theory of choice-reaction times is presented, alternative to the Communication Theory which was criticised in Chapter 1. When there are only two alternative signals the decision process can be represented by a random walk between two parallel absorbing boundaries. A two-choice model is described in §3.2 using a simple example as a mathematical illustration. This is a development of the two-choice sequential model proposed by Stone (1960). When there are more than two alternative signals the geometric representation of the decision process is more complicated (a random walk between curvilinear boundaries) and there are few explicit mathematical results. However a multi-choice counterpart to the two-choice model is described in §3.2.1. and illustrated by reference to a three-choice experiment. Both models are developed to points at which meaningful comparisons with experimental results can be made. For the most part intuitive arguments are used, illustrated with diagrams, so that the models should be intelligible to those with only a little knowledge of mathematics. A rigorous mathematical development of the theory for both two- and multi-choice experiments may be found in Appendices A and B.

§3.3 contains a formal statement of four axioms interleaved with comments on their meaning and application. In §3.4 the mathematical relation between the measure of information used here and the measure used in Communication Theory is explored; the choice between these measures has implications of fundamental importance to the theoretical study of choice-reaction times. §3.5 contains five comparisons between the random walk model and previous experimental results, and §3.6 lists three predictions which will be compared with further experimental results in Chapter 5.

3.2. The random walk model.

In a typical choice-reaction experiment the subject is shown on each of a series of trials a signal drawn at random from a finite set, $\{S_A, S_B, S_C \ldots \}$, which is well-known to the subject. To each signal in this set there corresponds a unique member of the response set, $\{R_A, R_B, R_C \ldots \}$. The subject is asked to make the appropriate response as soon as possible after each signal appears. The response that the subject actually makes (which may not be the correct one) and the time he takes to make it are recorded.

For the present, consider an experiment with only two alternative signals, S_A and S_B. It is a fundamental hypothesis of the model that the subject takes in from the signal a stream of information, which continues so long as the signal is present. This information is inherent in the sensory input arising from the signal, and successive increments of information are mutually independent. Another way of looking at the stream of information is to think of the subject as making a series of brief observations of the signal, represented by the series of random variables, x_1, x_2, x_3, ... The X_r (X is used to denote a generic random variable and x a specific value of X) are assumed independent and identically distributed, but with their common distribution dependent on the signal presented. It must be emphasised that this series of observations made by the subject does *not* correspond to a series of discrete presentations of the same signal, but rather, to each discrete presentation of a signal there corresponds a complete series of observations. The observations do not have any interpretation

FIGURE 3.1

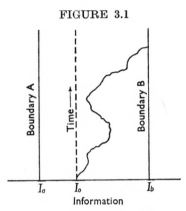

The random walk generated by I_n.

in terms of experimental events or conditions; they are purely hypothetical and have been introduced merely to assist in the presentation of the model. The axiomatic approach followed in the appendices treats the observations as a mathematical construction, as in proving certain theorems in Euclidean geometry.

δI will be used to represent an increment of information, and the increment contributed by the rth observation is defined by

$$\delta I_r = \log\{P(x_r|S_B)/P(x_r|S_A)\}, \tag{3.1}$$

where $P(x|S_i)$ is the probability of $X = x$ given that S_i is presented. Suppose, by way of illustration, that the X_r are normal, (μ_a, σ^2) or (μ_b, σ^2) according as S_A or S_B is presented. Then

$$\delta I_r = \log \frac{(2\pi\sigma^2)^{-\frac{1}{2}} \exp\{-(x_r-\mu_b)^2/2\sigma^2\}}{(2\pi\sigma^2)^{-\frac{1}{2}} \exp\{-(x_r-\mu_a)^2/2\sigma^2\}} = \frac{\mu_b-\mu_a}{\sigma^2}\left(x_r - \frac{\mu_b+\mu_a}{2}\right). \tag{3.2}$$

Suppose further that each observation takes a time δt. Then the total information available to the subject at time $n\,\delta t$ is $I_n = I_0 + \sum_{r=1}^{n} \delta I_r$, where I_0 is the *a priori* information, $\log\{P(S_B)/P(S_A)\}$, which the subject has before the signal is presented. If the probability of S_B being presented is p, then $I_0 = \log\{p/(1-p)\}$. Hence

$$I_n = \log\{p/(1-p)\} + \{(\mu_b-\mu_a)/\sigma^2\} \sum_{r=1}^{n} \{x_r - \tfrac{1}{2}(\mu_a+\mu_b)\}. \tag{3.3}$$

This is the equation of a random walk and a possible realisation of it is shown in Figure 3.1. In that figure I_0 is the point from which the random walk starts. If S_B is presented, the expectation of δI, $E\{\delta I|S_B\} = (\mu_b-\mu_a)^2/2\sigma^2$, and the walk will usually drift to the left as in Figure 3.1; if S_A is presented, $E\{\delta I|S_A\} = -(\mu_b-\mu_a)^2/2\sigma^2$

and the walk will usually drift to the right. But the actual path followed by the walk is random and may go to the left when S_B is presented or to the right when S_A is presented.

A response is made as soon as $I_n \leqslant I_a$ or $I_n \geqslant I_b$ for some value of n, where $I_a < I_0 < I_b$. If $I_n \leqslant I_a$, response R_A is made; if $I_n \geqslant I_b$, response R_B. I_a is the information required to make response R_A; it is constant and is represented in Figure 3.1 by an absorbing boundary parallel to the time axis. I_b is represented by another absorbing boundary. The random walk continues until it reaches one boundary or the other and it can be shown (see Theorem A.1 on p. 126) that this is certain to happen, sooner or later. It is clear from the description of the random walk that when S_A is presented the walk will not necessarily finish on boundary A with $I_n = I_a$. Although this will usually happen, there is a small probability, denoted by α, that the random walk will go to the right and finish on boundary B. In that case the wrong response will be made. In the same way there is a small probability, β, that the random walk will finish on boundary A when S_B is presented. α and β are therefore the probabilities of the two sorts of error, making R_B when S_A is presented and making R_A when S_B is presented.

Substituting from equations (3.2) and (3.1) into (3.3),

$$I_n = \log \frac{P(S_B)}{P(S_A)} + \sum_{r=1}^{n} \log \frac{P(x_r|S_B)}{P(x_r|S_A)} = \log \frac{P(S_B)P(x_1 \dots x_n|S_B)}{P(S_A)P(x_1 \dots x_n|S_A)}, \tag{3.4}$$

since the X_r are mutually independent. I_n is therefore the logarithm of the likelihood ratio[1] at time $n\,\delta t$. Now R_A is made as soon as $I_n = I_a$; hence

$$I_a = \log\{P(S_B)P(R_A|S_B)/P(S_A)P(R_A|S_A)\} = \log\{p\beta/(1-p)(1-\alpha)\}, \tag{3.5}$$

since $\alpha = P(R_B|S_A)$ and $\beta = P(R_A|S_B)$, and

$$I_b = \log\{p(1-\beta)/(1-p)\alpha\}. \tag{3.6}$$

The time taken to reach a decision is directly proportional to the number of observations required. Let this number be n; then the decision latency is $n\,\delta t$. Expressions for the mean decision latency in terms of the probabilities of error may be obtained by substituting for I_0, I_a, I_b, $E\{\delta I|S_A\}$ and $E\{\delta I|S_B\}$ in equations (A.8) and (A.9) on p. 127:

$$E\{n\delta t|S_A\} = \frac{-2\sigma^2\delta t}{(\mu_b - \mu_a)^2}\left\{\alpha \log \frac{1-\beta}{\alpha} + (1-\alpha) \log \frac{\beta}{1-\alpha}\right\}, \tag{3.7}$$

$$E\{n\delta t|S_B\} = \frac{2\sigma^2\delta t}{(\mu_b - \mu_a)^2}\left\{(1-\beta) \log \frac{1-\beta}{\alpha} + \beta \log \frac{\beta}{1-\alpha}\right\}. \tag{3.8}$$

These equations give the mean conditional duration of the random walk, that is, the average time required to reach a decision conditional on each signal. But in any realisable experiment it is the complete reaction time that is measured, and this includes the time taken by the sensory input to pass through the perceptual system (input time) and the time required to execute the response (movement time) as well as the time required to reach a decision. In analysing experimental data it will be assumed that input time and movement time are independent of the experimental variables under comparison (cf. Stone 1960, pp. 251–3), so that these factors appear as an additive constant in the mean reaction time equations,

e.g. $$E\{R.T.|S_A\} = E\{n|S_A\}\,\delta t + constant.$$

This assumption can be verified experimentally and this has been done (see pp. 62–3).

[1] For a simple exposition of the use of likelihood ratios in testing statistical hypotheses see Mood and Graybill (1963, §12.2).

Now, α, β and the distribution of reaction time conditional on each signal depend on the position of the boundaries. If the subject is shown a series of signals in which S_A and S_B occur in the proportions $1-p : p$, and if he is required not to make a proportion of errors greater than ϵ, then there is a unique position for each boundary such that his average reaction time shall be a minimum. This problem is equivalent to minimising

$$E\{n\} = (1-p)E\{n\,|\,S_A\}+pE\{n\,|\,S_B\} \qquad (3.9)$$

subject to

$$(1-p)\alpha+p\beta \leqslant \epsilon. \qquad (3.10)$$

It is obvious that the minimum will only be attained when (3.10) is an equality and the minimum value of $E\{n\}$ may be found by differentiating (3.9) with respect to α subject to equation (3.10). At the minimum

$$\alpha = \epsilon(p-\epsilon)/(1-p)(1-2\epsilon), \qquad \beta = \epsilon(1-p-\epsilon)/p(1-2\epsilon) \qquad (3.11)$$

and

$$E_{min}\{n\} = \frac{2\sigma^2}{(\mu_b-\mu_a)^2}\left\{(1-2p)\log\frac{p}{1-p} + (1-2\epsilon)\log\frac{1-\epsilon}{\epsilon}\right\}. \qquad (3.12)$$

These values represent an optimal choice amongst the possible sets of decision parameters and this optimum will prove important in the examination of the experimental evidence.

By substitution in equations (3.5) and (3.6) it is found that $I_a = \log\{\epsilon/(1-\epsilon)\}$, $I_b = \log\{(1-\epsilon)/\epsilon\}$. But, applying Bayes theorem to equation (3.5),

$$I_a = \log\{P(S_B\,|\,R_A)/P(S_A\,|\,R_A)\}.$$

Hence $\epsilon = P(S_B\,|\,R_A)$, the probability of error when response R_A is made. In the same way it can be shown that $P(S_A\,|\,R_B) = \epsilon$, too. Herein lies the optimal nature of the minimum: every response is made with the same degree of accuracy; a decision is made as soon as the probability of being wrong reaches a certain small constant value, ϵ. Figure 3.2 shows a realisation of the random walk process with

FIGURE 3.2

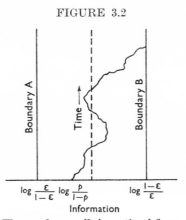

The random walk in optimal form.

the boundaries in their optimal positions. Since the positions of the boundaries are independent of p, and this factor enters only into the position of the starting point, it follows that the effect of bias in the series of signals presented can be represented by an appropriate choice of starting point for the random walk, while the boundaries remain fixed.

3.2.1. The multi-choice random walk model.

There are certain difficulties in presenting a model for decisions between three **or** more alternative signals, because the response criterion takes a form such as that of inequality (B.8, p. 155) and does not admit an explicit solution. There are three ways of looking at the multi-choice model, each of which yields its own particular insights. These three ways will be illustrated by reference to a three-choice decision process.

(i) Let S_A, S_B and S_C be three alternative signals which appear with *a priori* probabilities p_a, p_b, and p_c. After some information relevant to the decision has been processed, these *a priori* probabilities are replaced by the *a posteriori* probabilities, π_a, π_b and π_c. Any set of values (π_a, π_b, π_c) may be interpreted as the homogeneous coordinates of a point in the interior or on the boundary of triangle ABC in Figure 3.3, and the course of the decision process can be represented by the movement of a point

FIGURE 3.3

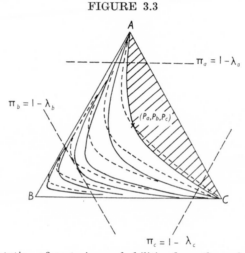

The plane representation of posterior probabilities for a three-choice decision process. (Solid curves are n-contours, broken curves $\Sigma \, x_r$ -contours).

inside the triangle. The process always starts from (p_a, p_b, p_c) and terminates as soon as it reaches one of the three straight lines, $\pi_a = 1-\lambda_b$, $\pi_b = 1-\lambda_b$, and $\pi_c = 1-\lambda_c$. These three boundaries separate those points at which R_A, R_B and R_C respectively are initiated from those points at which the decision process is continued. The position of each boundary determines the accuracy with which the corresponding response is made; λ_i is the probability of error when response R_i is initiated.

Without some assumptions about the information structure of the decision process there is little more that can be said. §B.3. develops a model in which the signals are represented by a set of univariate normal distributions with a common variance. This normal multi-choice model exhibits an interesting structure which will be described here. The mean values associated with the signals can be ordered on a single dimension, and it will be supposed that $\mu_a < \mu_b < \mu_c$.

Consider the sequence of observations $x_1, x_2, x_3, \dots$. Σx_r and n are joint sufficient statistics for this sample and they each determine a family of contours. After exactly n_0 observations the point reached by the decision process must lie on the contour determined by $n = n_0$ (equation B.10, p. 155). This is a smooth curve joining the vertices A and C, and several curves of the family are shown as the solid curves in Figure 3.3. Similarly if $\Sigma\, x_r = y$ (regardless of the value of n), the decision process must have reached a point on the contour determined by $\Sigma\, x_r = y$ (equation B.11). This is also a smooth curve joining the vertices A and C, and several curves of this family are shown as the broken curves in Figure 3.3. The point reached by the decision process always lies at the intersection of the contours determined by n and $\Sigma\, x_r$ and is unique. Each observation takes the process forward to somewhere on the next n-contour, always moving in the same direction, and the decision process can never enter the shaded area of the triangle in Figure 3.3, which corresponds to

FIGURE 3.4

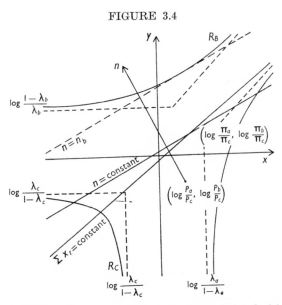

The log. probability ratio representation of a three-choice decision process.

negative values of n. The two contours through the starting point have zero parameters.

With four alternative signals the set of posterior probabilities may be interpreted as the interior and boundary points of a tetrahedron. The boundaries are then planes cutting off each of the vertices. The two sets of contours (equations B.10 and B.11) become families of three-dimensional curves inside the tetrahedron, lying on a certain two-dimensional surface (equation B.12). This idea may be extended analytically to any finite number of alternative signals, although the geometrical interpretation cannot be extended beyond four. Equation (B.12) implies that the decision process is confined to a two-dimensional surface irrespective of the number of alternatives, and is therefore capable of two-dimensional representation.

(ii) Figure 3.4 shows the three-choice decision process referred to a different set of coordinates, $x = \log\,(\pi_a/\pi_c)$, $y = \log\,(\pi_b/\pi_c)$. The boundaries, which formerly were straight lines, are now exponential curves, but the contours (equations B.10 and B.11) have become families of parallel straight lines. Each decision process starts at the point $\{\log (p_a/p_c), \log (p_b/p_c)\}$. Changes in the *a priori* signal probabilities may be represented by choosing a different starting point, while the boundaries remain fixed. With each observation the decision moves a unit distance perpendicular to the n-contours and a variable distance along them, executing a one-dimensional random walk with exponential absorbing boundaries.

The n-contours do not cut the boundary R_B for n less than a certain minimum value, n_b, given by equation (B.15). So it is not possible to initiate R_B until at least n_b observations have been made. This result follows essentially from the fact that μ_a, μ_b and μ_c can be ordered on a single dimension with μ_b between μ_a and μ_c. S_B is called an "interior" signal, R_B an "interior" response, while S_A and S_C are called "exterior" signals, R_A and R_C "exterior" responses. This is a distinction between one-sided and two-sided discriminations. If a subject judges a signal less than S_B, then he simultaneously judges it less than S_C and identifies it as S_A. But if he judges it smaller than S_C only, he must make another independent comparison before he can identify it as S_B. It is shown in §B.3.3 that an exterior signal in general affords information at a faster rate than does an interior signal and hence is easier to distinguish from the remainder of the signal set.

With more than three alternative signals the log (probability ratio) transformation (equation B.13, p. 156), transforms into more than two dimensions. The boundaries become exponential hypersurfaces. But the decision process is still represented by a one-dimensional random walk in a plane, which is the transform of equation (B.12). The two families of contours still transform into families of parallel lines in this plane. $(m-1)$ dimensions, however, are required to represent all the possible positions of the starting point, and a change in the position of the starting point may be accompanied by a change in the plane of the random walk. As in a three-choice decision, certain of the boundaries—all but the two corresponding to exterior responses—cannot be reached until certain minimum numbers of observations have been made.

(iii) Although (B.8), regarded as an equality, does not have any explicit solution, it is possible to determine those values of $(n, \Sigma\, x_r)$ for which each response should be made and to tabulate the values in a two-way table or to plot them in a two-dimensional diagram. This may be done however many alternative signals there are, since n and $\Sigma\, x_r$ are joint sufficient statistics for the sequence of observations. Figure 6.1 (p. 86) shows a map for a five-choice decision process. The course of the decision is represented on this map by the movement of the point $(n, \Sigma\, x_r)$. It starts from the origin and a response is initiated as soon as it strikes one of the boundaries. The boundaries are calculated for specific values of the *a priori* probabilities, but it is sometimes possible to use the map with other *a priori* probabilities by starting from some point other than the origin. Such a map brings the multi-choice model to a form in which it might have practical application.

3.3. The axioms.

A formal statement of the axioms for a discrimination between m mutually exclusive signals, S_i, $i = 1, ..., m$, is given here, with some comments on the application of each one. The comments are interleaved between the axioms, and the formal statement of each axiom is distinguished from the surrounding text by the use of italics. The axioms are a minimal set and are stated in the most general form likely to be needed either here or in future developments of the theory. They do not contain all the assumptions implicit in the illustrative models of §3.2 and §3.2.1. A mathematical exposition may be found in Appendices A and B.

(1) *Whilst a signal is present the subject extracts information from it continuously. The total information available to the subject at time t is a single valued random function of t.*

The stream of information from the signal to the subject is the primary concept of this theory. The total information, including *a priori* information, available to the subject at time t in favour of S_i against all other signals will be denoted by $I(S_i : \underset{j \neq i}{\cup} S_j; t)$ (where $\underset{j \neq i}{\cup} S_j$ denotes the union of the signals), though this will often be abbreviated to $I(S_i; t)$. The "sequence of observations" introduced in §3.2 is of the nature of a mathematical construction. Axiom 2, below, contains the necessary and sufficient conditions for this construction to be possible. In the statement of this axiom $\boldsymbol{I}(t)$ denotes the vector with components $I(S_i; t)$, $i = 1, ..., m$, $g(\boldsymbol{I}|S_i; t)$ is the probability density function of $\boldsymbol{I}(t)$ when S_i is presented, and $\pi_i(t) = [1 + \exp\{-I(S_i; t)\}]^{-1}$.

(2) (i) $\sum_{i=1}^{m} \pi_i(t) = 1$ *for each* $t \geqslant 0$.

   (ii) *For each fixed* $t \geqslant 0$, $p_i g(\boldsymbol{I}|S_i; t)/\pi_i(t)$ *is independent of* i, $i = 1, ..., m$, *where* p_i *is the* a priori *probability of* S_i.

   (iii) *For all* $t_2 > t_1 \geqslant 0$ *the random variables* $log\{\pi_i(t_2)\pi_j(t_1)/\pi_j(t_2)\pi_i(t_1)\}$ *and* $log\{\pi_i(t_1)/\pi_j(t_1)\}$ *are independent.*

The mathematical conditions of Axiom 2 are properties of the information stream provided by nature. They are equivalent to the verbal requirement that the information stream shall contain all that is relevant to the discrimination to be made and nothing that is irrelevant. For example:

(i) If $\Sigma \pi_i > 1$, certain information necessary for the discrimination is missing, and if $\Sigma \pi_i < 1$ the information available is confused with certain other irrelevant information relating to alternatives that do not have to be discriminated.

(ii) The second condition is essential to the definition of the information measure.

(iii) The third condition requires that disjoint increments of information relating to a discrimination between any pair of signals shall be independent and therefore additive. It also ensures that the information stream shall be consistent between different experiments. In Appendix B it will be shown that each signal in an experiment can be represented by a probability distribution that is, as it were, a specification of the signal. The information stream is consistent between experiments in the sense that it is possible so to choose the probability distributions representing a set of signals that they are common to any experiment employing a subset of the signals.

If these three conditions hold, the sequence of observations may be constructed with as fine a dissection of the time continuum as one pleases. If, on the other hand, the sequence of observations was regarded as the primary concept, and information defined in terms of *a priori* probabilities and the observations, then the conditions of Axiom 2 would become basic properties requiring proof.

Theorem B.3 (p. 149) imposes an additional condition on the information stream such that the rate of accumulation of information for a discrimination between any pair of signals shall be stationary in time. It is then possible to use the mathematics of discrete random walks (e.g. Wald, 1947), yet at the same time to derive exact results because there is no "excess over the boundary". The sequence of observations is a mathematical approximation to the continuous information flow, and this approximation can be made arbitrarily close by choosing a sufficiently fine dissection of the time continuum. This is the purpose behind the particular axiomatic approach that has been followed here. On the other hand the additional condition of Theorem B.3 has not been incorporated in the axioms because, as is pointed out on p. 149, it ought not to hold exactly in practice. Nonetheless the resultant mathematical model appears to be an adequate approximation to the experimental situations studied here.

(3) *The $g(I|S_i; t)$ are all distinct for sufficiently large t.*

This axiom is equivalent to saying that the signals to be discriminated are indeed distinguishable.

(4) *Provided no other response has previously been made, R_i is initiated as soon as $I(S_i: \bigcup_{j \neq i} S_j; t) \geqslant log \{(1 - \lambda_i)/\lambda_i\}$, $i = 1, ..., m$, where the λ_i are constants, $0 < \lambda_i < 1$, such that $\lambda_i + \lambda_j < 1$ for all i, j.*

A response is made as soon as the probability of its being wrong reaches a certain small fixed value λ_i (which may be different for different responses). The response criteria are specified with "$\geqslant$" because the random walk may jump over the boundary. The λ_i in the criteria are such that no two criteria can be satisfied simultaneously and the response is therefore unique. By making each response to a predetermined accuracy a most efficient use is made of the available information, and since the information flow is variable, so the decision latency is also inherently variable.

(5) *In the absence of any experimental instructions or conditions to the contrary the subject will tend to optimise his decision process in the sense of achieving the fastest total performance compatible with a given proportion of errors.*

A "decision process", in the context of this axiom, means a choice of $\lambda_1, ..., \lambda_m$. The axiom means that in suitable circumstances and in the light of the experimental conditions, including the *a priori* signal probabilities, subjects choose the $\lambda_1, ..., \lambda_m$ such that the mean decision latency is a minimum subject to a maximum average probability of error. Unless the experimental instructions or conditions make one sort of error more important than another, it seems reasonable that the subject should learn from his experience of the experimental task, and perhaps from similar perceptual problems outside the experiment, to make responses as quickly as possible compatible with a given overall level of accuracy. This axiom leads to a further simplification of the theoretical results, and it is worthy of note that my interest was first drawn to the random walk model because a prediction derived from this axiom in particular seemed to make sense of some otherwise surprising experimental data (see §3.5.5 and Table 3.1).

The expression "suitable circumstances" used above has deliberately been left ill-defined. Experiments 1 and 2 of Chapter 5 would be expected to conform to Axiom 5, while Series 3 and 4 of Experiment 3, in which a differential emphasis was laid upon the two sorts of error, would not. It seems likely that Axiom 5 will sometime be replaced by a more general axiom expressed in terms of loss functions, valid for a wider range of experiments (including Experiment 3) and leading to a more general concept of optimality (see Edwards, 1965). In the present state of knowledge, however, Axiom 5 is as much as can confidently be postulated.

In the mathematical theory of Appendices A and B there is implicit the assumption that measurements on successive trials of a choice-reaction experiment are statistically independent. This is not so, as will be seen in Chapter 8. It will appear there that the data from a choice reaction experiment form a complicated time-series whose probability structure has yet to be elucidated. Until this structure is understood little worthwhile analysis of the data can be done beyond an examination of the mean level of performance. Predictions of variances will certainly be inaccurate, but predictions of mean reaction times and numbers of errors will be perturbed by effects of second order only. The testing of the theory against the experimental evidence will therefore be confined to an examination of mean performance.

3.4. The relation of the random walk model to Communication Theory.

The random walk model bears some relation to the ideal communication channel analogy, which has traditionally been used to analyse choice-reaction experiments (see Chapter 1). The idea of a mean reaction time, which is a linear function of the average amount of information required to reach a decision, is common to both models (cf. Shannon, 1949, Theorem 11 and Theorem A.2, p. 126 here). The measures of information used are different, but nonetheless related.

The measure of information used in the random walk model is defined by Kullback (1959, p. 5) as follows:

If X is a generic random variable and x a specific value of X,

$$I(H_1: H_0; x) = \log\{P(x\,|\,H_1)/P(x\,|\,H_0)\}$$

is *the information in $X = x$ for discrimination in favour of H_1 against H_0*, where H_0 is usually identified with S_A, H_1 with S_B. But if H_0 is identified with the whole set of signals and H_1 with S_i, one member of the set, which is uniquely specified by $X = x_i$,

$$I(S_i : H_0; x_i) = -\log P(S_i),$$

and the average information per signal

$$E\{I(S_i: H_0)\,|\,H_0\} = -\sum_i P(S_i)\log P(S_i)$$

(Kullback, 1959, p. 7, Examples 4.1, 4.2), which is Shannon's measure of entropy. Hence the uncertainty about which signal will appear is equal to the average information contained in specifying the signal, in favour of the hypothesis that the specification is correct, against the alternative hypothesis that the information is irrelevant.

This comparison between prior and posterior probabilities has been developed by Powers (1956) in terms of generalized probability measures:

The information contained in an event, E, is $\int \log(d\nu/d\rho)\,d\nu$, where ρ is the prior and ν the posterior probability measure and ν is absolutely continuous with respect to ρ. This measure is a generalization of that due to Wiener (1948, p. 75). It is the information contained in the event E in favour of the hypothesis that such events may be taken at their "face value" against the alternative hypothesis that they tell us nothing we did not know before. If E is a message received through a communication channel, then the question is whether such messages mean what they appear to mean, or whether they are independent of the input to the channel. Hence the average information transmitted by such messages, $\iint \log(d\nu/d\rho)\,d\nu d\rho$ (a generalization of Shannon's measure) is a measure of the fidelity of the channel. The uncertainty of the message source is equal to the fidelity required for undistorted transmission and channel capacity is "fidelity per unit time". $\int \log(d\nu/d\rho)\,d\nu$ is a measure of "how much" message has been sent; it does not specify which message has been sent.

On the other hand Fano (1961, p. 27) defines information *about* an event:

$I(S_i;\ x) = \log\{P(S_i|x)/P(S_i)\}$ is *the information in* $X = x$ *about* S_i. From this definition he develops the familiar formulae of Communication Theory.

$$\int \log(d\nu/d\rho)\ d\nu = \sum_i P(S_i|x)\log\{P(S_i|x)/P(S_i)\}$$

is the average information about the signals $\{S_i\}$. If S_A and S_B are two exclusive and exhaustive signals, the information about S_A does not bear a simple relation to that about S_B, but

$$I(S_B;\ x) - I(S_A;\ x) = I(S_B:S_A;\ x),$$

so that Kullback's measure of information may be defined in terms of Fano's measure. Kullback's measure is the information (Fano's measure) about S_B minus the information about S_A in $X = x$.

The distinction between the random walk model presented here and the traditional Communication Model is not an arbitrary choice between two related measures of information. The Communication Model on the one hand supposes that the information presented to the subject is clear cut and decisive, and that its form can somehow be adjusted to pack it into the minimum message space required for transmission. Mean reaction time is determined by this minimum message space. In the random walk model on the other hand, the form of the information is invariant, so that it might be associated with the sensory impressions generated by the signals. Although it is possible to collect sufficient information to give a very high degree of confidence about external events, it is not possible to achieve absolute certainty within any finite time. The random walk process implies efficient use of the information and reaction time is determined by the time taken to collect a prescribed quantity.

The distinction therefore is between two different sorts of information. They have different measures, the one a undirected measure of quantity, the other a vector, and they lead to quite disparate mathematical theories. The Communication Theory focusses principally on *a priori* probabilities, the random walk model principally on errors.

3.4.1. The relation of the random walk model to other uses of statistical decision theory in psychology.

It is obvious from the extent to which the mathematical exposition follows Wald (1947) that the theory proposed here is but a development of Stone's (1960, p. 253) suggestion that a sequential probability ratio test might be used to represent the decision process in a two-choice reaction task. The formulation of the model published by Laming (1962) represents an interim stage of this development. In its present form the theory is applicable to multi- as well as two-choice tasks. It is here expressed in terms of information, but this is only a change of terminology in the interests of axiomatic simplicity, rigour and clarity.

There is a less direct connection with the signal detection theory of Swets, Tanner and Birdsall (1961). The relation with the work of Becker (1958), Swets and Green 1961) and Sanders and Ter Linden (1967), where the sequential probability ratio test has also been used as a model, is tenuous. In these last two papers observations were defined as discrete, experimentally observable and controllable events. This is quite different to the way in which the idea of an observation has been used here (see p. 31).

3.5. Comparisons with previous work.

Most previous studies have been made in the context of Communication Theory, and the published data have usually been summarised in ways which do not permit comparison with the random walk model. Errors have usually been ignored and the relationship between reaction time and *a priori* signal probability has been regarded as fundamental. In the random walk theory the fundamental relation is that between reaction time and the probabilities of error. *A priori* signal probability enters only through Axiom 5, which is not an invariable rule. In order to facilitate meaningful comparisons with previous results, which would otherwise be difficult, it will be assumed (so far as is reasonable) that the decision process is both symmetric and optimal.

The following five comparisons with previous results can now be made:

(*a*) *Mean reaction time as a function of* $P(S_B)$. Figure 3.5 compares equation (A.12) with the corresponding equation (1.3) from Communication Theory. Both equations are symmetric in p and $(1-p)$ and only one half of each curve is shown. The constants

FIGURE 3.5

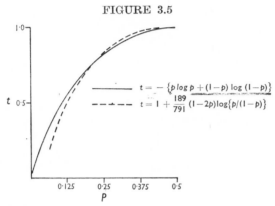

A comparison of the random walk equation (A.12) with the corresponding equation from Communication Theory (1.3). (The constants of equation A.12 have been chosen to make it coincide with equation 1.3 at $p = \frac{1}{2}$ and $p = \frac{1}{4}$.)

in the random walk equation have been chosen to make the two curves coincide at $p = \frac{1}{2}$ and $p = \frac{1}{4}$. Over the range of p-values that has usually been studied ($0.1 < p < 0.9$) there is little vertical separation between these curves.

(*b*) *Mean reaction times to individual signals.* Theorem A.4 (p. 129) shows that the response to the frequent signal is faster than that to the infrequent one. This, as an experimental result, was obtained by Hyman (1953). He also found that while equation (1.3), with constants estimated by a regression of series mean reaction time on series entropy, fitted the data well, equation (1.4), with the same values of the constants did not in general give adequate predictions of mean reaction times conditional on given signals. In a biased two-choice series the difference between the two conditional means was not so great as a consideration of the respective signal entropies would require. But the argument of §A.3.1 on the basis of the random walk model leads to a discrepancy from equation (1.4) in precisely this direction.

Another way of looking at this result is afforded by Figures 3.6 and 3.7. The mean reaction time to S_A, derived from the random walk model, is shown as a function of p in Figure 3.6 and of $-\log(1-p)$ in Figure 3.7; the series mean is shown as a dotted line. If in an experiment involving several series of signals equation (1.3) is fitted by a linear regression on entropy of (i) the series means, (ii) the mean reaction times to

S_A and S_B, it is clear that different sets of coefficients will be obtained, with a greater slope in case (i). This was Hyman's finding.

(c) *Comparison of B- and C- reactions.* Donders (1868) found that the C-reaction was faster than the B-reaction. Equation (A.45) shows that this result follows from

FIGURE 3.6

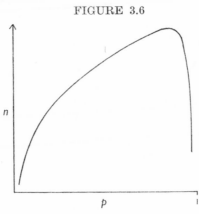

$E\{n|S_A\}$ as a function of p.

FIGURE 3.7

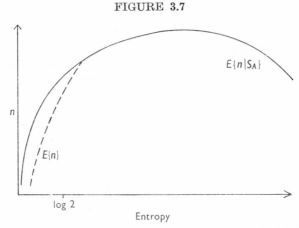

$E\{n|S_A\}$ and the unconditional $E\{n\}$ as functions of entropy.

the random walk model for a substantial range of values of p, where p is the *a priori* probability of the signal to which a response has to be made. If errors are made on, say, 3 per cent of all signals presented, then this result is true for the range, $0.35 < p < 0.97$.

(d) *Asymmetry between two signals.* Laming (1962, Experiment 1), found that a pack of cards containing 30 long stripes and 18 short ones took longer to sort than a pack containing 18 long and 30 short, and Shallice and Vickers (1964, p. 43) found that when the two lines were equiprobable more errors were made on the short lines than on the long. These results are compatible with the random walk model provided some asymmetry between the two signals is postulated. Asymmetric random walks are discussed in §A.5, and it is shown there that if the short stripe affords information at a faster average rate than does the long stripe, the minimum mean reaction time for a given average probability of error will be less for a pack with a majority of short stripes than for a pack with the corresponding majority of long stripes.[2]

(e) *Ratio of numbers of errors.* Laming (1962, Experiment 2), in a two-choice experiment with unequal signal frequencies found that more errors were made in response to the infrequent signal than in response to the frequent one. The total numbers of errors of each sort recorded in that experiment are shown in Table 3.1 together with

TABLE 3.1.   ERROR SCORES FROM LAMING (1962, EXPERIMENT 2) COMPARED WITH PREDICTIONS[3] FROM EQUATION (A.13).

$P(S_A) = 1-p$	0·25	0·375	0·5
Error scores:			
Total errors $\vert S_A$	212	175	159
Total errors $\vert S_B$	31	55	83
Total errors	243	230	242
$\hat{\epsilon}$ = errors/trials	0·018	0·017	0·018
Ratios of error scores:			
$\hat{R}_\epsilon = \dfrac{\text{total errors } \vert S_A}{\text{total errors } \vert S_B}$	0·15	0·31	0·52
Predicted $R_\epsilon = (1-p-\hat{\epsilon})/(p-\hat{\epsilon})$	0·31	0·59	1·00
Ratios of error rates:			
$(\hat{\beta}/\hat{\alpha}) = \hat{R}_\epsilon(1-p)/p$	0·05	0·19	0·52
Predicted $(\beta/\alpha) = R_\epsilon(1-p)/p$	0·10	0·35	1·00
$(\hat{\beta}/\hat{\alpha}) = \hat{R}_\epsilon/R_\epsilon$	0·48	0·53	0·52

the ratios of these numbers predicted from equation (A.13). The observed distributions of errors are all weighted too heavily towards S_A, but this might be so because S_A was not more frequent than S_B in any of the experimental conditions. In any case the similarity between the predicted and the observed ratios is interesting.[4]

No attempt will be made to discuss the effects of discriminability (Crossman, 1955; Welford, 1960, §2.5), stimulus-response compatibility (Fitts and Seeger, 1953) or practice (Mowbray and Rhoades, 1959) in terms of the random walk model. So far

[2] It is necessary here that the faster average information rate be associated with the short stripe rather than the long one, and this is perhaps the opposite of what one would expect. If the decision process is represented by a normal model with unequal variances (§A.4.2), then the greater variance must be associated with the short stripe; similarly if the decision process is represented by a Poisson model (§A.4.3), the greater Poisson parameter must correspond to the short stripe.

[3] The predictions are technically estimates obtained by inserting an estimated parameter into equation (A.13).

[4] This result more than any other first encouraged me to explore the random walk model as an alternative to Communication Theory. It is ironic that the same theoretical prediction can be obtained from Communication Theory by adjusting the coding of the messages to achieve the shortest average message length compatible with a given accuracy of transmission: I did not realise this at that time. Equation (A.13) is true of any system in which every response is made with the same probability of error.

as it has been stated here the theory is concerned only with relations between reaction times and probabilities of error for a given set of signals. It seems likely that effects such as those mentioned above will prove capable of representation in terms of certain parameters of the probability distributions constructed to represent the signals. But the experiments reported in Chapter 5 do not bear upon these issues and they will not be discussed here.

3.6. Three predictions from the model.

A. *In a two-choice experiment the ratio between the numbers of errors of each sort changes with bias in the signal sequence and approximates a certain optimal value* $R_\epsilon(S_B/S_A)$.

B. *In a two-choice experiment that signal which elicits the faster reaction, on average, has the smaller probability of error, and conversely.*

C. *For a given response the distribution of reaction time is the same whether the response is correct or an error.*

Prediction A has been stated before (Laming, 1962). For a symmetric decision process the value of the error ratio is $(1-p-\epsilon)/(p-\epsilon)$, given by equation (A.13); for an asymmetric process the value is bounded by inequality (A.41). Fitts, Peterson and Wolpe (1963) pointed out that the two probabilities of error conditional on the responses may be very different from the probabilities conditional on the signals. Equation (A.13) is equivalent to equal probabilities of error conditional on the responses.

Prediction B seems to be original. It is a restatement of Theorem A.5 (p. 129) which is exact only for a symmetric decision process; but the prediction is approximately true in the presence of small asymmetries (see p. 138). Essentially, if the subject is more ready to make one response, rather than the other, there is a reduction in errors and reaction time conditional on the corresponding signal. It does not matter whether the greater readiness is created by a biased signal sequence or by other methods such as differential instructions and rewards.

Prediction C was proved by Stone (1960, Appendix 1) for two-choice experiments. In §B.2.1 it is established for multi-choice experiments, and it can also hold for certain responses only and not for others in the same experiment. Schouten and Bekker (1967) have found errors faster than correct responses in a two-choice experiment, while Fitts (1966) failed to find any difference at all using a four-choice task. Seven experiments reported in Chapter 5 will be evaluated with reference to each of these predictions. The labels A, B and C will be used to indicate the results relevant to each prediction and the discussion of these results in Chapter 6.

CHAPTER 4

THE APPARATUS AND THE EXPERIMENTAL PROCEDURE

4.1. Introduction.

The same experimental task was used in all the experiments of Chapter 5. It was designed to simulate the card-sorting task used by Laming (1962) and, at the same time, to provide a complete record of individual signals, responses and reaction times listed in chronological order. It is convenient to describe here those details that are common to the experiments as a whole. Attention will be confined to those factors which are essential to an appreciation of the experiments and to their interpretation.

4.2. The signals and the Multiple Dodge Tachistoscope.

The signals used were vertical white stripes, 0·50 in. wide and of various lengths, mounted on black cards. In all the two-choice experiments the lengths were 4·00 in. and 2·83 in ($\log_2$ ratio $= \frac{1}{2}$). These signals were chosen because they were similar to those used in the card-sorting and because there was no frame round the stripe when shown to the subject. They were presented to the subject in a Multiple Dodge Tachistoscope,[1] which afforded a near instantaneous onset of the signal without any associated cues.

In its simple form the Dodge tachistoscope has a half-silvered mirror placed at an angle of 45° to the line of sight. On each side of the mirror is an electric light and a card. The cards are placed symmetrically with respect to the mirror, such that one of them is viewed by looking straight through the mirror, and the other, appearing in the same spatial position as the first, is seen by reflection in the mirror. Usually one of the cards carries a picture while the other is blank. The whole is contained in a light-tight box with a small aperture for viewing. Only one light is on at a time and only the corresponding card can be seen. If the current is switched from the "blank" to the "picture" light and back again, the picture is exposed for a well defined period of time.

Here there were five Dodge tachistoscopes mounted in series. Plate 4.1 shows a photograph of the device with the inside exposed. Five cards, each with a lamp in the same relative position, were arranged in echelon and viewed through a system of nine parallel plates of plain unsilvered window glass, such that the light from each card was reflected in one and transmitted through four plates of glass before entering the observer's eye. The five different paths traversed were optically equivalent, and the image of each signal card was coincident with a plain black card placed on the back wall of the tachistoscope, which was viewed when no signal was present by looking

---

[1] The author is indebted to Mr. R. L. Gregory of the Department of Experimental Psychology, Cambridge University, for suggesting the use of this device.

straight through all the mirrors. A viewing aperture, 7 in. × 4 in., was cut in the front wall of the tachistoscope and the subject sat some seven feet away.

Aluminium shields were placed round each lamp and in certain other places to prevent light shining into adjacent signal compartments. The interior of the tachistoscope, except for the reflecting surfaces around each lamp, was painted matt black. There were a few extraneous visual cues. The plain sheets of glass produced double images, by reflection at both front and back, and the signal appeared as a white stripe with fuzzy sides. The fuzziness, the light intensity and the black shadows at the sides of the signal varied a little from signal to signal, but these differences were negligible compared with the difference in length of the white stripes.

Nine-inch miniature discharge lamps were used in the tachistoscope. They had a special phosphor content, which gave a cold bluish light and a very short afterglow. In the chronologically earlier experiments (Nos. 1, 3, 6 and 7) the lamps were switched by relays, but later (Nos. 2, 4 and 5) a valve circuit was substituted.[2] With the latter circuit the rise and fall times were about 500 and 200 microseconds respectively. The output from each lamp was about 5 watts, and the illumination of the signal as seen by the subject was typically between 2·5 and 3·0 ft. lamberts. The experiments were mostly done with daylight excluded from the room and the signals were then easy to see.

4.3. The response keys and the recording apparatus.

The subject made his response by pressing one of a set of five keys, shown in Plate 4.2. Each key consisted of a strip of resin-bonded laminated paper, 4½ in. long and ¾ in. wide, pivoted at one end. Underneath was a microswitch and a pressure of about 4 oz. was required on the end of the key to operate the microswitch. The configuration of the keys was arranged so that they could be operated comfortably by the fingers and thumb of one hand. In the two-choice experiments, however, the two outside keys and the index fingers were used as in Plate 4.2. The depression of a response key caused the signal to disappear.

In the chronologically earlier experiments (Nos. 1, 3, 6 and 7) the sequence of events was controlled by a relay circuit and the data were recorded by hand. The experimenter had a list of signals which he presented to the subject one by one by pressing an appropriate key. The subject's response was shown to the experimenter by a set of lights, and the reaction time was measured to a hundredth of a second with a dekatron counter. These details had to be written down before the next signal was presented, so that the inter-trial interval (between a response and the following signal) was variable, averaging about two and a half seconds. The subject had a form of warning signal in the click from the experimenter's keys, and for Experiments 6 and 7 a buzzer was added specifically for this purpose.

In the chronologically later experiments (Nos. 2, 4 and 5) the programming of the signals and the recording of the data were automatic. The sequence of signals to be presented was punched in code in paper tape and the data were recorded in the same way. Reaction times were measured in milliseconds and the sequence of events in the experiment was controlled by a transistor switching circuit, whose latency was

---

[2] The author is indebted to Dr. A. Carpenter of the Medical Research Council's Applied Psychology Research Unit, Cambridge, for suggesting this means of switching and for designing the circuit.

PLATE 4.1

The Multiple Dodge Tachistoscope with the top removed.

PLATE 4.2

The response keys.

negligible compared with the unit of measurement. The inter-trial interval could be set to any chosen value up to 4096 milliseconds.

4.4. The subjects and the experimental procedure.

The subjects were volunteer university students and were occupied for about one hour each. They were not paid for taking part in the experiment. At the start of each session the task was explained to the subject. He was shown the signals and the corresponding response keys, and he was practised until there no longer appeared any uncertainty about the signal-response relations. Then the subject was tested with four or five series of signals (usually 200 signals/series) arranged in random order. The order of presentation of the signals was predetermined by means of random number tables and was the same for all the subjects in any one experiment. Subjects worked continuously throughout each series, but rested for about two minutes between series.

The subjects were told little about the ultimate purpose of the experiment, lest it influence their performance, and leading questions were put off until they had finished the session. Instructions relating to speed and accuracy were deliberately vague. The subjects were told to make each decision "as quickly as possible", but usually no more than this. It was assumed that each subject tends to do the experimental task with that degree of accuracy that feels right to him. If an attempt is made to make the subject take a different attitude to the experimental task, his performance is likely to be less stable with a tendency to revert to the preferred level.

The subjects obtained some knowledge of their performance during the experiment. In the two-choice experiments they invariably realised when they had made a mistake, and in all except Experiments 1 and 3 (for which the necessary apparatus was not available) they were informed of their mean reaction time on completing each series. This was done to help maintain their interest in the experiment.

CHAPTER 5

THE EXPERIMENTS

5.1. Introduction.

In this chapter each experiment is described in turn followed by a section presenting some of its results. Only those results which are pertinent to the three predictions on p. 44 and certain others which yield information about the details of the probabilistic structure of the decision process are presented here, and this material is evaluated in Chapter 6. Those results which are pertinent to other reaction-time models are described in Chapter 7, and Chapter 8 contains a sequential analysis of the two-choice data. This arrangement of the material has been adopted because a prediction from the random walk model may be compared with several or even all of the sets of experimental data, and the interpretation of the results is therefore best delayed until all the relevant evidence has been presented.

The experiments are listed in the table of contents. Those details common to them all—the apparatus and the general procedure—have already been described in Chapter 4. The descriptions given here include only those details peculiar to individual experiments. The design of each experiment is usually specified in one or more tables, and in the enumeration of the tables in this chapter there is an extra digit (the middle one), which is the number of the corresponding experiment.

The presentation of the results from each experiment usually follows a set pattern. Sections which are pertinent to any of the three predictions of p. 44 are clearly labelled. The testing of Prediction C required a little ingenuity in the treatment of the data; the details of this treatment may be found in the appendices, §C.1. An attempt has been made to be rigorous in the treatment of the data. But in some places, notably in comparisons with the multi-choice model of §B.3, only a tentative and heuristic treatment has been possible.

Some details of these experiments will appear more reasonable in the light of certain restrictions on the experimental method. Subjects were easy to come by, but were only available for one period of one hour each. Partly for this reason, partly for the increased validity of the results, these experiments were designed as "once only" tests of a relatively large population of subjects. Practice at the experimental task was strictly limited, in order to obtain the maximum of working data from each subject. The first experiment of Laming (1962) underlined the need for each subject to be tested under all the experimental conditions. So the length and number of signal series and the character of the design of each experiment were closely determined. One set of apparatus permitted the control of several interesting factors, and the experiments fall into a regular pattern.

5.2. Experiment 1: Variation of *a priori* signal probability—1.

It is evident from the work of Hyman (1953) and Crossman (1953) that *a priori* signal probability is an important determinant of choice-reaction time. Laming

(1962) obtained evidence from sorting packs of cards showing, for a two-choice task at least, that equation (1.2) is at best an approximation of limited accuracy, and he also demonstrated other effects of signal probability, notably in the distribution of errors. But Laming's experiments with cards did not clarify the role of *a priori* signal probability. An interpretation of this role, alternative to that of equation (1.2) is implied in Chapter 3, p. 33. In order to test the theory a more sophisticated repeat of Laming's (1962) second experiment was attempted.

Four groups of six subjects were tested with five two-choice random series of 200 signals, with $P(S_A) = 0.25$, 0.375, 0.5, 0.625 and 0.75. Table 5.1.1. shows the order

TABLE 5.1.1. VALUES OF $P(S_A)$ IN THE SIGNAL SERIES OF EXPERIMENT 1.

	Order of series in experimental session				
Group	*1st*	*2nd*	*3rd*	*4th*	*5th*
K	0.25	0.375	0.5	0.75	0.625
L	0.375	0.25	0.5	0.625	0.75
M	0.75	0.625	0.5	0.25	0.375
N	0.625	0.75	0.5	0.375	0.25

in which the series were given to the subjects. The signals used have already been described on p. 45. The subjects responded to the long line with the left forefinger and to the short line with the right forefinger. Before starting each series the subjects were told how many of each signal it contained. They were instructed to go as fast as they could, not worrying too much about mistakes. This experiment was the first to be done and was programmed and recorded by hand. The subjects did not receive any indication of their speed.

5.2.1. Results of Experiment 1.

Prediction A: The relation between error scores and *a priori* signal probability.

Table 5.1.2 shows the error scores summed over all 24 subjects, together with certain parameters estimated from them. The prediction relating to these data is expressed in equation (A.13)

$$R_\epsilon\left(\frac{S_B}{S_A}\right) = \frac{\text{Expected no. of errors}|S_B}{\text{Expected no. of errors}|S_A} = \frac{1-p-\epsilon}{p-\epsilon}, \tag{5.1}$$

where ϵ is the mean probability of error. This might also be expressed

$$\beta/\alpha = (1-p)(1-p-\epsilon)/p(p-\epsilon), \tag{5.2}$$

where α and β are as defined on p. 32.

In Table 5.1.2 $\hat{R}_\epsilon$ and $(\hat{\beta}/\hat{\alpha})$ are estimated from the numbers of errors actually observed, while predicted values for these parameters are obtained by putting $\epsilon = \hat{\epsilon}$ in equations (5.1) and (5.2). It is clear from the values of $(\hat{\beta}/\hat{\alpha})$ that the ratio between the two probabilities of error varies considerably from one series to another in the predicted direction, but the range of this variation is not so great as equation (5.2) predicts. If (5.2) were exactly correct, the index $\hat{R}_\epsilon/R_\epsilon$ in the bottom line of Table 5.1.2 would be unity throughout.

A statistical test of Prediction A is summarised in Table 5.1.3. This test is based upon the individual error scores lest a very few subjects making many errors should

TABLE 5.1.2. ERROR SCORES AND PARAMETERS IN EXPERIMENT 1.

$P(S_A) = 1-p$	0·25	0·375	0·5	0·625	0·75
Error scores:					
Total errors $\lvert S_A$	78	108	73	67	60
Total errors $\lvert S_B$	58	77	90	114	81
Total errors	136	185	163	181	141
$\hat\epsilon =$ errors/trials	0·028	0·038	0·034	0·038	0·029
Ratios of error scores:					
$\hat R_\epsilon = \dfrac{\text{total errors} \lvert S_B}{\text{total errors} \lvert S_A}$	0·74	0·71	1·23	1·70	1·35
Predicted $R_\epsilon = (1-p-\hat\epsilon)/(p-\hat\epsilon)$	0·31	0·57	1·00	1·74	3·27
Ratios of error rates:					
$(\hat\beta/\hat\alpha) = \hat R_\epsilon(1-p)/p$	0·25	0·43	1·23	2·83	4·05
Predicted $(\beta/\alpha) = R_\epsilon(1-p)/p$	0·10	0·34	1·00	2·90	9·81
$(\hat\beta/\hat\alpha)/(\beta/\alpha) = \hat R_\epsilon/R_\epsilon$	2·38	1·25	1·23	0·98	0·41

dominate the outcome. Since in this experiment ϵ is small relative to p, equation (5.1) is approximately equivalent to

$$p(Expected\ no.\ of\ errors\lvert S_B) = (1-p)(Expected\ no\ of\ errors\lvert S_A), \qquad (5.3)$$

so the index

$$D = (1-p)(No.\ of\ errors\lvert S_A) - p(No.\ of\ errors\lvert S_B)$$

should have a mean value approximately zero. For each series there are 24 values of D and these have been subjected to a t-test yielding the 0·05 confidence intervals, values of t and two-tailed probability levels shown in Table 5.1.3. Combining the five

TABLE 5.1.3. A SUMMARY OF THE T-TEST APPLIED TO THE INDEX
$D = \{(1-p)(No.\ of\ errors\ \lvert S_A) - p(No.\ of\ errors\ \lvert S_B)\}$ IN EXPERIMENT 1.

$P(S_A)$	0·25	0·375	0·5	0·625	0·75
5% Confidence interval	−0·42 −1·58	0·60 −1·21	0·42 −1·12	0·68 −0·76	1·75 0·26
t, (23 d.f.)	−3·58	−0·70	−0·95	−0·10	2·81
p, (2-tailed)	0·0016	0·4885	0·3520	0·9204	0·0100

probability levels by the method suggested by Fisher (1934, §21.1) gives $\chi^2 = 25\cdot8$ with 10 d.f., which is significant at the 0·005 level.

5.2.2. The order of the test series.

The evidence given above is not conclusive against Prediction A because the error scores depend in part upon the order in which the test series were given to the subject. Table 5.1.4 presents a comparison between the four experimental groups; each cell shows

    (i) position in the order of presentation,

    (ii) $(Total\ errors\lvert S_A)$, $(Total\ errors\lvert S_B)$,

(iii) $\dfrac{\hat{R}_\epsilon}{R_\epsilon} = \left(\dfrac{p-\hat{\epsilon}}{1-p-\hat{\epsilon}}\right)\left(\dfrac{Total\ errors\,|\,S_A}{Total\ errors\,|\,S_B}\right),$

(iv) a "direction of movement" symbol. " → " indicates that the value of p for the present series is less than that for the series preceding it in order (i.e. movement to the right among the columns of Table 5.1.4). " ← " has the opposite meaning.

TABLE 5.1.4. INTERACTION BETWEEN EXPERIMENTAL CONDITIONS AND ORDER OF SERIES IN EXPERIMENT 1 (For explanation see text).

$P(S_A)$		0·25	0·375	0·5	0·625	0·75
Group K	(i)	1st	2nd	3rd	5th	4th
	(ii)	16, 13	16, 11	14, 17	14, 29	19, 14
	(iii)	2·62	1·18	1·22	1·19	0·23
	(iv)		→	→	←	→
Group L	(i)	2nd	1st	3rd	4th	5th
	(ii)	24, 9	23, 27	28, 16	22, 20	21, 16
	(iii)	1·22	2·06	0·57	0·52	0·23
	(iv)	←		→	→	→
Group M	(i)	4th	5th	3rd	2nd	1st
	(ii)	25, 23	50, 22	24, 24	13, 38	12, 32
	(iii)	3·10	0·79	1·42	1·67	0·80
	(iv)	←	→	←	←	
Group N	(i)	5th	4th	3rd	1st	2nd
	(ii)	13, 12	19, 16	7, 23	19, 26	8, 19
	(iii)	2·94	1·45	3·28	0·79	0·74
	(iv)	←	←	←		→

TABLE 5.1.5. ORDER EFFECT IN EXPERIMENT 1

"Direction of Movement"	→	←
$\hat{R}_\epsilon/R_\epsilon > 1$	2	8
$\hat{R}_\epsilon/R_\epsilon < 1$	6	0

In Table 5.1.5 the indices, $\hat{R}_\varepsilon/R_\varepsilon$ are dichotomised at the value 1. There is a correlation between the value of $\hat{R}_\epsilon/R_\epsilon$ and the direction of movement which is significant at the 0·01 level on a Fisher exact probability test (Siegel, 1956, pp. 96–104).

The sign of the correlation is such that the ratio of the error scores, $\hat{R}_\epsilon$, is intermediate in value between the optimum for the given series, $(1-p-\epsilon)/(p-\epsilon)$, and the optimum for the series preceding it. The first series given to each group has of necessity been omitted from Table 5.1.5, but in each case the value of $\hat{R}_\epsilon/R_\epsilon$ is consistent with the hypothesis that the subjects begin the experiment as if the signals were appearing with equal frequencies. By the end of the first series an appropriate *a priori* expectation has been built up and this is carried over to the second series. It appears that subjects are slow to adapt to changes in *a priori* probability, slow relative to the length of an experimental series (200 signals), and they are slow to adapt even though they are informed in advance of the composition of each series.

Herein lies a sufficient explanation of the departures from Prediction A in Tables 5.1.2 and 5.1.3. If the cells in Table 5.1.4 corresponding to the series given first to each group are assigned a "direction of movement" symbol as if they had been preceded by a series with $p = 0·5$ (this is reasonable since each subject began with a short practice in which the signals appeared with approximately equal frequencies), then the following is true: The series with $p = 0.625$, 0.5 and 0.375 are approached equally often from either side and in the experimental sample as a whole the order effects should cancel, more or less. The series with $p = 0.75$ and 0.25 are always approached from the centre so that the order effect operates on each group in the same direction, causing every group to be more conservative than equation (5.1) predicts. It can be seen from Table 5.1.3 that the evidence against Prediction A comes entirely from the series with $p = 0.75$ and 0.25, where the deviations are in the directions one would expect from a knowledge of the order effect.

5.2.3. Prediction B: The qualitative relationship between mean reaction times and error scores.

Let t_A, t_B be the mean reaction times conditional on S_A, S_B and $\hat{\alpha}$, $\hat{\beta}$ the maximum likelihood estimates of α, β, defined on p. 32. Theorem A.5 (p. 129) requires that there should be an association between $t_A > t_B$ and $\hat{\alpha} > \hat{\beta}$, and between $t_A < t_B$ and $\hat{\alpha} < \hat{\beta}$. In Table 5.1.6 each test series is classified according to $t_A >$ or $< t_B$ and $\hat{\alpha} >$ or $< \hat{\beta}$. The data in this table are derived from the individual means and error scores of 120 series of reactions of which 13 are omitted from this analysis because $\hat{\alpha} = \hat{\beta}$. The mean reaction times averaged over all subjects are shown in Figure 5.1

FIGURE 5.1

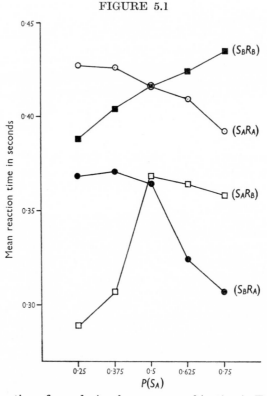

Mean reaction times for each signal-response combination in Experiment 1.

and the total error scores in Table 5.1.2. The five experimental conditions are not distinguished in Table 5.1.6 since Prediction B holds irrespective of the value of p.

Table 5.1.6 is evaluated as a 2×2 contingency table yielding a χ^2 variate with 1 d.f., corrected for continuity (Siegel, 1956, equation 6.4). But since the prediction is a correlation in a specified direction, a one-tailed test is appropriate and the probability

TABLE 5.1.6. QUALITATIVE RELATION BETWEEN MEAN REACTION TIMES AND ERROR SCORES IN EXPERIMENT 1.

	$t_A > t_B$	$t_A < t_B$
$\hat{\alpha} > \hat{\beta}$	36	12
$\hat{\alpha} < \hat{\beta}$	21	38

usually associated with the χ^2 variate should be halved. Here the correlation is in the predicted direction and $\chi^2 = 14 \cdot 75$ with 1 d.f., which is significant at the 0·001 level.

5.2.4. Prediction C: The relation between error- and correct-reaction times.

Theorem B.6 (p. 152) requires that the distribution of reaction time conditional on a given response shall be the same whether the response is correct or an error. Although each subject makes only a very few errors, it is possible to rank each error reaction time with respect to the corresponding sample of correct reaction times, and if the prediction is true this rank will have a rectangular distribution. Further, it is possible to collate the ranks from different subjects, from different responses and from different series and compare the sample so obtained with the theoretical rectangular distribution by a Kolmogorov-Smirnov one sample test (Siegel, 1956, pp. 47–52), which is sensitive to any kind of discrepancy. An exact specification of this procedure may be found in Appendix C, and the results are shown in Table 5.1.7.

TABLE 5.1.7. THE KOLMOGOROV-SMIRNOV STATISTICS AND THE NUMBER OF ERRORS IN EACH SAMPLE ARISING FROM THE TEST OF PREDICTION C IN EXPERIMENT 1. (A double underlining indicates significance at the 0·01 level.)

$P(S_A)$	0·25	0·375	0·5	0·625	0·75	All series together
Response R_A	0·247	0·259	0·239	0·379	0·395	0·297
	58	77	90	114	81	420
Response R_B	0·468	0·407	0·306	0·298	0·407	0·358
	78	108	73	67	60	386
Both responses together	0·358	0·334	0·260	0·348	0·391	0·326
	136	185	163	181	141	806

Obviously Prediction C is not true. From an examination of the distributions under comparison it appears that the difference is principally one of location; errors are everywhere faster than the same response made correctly. This is confirmed by Figure 5.1 which shows the mean reaction time for each signal-response combination in each series. Under variation of *a priori* signal probability the mean reaction time when an error is made, say $(S_B R_A)$, changes in much the same way as the mean reaction time for the same response made correctly, $(S_A R_A)$, but in contrary fashion to the mean reaction time for a correct response to the same signal, $(S_B R_B)$. It looks as though the difference in mean between the distributions of error- and correct-reaction times for the same response is more or less constant, independent of changes in the bias of the signal sequence.

5.3. Experiment 2: Variation of *a priori* signal probability—2.

In Experiment 1 there was found an important effect of the order in which the test series were given to each subject, and on pp. 50–2 it was shown that this order effect afforded a sufficient explanation of the departure from Prediction A. There are two ways in which this order effect might be circumvented: if the series were, say, 400 signals long and the first half of each series was omitted from the analysis, then the size of the order effect would be reduced, perhaps much reduced. Alternatively, it is possible to compare two groups experiencing the experimental conditions in opposite orders in such a way that the order effect is balanced in the experimental sample as a whole. This second alternative was preferred because it was the more practicable at that time, and it lead to Experiment 2.

As in Experiment 1 four groups of six subjects were each tested with five two-choice series of 200 signals. Table 5.2.1 shows the composition of the two sets of series and

TABLE 5.2.1. Values of $P(S_A)$ in the signal series of Experiment 2.

Order of series in experimental session

Groups	1st	2nd	3rd	4th	5th	6th	7th
K, M	0·5	0·875	0·75	0·625	0·5	0·375	0·25
L, N	0·5	0·125	0·25	0·375	0·5	0·625	0·75

the order in which they were given to the subjects. The first series (100 signals) was intended to give the subjects practice, and in this series only they were obliged to correct any mistakes they made. The second series was intended solely to balance the order effects on the third series, and it was omitted from the analysis. There follow the five test series, in which p increases or decreases by equal amounts between successive series. It was expected that the order effect would be balanced for all five test series, acting for Groups K and M in the opposite direction to that for Groups L and N. Table 5.2.2 shows the signal-response combinations pertaining to each group.

TABLE 5.2.2. Response forefingers in Experiment 2.

Signal	S_A	S_B
Height in ins.	4·00	2·83
Groups K, L	left	right
Groups M, N	right	left

This experiment was done with the apparatus in its ultimate fully automatic state, and the interval between each response and the subsequent signal was set at 1500 milliseconds. The subjects were told nothing about the composition of the test series, lest such information interact with the order effects. On completing each series subjects were told how long they had taken (the times were measured with a stop watch) to help maintain their interest in the experiment.

5.3.1. Results of Experiment 2.

Prediction A: The relation between error scores and *a priori* signal probability.

Table 5.2.3 shows the error scores summed over all 24 subjects, together with certain parameters estimated from them. This table shows the same details as Table 5.1.2,

TABLE 5.2.3. ERROR SCORES AND PARAMETERS IN EXPERIMENT 2.

$P(S_A) = 1-p$	0·25	0·375	0·5	0·625	0·75
Error scores:					
Total errors $\vert S_A$	79	74	70	58	28
Total errors $\vert S_B$	33	49	59	83	83
Total errors	112	123	129	141	111
$\hat{\epsilon}$ = errors/trials	0·023	0·026	0·027	0·029	0·023
Ratios of error scores:					
$\hat{R}_\epsilon = \dfrac{\text{total errors}\vert S_B}{\text{total errors}\vert S_A}$	0·42	0·66	0·84	1·43	2·96
Predicted $R_\epsilon = (1-p-\hat{\epsilon})/(p-\hat{\epsilon})$	0·31	0·58	1·00	1·73	3·20
Ratios of error rates:					
$(\hat{\beta}/\hat{\alpha}) = \hat{R}_\epsilon(1-p)/p$	0·14	0·40	0·84	2·38	8·89
Predicted $(\beta/\alpha) = R_\epsilon(1-p)/p$	0·10	0·35	1·0	2·88	9·61
$(\hat{\beta}/\hat{\alpha})/(\beta/\alpha) = \hat{R}_\epsilon/R_\epsilon$	1·34	1·14	0·84	0·83	0·93

and the prediction relating to these data and the method of testing it have already been described on p. 49. The error scores in this experiment conform well to equation (5.1). The results of t-tests on the error indices

$$D = (1-p)(No.\ of\ errors\,|\,S_A)-p(No.\ of\ errors\,|\,S_B)$$

from individual subjects are summarized in Table 5.2.4, and the combined probability levels give $\chi^2 = 5\cdot33$ with 10 d.f., which is not significant.

TABLE 5.2.4. A SUMMARY OF THE T-TEST APPLIED TO THE INDEX
$D = \{(1-p)(No.\ of\ errors\,|\,S_A)-p(No.\ of\ errors\,|\,S_B)\}$ IN EXPERIMENT 2.

$P(S_A)$	0·25	0·375	0·5	0·625	0·75
5% Confidence interval	0·38 −0·80	0·41 −0·65	0·48 −0·94	0·83 −0·40	0·44 −0·42
t, (23 d.f.)	−0·75	−0·47	0·67	0·72	0·05
p, (2-tailed)	0·462	0·644	0·510	0·476	0·481

5.3.2. The order of the test series.

Table 5.2.5 shows the total error scores in the form

$$\{(No\ of\ errors\,|\,S_A),(No.\ of\ errors\,|\,S_B)\}$$

for each order of presentation of the test series. Groups K and M move from right to left in order among the columns of Table 5.2.5, and Groups L and N from left to

TABLE 5.2.5. ERROR SCORES FROM DIFFERENT GROUPS IN EXPERIMENT 2 IN THE FORM $\{(No.\ of\ errors\,|\,S_A),\ (No.\ of\ errors\,|\,S_B)\}$.

$P(S_A)$	0·25	0·375	0·5	0·625	0·75
Groups K, M	38, 26	35, 38	26, 39	23, 41	9, 45
Groups L, N	41, 7	39, 11	44, 20	35, 42	29, 38
χ^2, 1 d.f.	7·75	9·87	9·59	0·94	8·65

right. There is here the same slowness of adaptation to changes in *a priori* signal probability that was found in Experiment 1 (§5.2.2). The values of χ^2 in the bottom row of Table 5.2.5 are obtained by considering the four scores from each series as an independent 2×2 contingency table. Four of these values are significant at the 0·01 level and their sum $\chi^2 = 36\cdot80$ with 5 d.f. is significant at the 0·001 level. The effect on the individual error scores is to separate them partially into two groups, corresponding to the two series orders. Table 5.2.3 presents the mean of these two groups, and it appears that in this experiment the order effects were more or less balanced.

5.3.3. Prediction B: The qualitative relationship between mean reaction times and error scores.

In Table 5.2.6 the test series are classified exactly as in Table 5.1.6. The mean reaction times averaged over all subjects are shown in Figure 5.2 and the total error

TABLE 5.2.6. QUALITATIVE RELATION BETWEEN MEAN REACTION TIMES AND ERROR SCORES IN EXPERIMENT 2.

	$t_A > t_B$	$t_A < t_B$
$\hat{\alpha} > \hat{\beta}$	47	15
$\hat{\alpha} < \hat{\beta}$	7	48

scores have been presented in Table 5.2.3. Altogether there are 120 series of data, of which three are omitted because $\hat{\alpha} = \hat{\beta}$. The prediction and the method of testing it have already been described on p. 52. The correlation is in the predicted direction and $\chi^2 = 44\cdot1$ with 1 d.f., which is significant at the 0·001 level.

5.3.4. Prediction C: The relation between error- and correct-reaction times.

Table 5.2.7 summarises the results of a comparison between the distributions of error- and correct-reation times. The prediction tested and the approximate method of testing it have already been described on p. 53; an exact specification may be found in Appendix C.

Prediction C is clearly not true of this experiment. The difference detected by the test is principally one of location; as in Experiment 1 errors are everywhere faster than the corresponding correct responses. The mean reaction times for each signal-response combination are shown in Figure 5.2, which has a pattern very similar to

FIGURE 5.2

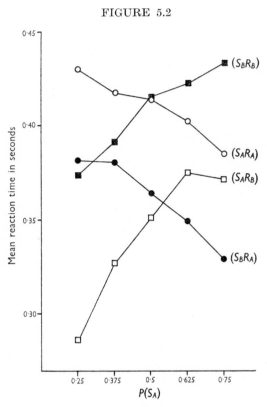

Mean reaction times for each signal-response combination in Experiment 2.

TABLE 5.2.7. THE KOLMOGOROV-SMIRNOV STATISTICS AND THE NUMBER OF ERRORS IN EACH SAMPLE ARISING FROM THE TEST OF PREDICTION C IN EXPERIMENT 2. (A double underlining indicates significance at the 0·01 level.)

$P(S_A)$	0·25	0·375	0·5	0·625	0·75	All series together
Response R_A	0·337	0·165	0·167	0·414	0·420	0·299
	33	49	59	83	83	307
Response R_B	0·488	0·440	0·317	0·260	0·329	0·367
	79	74	70	58	28	309
Both responses together	0·428	0·321	0·236	0·347	0·374	0·325
	112	123	129	141	111	616

that of Figure 5.1. As in Experiment 1, so here, it appears that the difference in mean between the distributions of error- and correct-reaction times is more or less independent of changes in the bias of the signal sequence.

5.4. Experiment 3: Variation of error scores by experimental instructions.

In the random walk model of Chapter 3 *a priori* signal probability is relevant only as a determinant of the parameters of the optimum decision process. If the probabilities of each sort of error, α and β, are specified, then the performance of the model for a given pair of signals is completely determined. Variation of *a priori* signal probability in Experiments 1 and 2 served as a means, a very effective means, of varying α and β. Any other means of varying the probabilities of error should produce a comparable result. In this experiment an attempt is made to do this by giving special experimen-

TABLE 5.3.1. EXPERIMENTAL   INSTRUCTIONS   AND   POINTS   AWARDED   IN EXPERIMENT 3.

Series	*1*	*2*	*3*	*4*	*5*
Groups K, K', M, M'	Careful, avoid mistakes. Max. points = 200, less 5/error	Faster. Max. points = 400, less 5/error	Respond quickly to S_B. Max. points = 400, less 3/error on S_A 7/error on S_B	Faster to S_B. Max. points = 400, less 2/error on S_A 8/error on S_B	"As fast as you possibly can."
Groups L, L', N, N'			Respond quickly to S_A. Max. points = 400, less 7/error on S_A 3/error on S_B	Faster to S_A. Max. points = 400, less 8/error on S_A 2/error on S_B	Max. points = 800, less 5/error

TABLE 5.3.2. RESPONSE FOREFINGERS IN EXPERIMENT 3 AND ORDER OF SERIES IN EXPERIMENTAL SESSION.

Signal	S_A	S_B	*Order of series in experimental session*
Height in ins.	4·00	2·83	
Groups K, L	left	right	**1**, 2, 3, 4, 5
K', L'	right	left	
Groups M, N	left	right	**5**, 4, 3, 2, 1
M', N'	right	left	

tal instructions before each of five test series, in which S_A and S_B appear equally often.

Eight groups of three subjects were tested with five two-choice series of signals. Each series contained 100 each of S_A and S_B, and was prefaced by special instructions. The instructions peculiar to each series are shown in Table 5.3.1. In series 3 and 4 there was an emphasis in the instructions on one of the two signals; this was on S_B for groups K, K', M, M', and on S_A for groups L, L', N, N'. Table 5.3.2 specifies the signal-response combinations and the order of the test series for each experimental group.

Besides the special experimental instructions a points system was used as an additional means of influencing the error probabilities. At the end of each series the subject's mean reaction time was estimated and points awarded, basically as follows: mean reaction time < 0.25 sec—200, < 0.30—175, < 0.35—150, and so on; $\geqslant$ 0.60—0. The scale was doubled for series 2, 3 and 4 and quadrupled for series 5. Points were deducted for every mistake made and the scale of these deductions is shown in Table 5.3.1. After completing each series the subject was informed of his mean reaction time, the mistakes he had made and the points he had scored.

This system of awarding points was crude, but at that time this was the only available way of putting relative values to speed and accuracy. By itself it had very little effect, as was shown by a few initial discarded sets of data. When it was coupled with the experimental instructions of Table 5.3.1 a reasonable spread of error scores was achieved; these scores, being numbers of errors occurring in 600 trials, are shown in Table 5.3.3. The encouragement given to the subjects was always phrased in terms

TABLE 5.3.3. ERROR SCORES IN EXPERIMENT 3 IN THE FORM
$\{(No. of errors | S_A), (No. of errors | S_B)\}.$

Series	1	2	3	4	5
Groups K, K'	15, 27	38, 39	31, 70	28, 84	68, 67
Groups L, L'	13, 17	33, 37	53, 30	85, 27	86, 54
Groups M, M'	15, 10	30, 33	26, 31	18, 58	53, 54
Groups N, N'	24, 29	28, 34	39, 36	43, 21	29, 28

of speed, and any explicit suggestion that they were required to make mistakes was carefully avoided. For groups M, M', N and N', who were given the test series in reverse order, the instructions prefacing the series were appropriately modified. One side effect of these instructions was an increased variability in performance. Some subjects responded well to the instructions, others relapsed part way through the series, while a few were hardly influenced at all. This method of varying the error probabilities was therefore not so effective as that of Experiments 1 and 2, but perhaps this was to be expected.

This experiment was done immediately after Experiment 1 with the apparatus in the same state as there. Under pressure to go fast some subjects tended a little to anticipate the signal and guess at the correct response. Where it was obvious that this had happened the measurement was repeated, but inevitably some anticipatory reaction-times were retained in the experimental data.

5.4.1. Results of Experiment 3.

Prediction B: The qualitative relationship between mean reaction times and error scores.

In Table 5.3.4 the test series are classified exactly as in Table 5.1.6, and the manner of evaluating the table has been described on p. 52. Altogether there are 120 series

TABLE 5.3.4. QUALITATIVE RELATION BETWEEN MEAN REACTION TIMES AND ERROR SCORES IN EXPERIMENT 3.

	$t_A > t_B$	$t_A < t_B$
$\hat{\alpha} > \hat{\beta}$	24	20
$\hat{\alpha} < \hat{\beta}$	18	36

of data, of which 22 are omitted because $\dot{\alpha} = \hat{\beta}$. The correlation is in the predicted direction and $\chi^2 = 3\cdot64$ with 1 d.f., which is significant at the 0·05 level on a one-tailed test.

5.4.2. Prediction C: The relation between error- and correct-reaction times.

The results of a comparison between the distributions of error- and correct-reaction times are presented in Table 5.3.5. The prediction and the approximate treatment of

TABLE 5.3.5.   THE KOLMOGOROV-SMIRNOV STATISTICS AND THE NUMBER OF ERRORS IN EACH SAMPLE ARISING FROM THE TEST OF PREDICTION C IN EXPERIMENT 3. (A double underlining indicates significance at the 0·01 level.)

Series	1	2	3	4	5	All series together
Response R_A	0·325	0·368	0·347	0·338	0·271	0·318
	83	143	167	190	203	786
Response R_B	0·254	0·332	0·321	0·315	0·333	0·304
	67	129	149	174	236	755
Both responses together	0·272	0·344	0·323	0·314	0·306	0·305
	150	272	316	364	439	1541

the data have been described on p. 53, and there is an exact specification in Appendix C. Here also there is overwhelming evidence against Prediction C. The difference is again principally one of location with errors everywhere faster than the corresponding correct responses.

5.5. Experiment 4: A comparison of the A-, B- and C-reactions.

There are two quite distinct objectives underlying this experiment. First it provides another means of making subjects vary their error probabilities. The C-reaction, in which the subject is instructed to make a response to only one of two alternative signals, may be represented by a random walk with one boundary at infinity. Provided the subject is allowed sufficient time to make a response, if he will, all his mistakes will consist of responses to the "no response" signal; the probability of an error of the other sort is zero.

The second objective is to compare the means and variances of choice-reaction times with those of simple reaction times (the A-reaction) measured under identical conditions. Suppose for the present that reaction time can be split into three components:

    input time, T_i,
    decision time, T_d
    and *movement time*, T_m,

where $T_d = 0$ for a simple reaction. Then the following questions will be investigated:

What is the approximate duration of T_d for the standard two-choice task used here? Is it independent of T_i and T_m?

Is T_i different for S_A and S_B?

Is T_m different for the left and right forefingers?

Twenty subjects, divided randomly into 10 groups of two, were each tested with five equiprobable series of 160 signals. Table 5.4.1 shows the composition of each series, the response instructions that went with it and the order in which the series were given to each group. The first series (of 100 signals) in each group was a practice

TABLE 5.4.1. (a) THE ORDER OF THE EXPERIMENTAL CONDITIONS, AND (b) THE ASSOCIATED INSTRUCTIONS IN EXPERIMENT 4.

(a) *Order of series in experimental session.*

Groups	1st	2nd	3rd	4th	5th	6th
J, J'	P	1	4	3	2	5
K, K'	P	2	1	5	3	4
L, L'	P	3	5	4	1	2
M, M'	P	4	3	2	5	1
N, N'	P	5	2	1	4	3

(b) *Series instructions.*

P, 1	B-reaction	Respond to both signals with different responses
1	C-reaction	Respond to S_A only
3	C-reaction	Respond to S_B only
4	A-reaction	Respond to both signals with right forefinger
5	A-reaction	Respond to both signals with left forefinger

TABLE 5.4.2. RESPONSE FOREFINGERS IN EXPERIMENT 4.

Signal	S_A	S_B
Height in ins.	4·00	2·83
Groups J, K, L, M, N	right	left
Groups J', K', L', M', N'	left	right

series, in which the subject was obliged to correct any mistakes he made. Thereafter the series are arranged in a Latin square design. Table 5.4.2 shows the signal-response combinations appropriate to each group.

This experiment was done with the apparatus in the fully automatic state of Experiment 2, and with the interval between each response and the subsequent signal set to 1500 milliseconds. Normally the signal disappeared when the subject made his response. But in series 2 and 3, if no response was made, the signal disappeared after 4096 milliseconds and the next signal appeared 1500 milliseconds later. In the simple reaction series, 4 and 5, the subjects tended to anticipate the signal. They were warned that any response made before the signal appeared would not be recorded and would have to be made again.

5.5.1. Results of Experiment 4.

The comparison of means and variances.

Table 5.4.3 shows the error scores, and the median values of the subject mean reaction times and variances for each series in this experiment. The calculation of the means and variances here includes error reaction times and this is also the case in subsequent tables, 5.5.3, 5.6.2, etc. The percentage of errors is substantially lower in the C-reaction than in the B-reaction, indicating a certain difference in attitude on the part of the subjects. Nonetheless the error scores vary in the way that was intended.

Although the median reaction times for the C-reaction are intermediate between that for the B- and those for the A-reaction, they are nearer the B-reaction median than Donders' (1868) results would lead one to expect. Every subject responded faster in both the A-reaction series than in any of the other three, but a comparison between the mean times for series 1, 2 and 3 showed no significant difference (Friedman

TABLE 5.4.3. ERROR SCORES, MEDIAN MEAN REACTION TIMES IN SECS. AND MEDIAN VARIANCES IN SECS². IN EXPERIMENT 4.

Series	1	2	3	4	5
Error scores:					
Total errors $\vert S_A$	68	0	44	—	—
Total errors $\vert S_B$	72	41	0	—	—
Total errors	140	41	44	—	—
$\hat{\epsilon}$ = errors/trials	0·0437	0·0128	0·0137	—	—
Median reaction time	0·419	0·384	0·385	0·228	0·220
Median variance	0·0078	0·0065	0·0072	0·0075	0·0077

Analysis of Variance by Ranks: $\chi_r^2 = 1\cdot6$ with 2 d.f.; Siegel 1956, pp. 166–172). This is probably a concomitant of the lower percentage of errors made in the C-reaction conditions. T_d for the standard two-choice task is approximately equal to the difference between the reaction time for a B-reaction and that for an A-reaction; here this difference is about 1/5th second.

The variances quoted in Table 5.4.3 are all of the same order, and there is no significant difference between them (Friedman Analysis of Variance by Ranks: $\chi_r^2 = 4\cdot64$ with 4 d.f.). It might have been expected that the B- and C-reactions would show greater variances than the A-reaction, and the important point here is that this has not been found to be so. This result suggests either that T_d is constant, or nearly so, throughout any one series (ample evidence will be cited on pp. 92–3 to show that this cannot be so), or that T_d is correlated with one or both of the other components of reaction time. However Snodgrass, Luce and Galanter (1967) have recently investigated this question in greater detail. They reached more complex and somewhat different conclusions, albeit under experimental conditions that differed from those here in critical details.

5.5.2. Differences in input and movement times.

Table 5.4.4 shows the mean reaction times for each signal-response combination under each experimental condition. The results of the analysis of the differences between these means are shown in Table 5.4.5.

Under the A-reaction condition a mean reaction time for each signal-response combination was obtained from every subject. So it is possible to calculate an input

TABLE 5.4.4. MEAN REACTION TIMES IN SECS. FOR EACH SIGNAL-RESPONSE COMBINATION IN EXPERIMENT 4.

	A-reaction		B-reaction		C-reaction	
	S_A	S_B	S_A	S_B	S_A	S_B
Right forefinger	0·2274	0·2271	0·4439	0·4012	0·4375	0·3883
Left forefinger	0·2242	0·2209	0·4109	0·4440	0·3854	0·4184

time (T_i), a movement time (T_m) and an interaction term $(T_i \times T_m)$ for each subject, and these variables are independent. There are therefore 20 measures of T_i and these are subjected to a t-test to see if their mean is significantly different from zero. T_m and $T_i \times T_m$ are treated in the same way and the results of these tests are shown in the top three lines of Table 5.4.5.

Under the B- and C-reaction conditions each subject contributes a mean reaction time for only two signal-response combinations and these two are diagonally opposed in the 2×2 tables of Table 5.4.4. There can therefore be no interaction term under these conditions. The difference $\{(Mean\ R.T.\,|\,S_B) - (Mean\ R.T.\,|\,S_A)\}$ represents

TABLE 5.4.5. RESULTS OF TESTS OF DIFFERENCES IN INPUT TIME AND MOVEMENT TIME IN EXPERIMENT 4.

Condition	Effect	Mean diff.	S.S.	d.f.	t	p
A-reaction	T_i	0·0018	0·00307	19	0·62	>0·50
	T_m	0·0047	0·00938	19	0·94	>0·30
	$T_i \times T_m$	0·0015	0·00235	19	0·61	>0·50
B-reaction	T_i	0·0050	0·00604	18	1·21	>0·20
	T_m	0·0048			1·17	>0·20
C-reaction	T_i	0·0081	0·00970	18	1·56	>0·10
	T_m	0·0110			2·12	<0·05

$T_i - T_m$ for groups J, K, L, M, N, who contribute the leading diagonals of the 2×2 tables, and the difference represents $T_i + T_m$ for groups J', K', L', M', N', who contribute the opposite diagonals. There are 10 independent measures of each of $(T_i - T_m)$ and $(T_i + T_m)$, and the problem reduces to a t-test between two independent samples. If the means of the two samples are the same, $T_m = 0$; if the means sum to zero, $T_i = 0$. Hence the bottom four rows of Table 5.4.5.

Only one of the seven t-values is significant (for T_m in the C-reaction), and that at only the 0·05 level. It is likely that this is a chance result. More particularly, the t-test assumes homogeneity of variances. Here the sample variances were significantly different at the 0·05 level (Variance ratio = 3·44 with 9, 9 d.f.) and if the test is adjusted to allow for this difference (cf. Welch, 1947) $t = 2·12$ is no longer significant.

Under the conditions of this experiment differences in input time and movement time were so small that they could not be detected. It follows that such differences can safely be ignored in the other two-choice experiments reported here. A slight reservation must be made however in respect of T_i in Experiments 1 and 3 (see p. 112).

5.5.3. Prediction B: The qualitative relationship between mean reaction times and error scores.

Series 1, 2 and 3 are classified in Table 5.4.6 exactly as in Table 5.1.6, and the manner of evaluating the table has been described on p. 52. The scores from series

TABLE 5.4.6. QUALITATIVE RELATION BETWEEN MEAN REACTION TIMES AND ERROR SCORES IN EXPERIMENT 4.

	$t_A > t_B$	$t_A < t_B$
$\hat{\alpha} > \hat{\beta}$	5 (16)	4
$\hat{\alpha} < \hat{\beta}$	4	4 (17)

2 and 3, provided at least one error is made, must necessarily fall in the bottom right and top left cells respectively; these scores are shown in brackets. The remaining scores are from series 1 (3 series have been omitted because $\hat{\alpha} = \hat{\beta}$) and show no correlation at all. But if the C-reaction scores are included (these certainly conform to Prediction B), $\chi^2 = 20 \cdot 48$ with 1 d.f., which is significant at the 0·001 level.

5.5.4. Prediction C: The relation between error- and correct-reaction times.

The results of a comparison between the distributions of error- and correct-reaction times is presented in Table 5.4.7. The prediction and the approximate treatment of

TABLE 5.4.7. THE KOLMOGOROV-SMIRNOV STATISTICS AND THE NUMBER OF ERRORS IN EACH SAMPLE ARISING FROM THE TEST OF PREDICTION C IN EXPERIMENT 4. (A double underlining indicates significance at the 0·01 level.)

Series	1	2	3
Type of reaction	B	C	C
Response R_A	0·282	0·955	—
	72	41	
Response R_B	0·408	—	0·940
	68		44

the data have been described on p. 53 and there is an exact specification in Appendix C. Since in the C-reaction conditions errors of only one sort were possible, there are two empty cells in the table. The evidence against Prediction C from the C-reaction conditions is even more decisive than that from the previous three experiments. Indeed, the error- and correct-reaction time distributions in series 2 and 3 are almost completely disjoint. Errors are again everywhere faster than correct responses.

5.6. Experiment 5 : Variation of the intertrial interval.

Although this experiment affords a test of the random walk model against variation of yet another parameter, this is not the primary objective here. The random walk model of Chapter 3 assumes implicitly that successive decisions are statistically independent. In practice this is not so; in Chapter 8 there will be presented abundant evidence of sequential relations in these experiments. The purpose here is to study these systematically. Bertelson (1961) showed that the time interval between each response and the subsequent signal (the intertrial interval) was one determinant of the sequential interactions. In this experiment the intertrial interval is varied systematically.

Five groups of five subjects were each tested with five equiprobable two-choice series of 200 signals. A different intertrial interval was set for each series. The intervals used, and the order in which the experimental conditions were given to each group are shown in Table 5.5.1. The first series (of 100 signals) in each session was for practice; thereafter, the intertrial intervals are arranged in a Latin square design. The response to S_A was made with the right forefinger, S_B with the left.

In the preceding experiments the signal remained visible until the subject made his response. If this had been the case in the short intertrial interval conditions here, the subject would have seen, when the signal changed, not a replacement of one signal by another, but a movement of the signal, a shortening or a lengthening. This "movement effect" is due to the persistence of vision, as in a cinema, and arises from an interaction between the images of the two successive signals on the retina. The perception is then qualitatively different and the discrimination easier. Accordingly, the signal was switched off after a fixed time interval in the short intertrial interval

TABLE 5.5.1. THE INTERTRIAL INTERVALS IN MILLISECONDS DEFINING THE EXPERIMENTAL CONDITIONS IN EXPERIMENT 5 AND THE ORDER OF THEIR PRESENTATION TO THE SUBJECTS.

	Order of series in experimental sessions					
Group	1st	2nd	3rd	4th	5th	6th
J	512	4096	1	64	512	8
K	512	512	64	8	4096	1
L	512	64	8	512	1	4096
M	512	8	4096	1	64	512
N	512	1	512	4096	8	64

conditions. On the other hand the signal could not be cut off short with an intertrial interval of 4 seconds, lest the subject missed the signal altogether, through being unprepared when it appeared. There was no easy solution to this problem. Different exposures were used with different intertrial intervals, and these are shown in Table 5.5.2, where "∞" indicates that the signal remained visible until the subject made his

TABLE 5.5.2. THE LENGTH OF EXPOSURE OF THE SIGNAL FOR EACH INTERTRIAL INTERVAL IN EXPERIMENT 5. (All times in milliseconds.)

Intertrial interval	4096	512	64	8	1
Exposure	∞	∞	256	192	192

response. For each series the exposure had to be short enough to prevent interaction between successive signals on all except a very small proportion of trials. On the other hand the exposure must not be so short as to increase the difficulty of the task. Data from another experiment (not reported here) suggested that the exposures in Table 5.5.2 were amply long enough.

This experiment was done with the apparatus in the fully automatic state of Experiment 2. Subjects were told in advance of each test series the approximate length of the intertrial interval (long, short, moderate, etc.) and whether the signal would be switched off before they made their response. An electromagnetic counter recorded errors as they were made, and the noise from this counter provided the subjects with a clear indication whenever they made a mistake. On completing each series subjects were told the total time they had taken and the number of mistakes they had made, in order to help maintain their motivation.

5.6.1. Results of Experiment 5.

General impressions.

A superficial impression of the effects of different intertrial intervals may be obtained from Table 5.5.3, which shows the error scores, the medians of the subject mean reaction times and the medians of the within subject variances for each signal and each intertrial interval. Errors increase uniformly as the intertrial interval decreases, with no systematic bias developing in their distribution. Variances increase likewise and so do reaction times, except for a slight reversal of this trend between the

TABLE 5.5.3. ERROR SCORES, MEDIAN MEAN REACTION TIMES IN SECS. AND MEDIAN VARIANCES IN SECS.^{2} IN EXPERIMENT 5.

Intertrial interval	4096	512	64	8	1
Error scores:					
Total errors $\vert S_A$	51	96	155	149	194
Total errors $\vert S_B$	43	92	160	215	193
Total errors	94	188	315	364	387
$\hat{\epsilon}$ = errors/trials	0·019	0·038	0·063	0·073	0·078
Median reaction times:					
Signal S_A	0·454	0·437	0·579	0·592	0·679
Signal S_B	0·455	0·446	0·578	0·593	0·653
Median variances:					
Signal S_A	0·0049	0·0051	0·0149	0·0277	0·0444
Signal S_B	0·0057	0·0064	0·0179	0·0212	0·0369

intervals 4096 and 512. This reversal is probably due to the greater temporal uncertainty attaching to the longer interval. But the important feature of Table 5.5.3 is the extent to which both means and variances increase from the 512 to the 1 millisecond interval. The variances increase by a factor of nearly 9 (standard deviation by a factor of 3). There is a substantial increase in reaction time from the 8 to the 1 millisecond interval, an increase much greater than the difference in length of the two intervals: yet the difference between these two intervals was not consciously appreciated by the subjects; under both conditions each signal appeared to the subject coincident with his preceding response. Unfortunately the results from individual subjects are dominated by the order in which they experienced the several experimental conditions and a more detailed analysis does not reveal any worthwhile information beyond what is already contained in Table 5.5.3. These results will be discussed further in Chapter 8, pp. 108–11, in the context of sequential relations.

Another valuable impression was obtained from sitting in on the experimental sessions. The apparatus indicator lights and noise from the response keys and error counter provided a continuous visual and auditory account of the experimental events. With the longer intertrial intervals the subjects' performance was fairly regular; with a very short interval there was a marked difference. For the first 30 or so signals of the series the subject responded, and accurately too, at a rate that one felt intuitively he could not maintain. In due course the subject would slow up, make one or two mistakes, pause perhaps, and then increase speed again. Thereafter his performance fluctuated, though not with any noticeably regular period. Every subject showed this effect under the short intertrial interval conditions, if only to a small degree. Two subjects were particularly resistant to it; both were competent musicians and both showed a strong rhythm in their pressing of the response keys. Their performances ranked among both the fastest and the most accurate under the short intertrial interval conditions.

5.6.2. Prediction B: The qualitative relationship between mean reaction times and error scores.

In Table 5.5.4 the test series are classified exactly as in Table 5.1.6, and the manner of evaluating the table has been described on p. 52. Altogether there are 125 series

TABLE 5.5.4. QUALITATIVE RELATION BETWEEN MEAN REACTION TIMES AND ERROR SCORES IN EXPERIMENT 5.

	$t_A > t_B$	$t_A < t_B$
$\dot{\alpha} > \hat{\beta}$	26	20
$\dot{\alpha} < \hat{\beta}$	23	30

of data, of which 26 are omitted because $\dot{\alpha} = $. The correlation lies in the predicted direction, but is not significant ($\chi^2 = 1 \cdot 182$ with 1 d.f.). This was perhaps to be expected since in this experiment no attempt was made to vary the distribution of the errors.

5.6.3. Prediction C: The relation between error- and correct-reaction times.

The results of a comparison between the distributions of error- and correct-reaction times are presented in Table 5.5.5. The prediction and the approximate treatment of

TABLE 5.5.5. THE KOLMOGOROV-SMIRNOV STATISTICS AND THE NUMBER OF ERRORS IN EACH SAMPLE ARISING FROM THE TEST OF PREDICTION C IN EXPERIMENT 5. (A double underlining indicates significance at the 0·01 level, a single underlining at the 0·05 level.)

Intertrial interval	4096	512	64	8	1	All series together
Response R_A	0·370	0·367	0·160	−0·078	0·109	0·124
	43	92	160	215	193	703
Response R_B	0·395	0·404	0·156	−0·143	0·096	0·151
	51	96	155	149	194	645
Both responses together	0·370	0·385	0·150	−0·100	0·102	0·134
	94	188	315	364	387	1348

the data have been described on p. 53, and there is an exact specification in Appendix C.

The results from the 4096 and 512 millisecond series are much the same as those from Experiments 1–4. At 64 milliseconds the test statistic is smaller, indicating a smaller deviation from the prediction. The results for the two shortest intervals show little consistency, and at 8 milliseconds the sign of the test statistics is reversed. An examination of the distributions under comparison shows that a difference of location at the two longest intervals decreases as the intertrial interval is reduced, and the error-reaction time distribution begins to show a greater dispersion than that of the correct reaction times. At 1 millisecond the difference between the two distributions is one of dispersion rather than location.

5.7. Experiment 6 : A five-choice task.

So far only two-choice experiments have been described, for which the analysis is relatively simple. But a two-choice experiment contains only a few degrees of freedom and therefore does not afford so stringent a test of the theory as a multi-choice experiment, provided, of course, that the latter can be adequately analysed. Theorem B.6 (p. 152) holds equally for multi-choice experiments, and affords a distribution-free test. A five-choice experiment was therefore designed to yield as sensitive a test as possible of Prediction C. Although the multi-choice problem is determinate, quantitative predictions about the error and mean reaction time matrices have not yet been derived. But it might be possible to deduce something about the structure of the decision problem from the matrices experimentally obtained.

Two groups of 12 subjects each were tested with a single five-choice series, 800 signals long. Five was the maximum number of signals that the apparatus could

TABLE 5.6.1. SIGNALS, RESPONSES AND SIGNAL PROBABILITIES IN EXPERIMENT 6.

Signal	S_A	S_B	S_C	S_D	S_E
Height in ins.	1·41	2·00	2·83	4·00	5·66
Group K:					
Approximate probability	$^1/_{15}$	$^2/_{15}$	$^3/_{15}$	$^4/_{15}$	$^5/_{15}$
Response finger	Thumb	Index	Middle	Ring	Little
Group L:					
Approximate probability	$^5/_{15}$	$^4/_{15}$	$^3/_{15}$	$^2/_{15}$	$^1/_{15}$
Response finger	Little	Ring	Middle	Index	Thumb

accommodate and a single long series was used in order to obtain large samples from the several reaction-time distributions. The data were recorded by hand and 800 items were as many as could conveniently be recorded within the hour for which each subject was available. The *a priori* probability was different for each signal in order to separate partially the several reaction-time distributions. The signals were stripes of various lengths, as in the two-choice experiments, and the responses were made by the digits of the right hand. The signal-response combinations and the approximate *a priori* probabilities for each group are shown in Table 5.6.1.

Crossman (1955) found that the ease of discrimination in a two-choice task is approximately a function of the ratio between the physical magnitudes of the two stimuli. So here the signal sizes were chosen to lie in a geometric series. The ratio between the lengths of any two adjacent signals is 1.41, which is the same as in the two-choice experiments. There were many available choices of signal probabilities and the set chosen here seemed as good as any other. Subjects responded with the digits of the right hand because this is the preferred hand for most people. The particular correspondence between response fingers and signal frequencies was chosen because the experimenter had to programme the series of signals with his *left* hand on a set of keys similar to that used by the subject; if the experimenter's little finger had become tired during the session it was possible that a differential noise cue might have been introduced. It would have been better if the pairing between response set and signal frequencies had been varied in a 2×2 factorial design. But while it was easy to change the signals around in the tachistoscope, it was somewhat more difficult to modify the relay circuit at that time.

Each subject began with a practice run during which he was told at once whenever he made a mistake. The practice continued until his responses became more or less error free. The test series of 800 signals was split into four sections and subjects had about two minutes rest between sections. The intertrial interval averaged about three seconds.

5.7.1. Results of Experiment 6.

Mean reaction times and error scores.

The signal-response matrix and the mean reaction times for each experimental group are shown in Table 5.6.2. Responses are clustered about the leading diagonal

TABLE 5.6.2. SIGNAL-RESPONSE MATRICES FROM EXPERIMENT 6.

Signal	Signal probability	R_A	R_B	R_C	R_D	R_E	Total signals	Mean reaction time in secs.
Group K:								
S_A	$^1/_{15}$	379	139	1	0	0	519	0·807
S_B	$^2/_{15}$	17	1336	130	7	0	1490	0·866
S_C	$^3/_{15}$	1	186	1799	83	0	2069	0·811
S_D	$^4/_{15}$	0	8	321	2146	14	2489	0·773
S_E	$^5/_{15}$	0	0	7	255	2771	3033	0·645
Total responses	—	397	1669	2258	2491	2785	9600	—
(total responses) —(total signals)	—	−122	179	189	2	−248	—	—
Mean reaction time in secs.	—	0·778	0·847	0·830	0·763	0·636	—	0·757
Group L:								
S_A	$^5/_{15}$	2715	330	5	0	0	3050	0·678
S_B	$^4/_{15}$	42	2287	158	0	0	2487	0·725
S_C	$^3/_{15}$	0	250	1753	49	0	2052	0·789
S_D	$^2/_{15}$	1	2	279	1192	21	1495	0·827
S_E	$^1/_{15}$	0	0	0	41	475	516	0·705
Total responses	—	2758	2869	2195	1282	496	9600	—
(total responses) —(total signals)	—	−292	382	143	−213	−20	—	—
Mean reaction time in secs.	—	0·656	0·740	0·798	0·822	0·706	—	0·738

of the signal-response matrix. When an error is made it usually consists of the substitution of a response appropriate to an adjacent signal, so that the signals appear to be organized subjectively, as well as objectively, on a single continuum. As was expected, the mean reaction times here are altogether longer than in the two-choice experiments; this happens even though the ratio between the lengths of adjacent signals is the same in both two- and five-choice experiments. Further, mean reaction times and the proportions of errors are greater for the interior responses, confirming the conjecture on p. 158.

5.7.2. The central tendency of judgment.

There is a highly significant difference between the marginal distributions of signals and responses in Table 5.6.2. The distribution of the signals is fixed by the experimenter, so that the signal totals are a set of population parameters for comparison with the distribution of the responses. The comparison gives: Group K, $\chi^2 = 22 \cdot 68$, Group L, $\chi^2 = 32 \cdot 36$, with 4 d.f., $p < 0 \cdot 001$. The responses move towards the centre of the scale relative to the signals. It is possible that this result is entirely due to the linear ordering of the response fingers—but this is unlikely. With this one reservation the phenomenon here appears to be the same as that called "The central tendency of judgment" by Hollingworth (1910).

5.7.3. The downward movement of the responses.

There is also a movement of responses towards signals of smaller physical size. In this experiment the effect is partially obscured by differences in *a priori* signal probability and the finite size of the signal set, but it may be demonstrated as follows: As well as moving towards the centre, responses may also be affected by differences in signal probability. If these were the only two factors operative, however, there should be no significant difference between the performance of the two groups when the signals (and responses) are identified by signal probability rather than by signal size (as has been done in Table 5.6.2). In Table 5.6.3 errors with the three interior

TABLE 5.6.3. AN ANALYSIS OF THE MOVEMENT OF ERRORS RELATIVE TO SIGNAL PROBABILITY IN EXPERIMENT 6.

Signal probability	$^2/_{15}$		$^3/_{15}$		$^4/_{15}$	
Movement of errors relative to signal probability	*lower* $^1/_{15}$	*higher* $^3/_{15}$ to $^5/_{15}$	*lower* $^1/_{15}, {}^2/_{15}$	*higher* $^4/_{15}, {}^5/_{15}$	*lower* $^1/_{15}$ to $^3/_{15}$	*higher* $^5/_{15}$
Group K	17	137	187	83	329	14
Group L	21	282	49	250	158	42
χ^2, 1 d.f.	1·76		161·0		33·7	

responses have been analysed according to their direction of movement relative to differences in signal probability. The scores entered under each value of signal probability have been evaluated as an independent 2×2 contingency table and the resultant values of χ^2 are shown in the bottom row. Errors with the exterior responses have been left out because they must necessarily give $\chi^2 = 0$. The sum of the χ^2-variates is highly significant ($\chi^2 = 196 \cdot 46$, with 3 d.f., $p < 0 \cdot 001$). The nature of the difference in the direction of movement of the errors is obscured for the responses to signals of probability 2/15 and 4/15 by their proximity to exterior responses; here the central tendency of judgment is dominant. But it is clear from the centre response (signal probability 3/15) that responses tend to be transposed towards signals of smaller physical size. A similar result has been obtained by Broadbent and Gregory (private communication) with the sorting of rods of various lengths and of dishes containing various numbers of ball bearings.

5.7.4. The rate of extracting information.

Although the mean information per observation is not constant with respect to successive observations in a multi-choice decision process (the expression for the information in favour of S_i in equation (B.1) does not decompose additively, so that the increment in information due to the $(r+1)^{th}$ observation, x_{r+1}, will depend in part upon the values of $x_1 \ldots x_r$), it is nonetheless possible to make meaningful, albeit tentative, comparisons between the rates at which information is afforded by different signals. Table 5.6.4 shows certain decision parameters for the two groups,

$$\lambda_i = P(error \,|\, R_i) = \sum_{j \neq i} P(S_j \,|\, R_i), \qquad (5.3)$$

so that $\hat{\lambda}_i$ is an estimate of the parameter of the response criterion for R_i (see axiom 4, p. 38), and

$$I_n = \log\{(1-\lambda_i)/\lambda_i\}, \qquad (5.4)$$

so that $\hat{I}_n$ is an estimate of the amount of information required to make R_i.

The signal lengths were chosen to lie in a geometric series; the evidence of Crossman (1955) suggested that the signal set would then be subjectively approximately symmetric about the centre signal, S_C. If this were exactly true the results from S_A (and

TABLE 5.6.4. DECISION PARAMETERS IN EXPERIMENT 6.

Response	R_A	R_B	R_C	R_D	R_E
Group K:					
Signal probability	$1/15$	$2/15$	$3/15$	$4/15$	$5/15$
$\hat{\lambda}_i$	0·045	0·200	0·204	0·139	0·005
$\hat{I}_n$	5·91	3·08	2·66	2·88	6·07
Mean reaction time	0·778	0·847	0·830	0·763	0·636
Group L:					
Signal probability	$5/15$	$4/15$	$3/15$	$2/15$	$1/15$
$\hat{\lambda}_i$	0·016	0·203	0·202	0·070	0·042
$\hat{I}_n$	4·90	2·42	2·68	4·28	5·98
Mean reaction time	0·656	0·740	0·798	0·822	0·706

hence R_A) for one Group should be comparable to the results from S_E (or R_E) for the other, because the corresponding signal probabilities are equal. Such a comparison can be made with the data in Table 5.6.4 as follows:

Comparing R_A (group K) with R_E (group K) and R_A (group L) with R_E (group K), it appears that

$$I_n |\, R_E > I_n |\, R_A$$

and
$$Mean\ Reaction\ Time |\, R_E < Mean\ Reaction\ Time |\, R_A,$$

so that the information when R_E is made comes at a faster rate than that when R_A is made. A similar comparison between R_B and R_D reveals that

$$I_n |\, R_D > I_n |\, R_B,$$

while no corresponding inequality can be stated for the mean reaction times. This evidence is only slight, but it suggests that the mean rate of information conditional on a given response, say R_i, increases as i moves from A to E through the response set. And since S_i is presented on at least 79·6 per cent of the occasions when R_i is made, the same conclusion would seem to apply to the signals, that is, within the signal set used in this experiment the mean rate of information afforded increases with the physical size of the signal.

5.7.5. Sequential relations in the data.

In the foregoing discussion the analysis of the data has been unsophisticated and the arguments have been heuristic, because the mathematics of the multi-choice decision model is relatively undeveloped. There is one reservation to add arising from qualitative observations made during the recording of the data.

Some subjects showed at times a certain confusion of the signals, which took the form of a transposition of one or more signals to adjacent responses, up or down the scale. These transpositions were transitory, though they might last for 50 responses and might occur several times during the same experimental session. The transposition of the signals was rarely complete and some correct responses occurred during these periods. In some cases it is known that such correct responses were regarded by the subject as errors.

Observations such as these indicate strong sequential interactions in the experiment and call for a sequential analysis of the data, which has not yet been done. It is sufficient to remark here that a substantial number of the errors recorded occurred during such periods of confusion of the signals. The conclusions reached in the preceding sections might need amendment in the light of further analysis of the data.

5.7.6. Prediction C: The relation between error- and correct-reaction times.

The results of a comparison between the distributions of error- and correct-reaction times are presented in Table 5.6.5. The prediction and the approximate treatment of the data have been described on p. 53, and there is an exact specification in Appendix C. There are two ways of pairing the responses of the two experimental

TABLE 5.6.5. THE KOLMOGOROV-SMIRNOV STATISTICS AND THE NUMBER OF ERRORS IN EACH SAMPLE ARISING FROM THE TEST OF PREDICTION C IN EXPERIMENT 6. (A double underlining indicates significance at the 0·01 level.)

(*i*) *Responses identified by signal height;*

Signal height in ins.	1·41	2·00	2·83	4·00	5·66
Number of errors	61	915	901	435	35
Kolmogorov-Smirnov test statistic	−0·162	−0·092	−0·073	−0·024	−0·198

(*ii*) *Responses identified by signal probability;*

Signal probability	$^1/_{15}$	$^2/_{15}$	$^3/_{15}$	$^4/_{15}$	$^5/_{15}$
Number of errors	39	423	901	927	57
Kolmogorov-Smirnov test statistic	0·161	0·015	−0·073	−0·093	−0·278

(*iii*)   Total number of errors   2347
        Combined test statistic   −0·064

groups: (i) by the size of the corresponding signal, and (ii) by the *a priori* probability of the corresponding signal. The first two parts of Table 5.6.5 correspond to these two alternatives.

There are several significant statistics here, indicating that Prediction C is not true of this multi-choice experiment either. But there are two differences from the two-choice results worthy of note. First, the Kolmogorov-Smirnov statistics are somewhat smaller in absolute size here, indicating smaller discrepancies between error- and correct-reaction time distributions. Secondly, wherever the statistic is significant, it is negative in sign, indicating that errors take longer than correct responses. From an examination of the distributions under comparison it appears that the difference between them is principally one of location, and there is some evidence that the relative locations of the two distributions change monotonically with *a priori* signal probability.

These differences with respect to the results from the two-choice experiment are not due to the extra long signal series (800 signals) used here. The calculations have been repeated using only the first 200 reactions from each subject and similar results to those in Table 5.6.5 were obtained. The differences may be essentially due to the increase in the number of alternative signals or they may be due, in part at least, to the concomitant decrease in discriminability.

5.8. Experiment 7: Variation of number of equiprobable alternatives.

The differences in the relation between error- and correct-reaction times found in Experiment 6, relative to the two-choice experiments, may be essentially due to the increase in the number of alternative signals, or they may be due in part to the concomitant decrease in discriminability. There are several ways in which further information on this issue might be obtained. Here equiprobable two-, three-, four-and five-choice series are compared, using the same type of signal as before, to see how the change in the relationship between error- and correct-reaction times with increasing number of alternative signals comes about. Different experimental groups are given tasks of different difficulty, to see whether this also affects the issue.

At the same time a limited comparison can be achieved with Hick's (1952) experiment, which has had so great an influence on subsequent work and theorising on choice-reaction times. It seems *prima facie* likely that the relation between mean reaction time and the number of alternative signals is determined in part by the particular signals used, but that if the signals are all mutually easily discriminable, equation (1.1) is a good approximation. Obviously one must not use unrelated sets of signals for the different experimental conditions. Hick formed his $(m+1)$-alternative set by adding one signal to his m-alternative set, and the same arrangement will be used here. But if the signal so added is difficult to discriminate from one or another member of the m-alternative set, there should be a bigger increase in reaction time, than if the new signal was easily distinguishable. By such means an attempt will be made to vary the form of the relation between mean reaction time and the number of alternative equiprobable signals.

Each of three groups of ten subjects was tested with four series of signals. The series contained two, three, four and five alternatives respectively, occurring in approximately equal numbers. Series 2 and 3 contained 200 signals, series 4 and 5 300 signals. All the groups were shown the same five signals in series 5, but were shown different subsets of the signal set in series 2, 3 and 4. The signal sets and the ratios between adjacent signals in each set are shown in Table 5.7.1. The signals for series 5 were so chosen that subsets of differing difficulty could easily be constructed. Group *L* had relatively difficult sets of signals, group *M* intermediate sets and group

TABLE 5.7.1. THE SIGNAL SETS USED IN EXPERIMENT 7.

	2-choice		3-choice		4-choice		5-choice	
Group	Height of signals	Ratio between heights of adjacent signals	Height of signals	Ratio between heights of adjacent signals	Height of signals	Ratio between heights of adjacent signals	Height of signals	Ratio between heights of adjacent signals
K	5·66" 2·59"	2·18	5·66" 2·59" 1·41"	2·18 1·83	5·66" 4·36" 2·59" 1·41"	1·30 1·68 1·83		
L	2·59" 2·18"	1·19	4·36" 2·59" 2·18"	1·68 1·19	5·66" 4·36" 2·59" 2·18"	1·30 1·68 1·19	5·66" 4·36" 2·59" 2·18" 1·41"	1·30 1·68 1·19 1·54
M	5·66" 4·36"	1·30	5·66" 4·36" 1·41"	1·30 3·08	5·66" 4·36" 2·18" 1·41"	1·30 2·00 1·54		

K relatively easy ones. Half of each group was tested with the order 2, 3, 4, 5; half in the reverse order. The responses were made with the digits of the right hand and the signal-response combinations, which were invariant throughout the experiment, are shown in Table 5.7.2.

TABLE 5.7.2. THE SIGNAL HEIGHTS AND THE CORRESPONDING RESPONSE FINGERS OF THE RIGHT HAND IN EXPERIMENT 7.

Signal	S_A	S_B	S_C	S_D	S_E
Height in ins.	1·41	2·18	2·59	4·36	5·66
Response finger	Little	Ring	Middle	Index	Thumb

This experiment was done immediately after Experiment 6 with the apparatus in the same state as there. Each subject began with a practice run and had further practice before commencing each test series to accustom him to the change in the signal set. The intertrial interval was about 3 seconds for series 5 and decreased a little with the number of alternative signals.

5.8.1. Results of Experiment 7.

A comparison with Hick's (1952) experiment.

Figure 5.3 shows the series mean reaction times for each group compared with the corresponding means obtained by Hick. The reaction times here are longer because the signals were harder to discriminate. In series 2, 3 and 4 the three experimental groups maintain the rank order intended in the design of the signal sets; the probability of this happening by chance is $1/(3!)^3 = 1/216$. The variation of difficulty among the groups is comparable, in terms of increase in reaction time, to the addition of an extra signal.

Although the sets of data shown in Figure 5.3 do not appear to vary much from a straight line, there is nonetheless a significant difference in the shape of the mean reaction time equation between the three groups. Suppose the equation can be written in the form

$$t(n) = a + b f(n), \qquad (5.5)$$

where $t(n)$ is the mean reaction time for a series with n equiprobable signals and a and b are constants peculiar to the subject. (Compare equation 1.1: $t(n) = b \log(n+1)$). Changes in $f(n)$ may be obscured in Figure 5.3 because each point there is the mean of

FIGURE 5.3

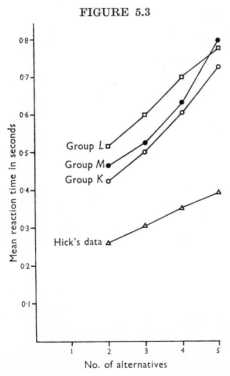

A comparison of the mean reaction times for each series in Experiment 7 with the corresponding data from Hick (1952).

ten readings from different subjects, for whom different values of the constants a and b may have been appropriate. But it is possible to extract the quadratic factor of $f(n)$ independently of a and b. For each subject a set of polynomial regression coefficients were easily calculated with the aid of orthogonal polynomials. The quadratic coefficient of $f(n)$ was estimated by the ratio of the quadratic regression coefficient divided by the linear one, and the results of an Analysis of Variance of this ratio are shown in Table 5.7.3.

The order effect in Table 5.7.3 arises from a comparison of the two orders in which the signal series were presented, $\{2, 3, 4, 5\}$ and $\{5, 4, 3, 2\}$. It is due to practice effects within the experimental session. Because of the particular orders of presentation used, practice at the experimental task also accounts, in part at least, for the positive quadratic component found in the experimental results as a whole (the top line of Table 5.7.3) and the interaction between groups and order. It is also possible that the group effect is entirely due to an interaction between practice and the

TABLE 5.7.3. ANALYSIS OF VARIANCE OF THE RATIO BETWEEN THE QUADRATIC AND LINEAR FACTORS OF MEAN REACTION TIME AS A FUNCTION OF THE NUMBER OF ALTERNATIVE SIGNALS IN EXPERIMENT 7.

Source of variation	S.S.	d.f.	F	p
Mean coefficient	1·2867	1	20·12	<0·001
Between groups	0·9480	2	7·49	<0·005
Between orders	0·6771	1	10·70	<0·005
Interaction: group × order	0·4968	2	3·92	<0·05
Error term	1·5215	24	—	—
Total	4·9301	30	—	—

different signal sets used with the different groups, so that it would not have appeared if the subjects had been practised sufficiently beforehand. But this is unlikely on the evidence of Table 5.7.3, because the interaction effect, which is certainly due to this cause, is weak relative to the group effect. There appears to be an inherent difference in the form of the equation for $t(n)$ for the three groups, so that $t(n)$ is a function of the particular signals used as well as their number, and this was the intention underlying the design of the signal sets.

5.8.2. The decision parameters in series 5.

In Table 5.7.4 the signals in series 5 are ordered according to their ratios with respect to each of the adjacent signals (writing ∞ for one ratio of an exterior signal). The decision parameters, λ_i and I_n, have already been defined on p. 71. The λ_i are in the same rank order as the responses, and this is consistent with the idea of an optimal multichoice decision process, which, as conjectured on p. 158, is a compromise between equal accuracy of response on the one hand and equal mean speed of response on the other. It also follows from this idea that mean reaction times should also be in the same rank order as the responses, but this is not exactly so here.

TABLE 5.7.4. DECISION IN PARAMETERS IN SERIES 5 OF EXPERIMENT 7.

Response	Signal height in ins.	Ratios with heights of adjacent signals	λ_j	$\hat{I}_n$	Mean reaction time in secs.
R_A	1·41	∞, 1·54	0·011	5·96	0·685
R_E	5·66	∞, 1·30	0·022	5·10	0·668
R_D	4·36	1·68, 1·30	0·068	3·94	0·751
R_C	2·59	1·68, 1·19	0·290	2·30	0·873
R_B	2·18	1·54, 1·19	0·320	2·20	0·838

5.8.3. Prediction C: The relation of error- and correct-reaction times.

The results of a comparison between the distributions of error- and correct-reaction times are presented in Table 5.7.5. The prediction and the approximate treatment of

TABLE 5.7.5. THE KOLMOGOROV-SMIRNOV STATISTICS AND THE NUMBER OF ERRORS IN EACH SAMPLE ARISING FROM THE TEST OF PREDICTION C IN EXPERIMENT 7. (A double underlining indicates significance at the 0·01 level, a single underlining at the 0·05 level.)

Series	Group	R_A	R_B	R_C	R_D	R_E	All responses together
2-choice	K	—	—	0·718	—	0·330	0·478
				13		15	28
	L	—	0·263	—0·252	—	—	—0·183
			38	55			93
	M	—	—	—	0·194	0·324	0·246
					23	17	40
3-choice	K	0·633	—	0·166	—	0·272	0·240
		8		23		5	36
	L	—	—0·066	—0·264	—0·377	—	—0·210
			35	136	5		176
	M	0·846	—	—	0·286	0·264	0·244
		2			30	11	43
4-choice	K	—0·244	—	—0·292	0·174	0·251	—0·156
		3		28	33	11	75
	L	—	—0·179	—0·227	—0·115	0·261	—0·183
			26	285	53	14	378
	M	0·363	—0·186	—	0·150	0·184	0·080
		11	61		38	17	127
5-choice	All groups together	0·334	—0·065	—0·148	—0·138	—0·109	—0·098
		16	555	581	129	41	1322

the date have been described on p. 53, and there is an exact specification in Appendix C. In series 2, 3 and 4 the experimental groups are analysed separately, since they worked with different signal sets; in series 5 they are taken together.

Table 5.7.5 contains test statistics indicating shifts of location in both directions and some increases of variance of the error- over the correct-reaction times. These statistics are not of the same small order as in Experiment 6, Table 5.6.6—perhaps the uneven spacing of the signal sizes and the shorter test series created greater variability here. About half the statistics are significant, but many more would achieve significance with larger numbers of errors in the sample.

In Table 5.7.6 there are certain interesting relations involving the signs of the test statistics. Group L, who had the most difficult set of tasks, show a higher proportion of negative statistics than Group K or Group M ($\chi^2 = 6\cdot70$, with 2 d.f. $p < 0\cdot05$). Interior responses seem to show a higher proportion of negative statistics than do exterior responses, but the difference here is not quite significant ($\chi^2 = 2\cdot75$ with 1 d.f., $p < 0\cdot10$). But there is no comparable change in the signs of the statistics with increasing number of alternative signals ($\chi^2 = 2\cdot22$ with 3 d.f., $p > 0\cdot50$); such trend as there appears to be might well be attributed to a concomitant increase in task difficulty.

CHAPTER 6

AN APPRAISAL OF THE RANDOM WALK MODEL

6.1. Introduction.

This chapter reviews the evidence presented in Chapter 5 pertinent to the three predictions on p. 44 and the probabilistic structure of the multi-choice model for Experiments 6 and 7. These four topics are discussed in successive subdivisions of the chapter. Because Prediction C fails, §6.4 also introduces two modifications to the random walk model to make it conform to the data. These modifications concern temporal uncertainty on the one hand and the limit to human discrimination on the other. Some of their implications are discussed.

6.2. Prediction A: The relation between the error scores and *a priori* signal probability.

In a two-choice experiment the ratio between the numbers of errors of each sort changes with the bias in the signal sequence and approximates a certain optimal value, $R_\epsilon(S_B/S_A)$, which is given for a symmetric decision process by equation (A.13),

$$R_\epsilon\left(\frac{S_B}{S_A}\right) = \frac{Expected\ no.\ of\ errors\,|\,S_B}{Expected\ no.\ of\ errors\,|\,S_A} = \frac{1-p-\epsilon}{p-\epsilon}. \tag{6.1}$$

The method of testing this prediction has already been described on p. 50 in presenting the results of Experiment 1.

The error scores from Experiment 1 may be disregarded because they are confounded with an order effect (see pp. 50–2); the data from Experiment 2 conform well to the prediction. If there is sufficient asymmetry in the decision process to be apparent in the error scores, the estimated ratio, $\hat{R}_\epsilon$, will be consistently greater than or consistently less than the value predicted by equation (6.1) (see inequality A.41). No such asymmetry is apparent in either experiment.

Prediction A could be obtained from certain other choice-reaction models. It was pointed out on p. 33 that the essence of the symmetric optimal decision process is that every response is made to the same degree of accuracy, irrespective of the response actually made or the signal presented. Any other choice-reaction model with this property would also lead to equation (6.1).

6.3. Prediction B: The qualitative relationship between mean reaction times error scores.

In a two-choice experiment that signal which elicits the faster reaction, on average, has the smaller probability of error, and conversely. This implies, in the terminology of §5.2.3, an association between $t_A > t_B$ and $\hat{\alpha} > \hat{\beta}$ and between $t_A < t_B$ and $\hat{\alpha} < \hat{\beta}$. The method of testing this prediction has been described on pp. 52–3 in presenting the results from Experiment 1.

To show the prediction false it is in fact necessary to demonstrate a significant correlation in the direction contrary to that predicted, although failure to find any correlation at all would also cast grave doubt upon the truth of the prediction. However the two-choice experiments have provided strong positive evidence. If there is but little variation in the ratio between the numbers of errors of each sort, there may not be any demonstrable correlation in either direction (Experiment 4, Series 1 and Experiment 5). But where the variation in the error ratio is sufficient, (Experiments 1, 2 and 3 and Experiment 4, Series 1, 2 and 3 combined), there is a significant correlation in the predicted direction. This implies a greater readiness to make one *response* than the other, rather than a differential treatment of the two signals. The prediction is only qualitative and might well follow from any choice-reaction model that incorporated a similar response bias.

6.4. Prediction C: The relation between error- and correct-reaction times.

For a given response the distribution of reaction time is the same whether the response is correct or an error. In this section comparisons will always be made between reaction times for different signals paired with the same response, and this prediction does not imply any relation between reaction times for different responses to the same signal. The prediction is derived in Theorem B.6 (p. 152) for any decision process in which the responses are determined according to a constant probability ratio criterion (i.e. Axiom 4, p. 38), provided that the information stream satisfies the constraints of Axiom 2. This prediction applies equally to multi-choice experiments as well as two-choice. The method of testing it is described roughly on p. 53 in presenting the results of Experiment 1 and there is an exact specification of the method in Appendix C.

Each and every experiment has yielded highly significant results contrary to Prediction C. It only remains to see whether the simple random walk model of Chapter 3 can be modified sufficiently to account for the data that have been recorded. The deviations from the prediction may be summarized as follows:

In those two-choice experiments with an intertrial interval not less than 1500 milliseconds (Nos. 1–4) errors are always faster than the same response made correctly. The difference between the distributions of error- and correct-reaction times is principally one of location. In Experiments 1 and 2 (see Figures 5.1 and 5.2) the difference between the means of these two distributions appears more or less constant, independent of the experimental conditions. In Experiment 5 the difference in location is diminished at short intertrial intervals and there is a difference in dispersion instead, such that the distribution of error-reaction times has the greater variance. In the multi-choice experiments (Nos. 6 and 7) errors frequently take longer than the same response made correctly, and this appears to be due to the increased difficulty of discrimination concomitant with the increase in the number of alternative signals.

6.4.1. Temporal uncertainty.

Hitherto it has been implicitly assumed in the random walk model that the subject knows exactly when the signal will appear and begins deciding at this precise moment. In practice this is not so and a modification to the model will be introduced here to allow for the subject's temporal uncertainty.

It is almost certain that the subjects in the experiments of Chapter 5 did not merely guess when the signal would appear but scanned the empty display while they were waiting and used the information it afforded. Woodrow (1930), measuring the accuracy of reproduction of empty temporal intervals, found that reproductions of an interval of 1500 milliseconds, which was the intertrial interval used in Experiment 4, had an average variance of 0.0193 sec^2. Now if the subjects merely guessed when the signal would appear the variance of their guesses would be a lower bound to the variance of their reaction times; yet the variance quoted from Woodrow is more than twice as large as the reaction time variances in Table 5.4.3. Snodgrass, Luce and Galanter (1967) have recently advanced this same argument and have confirmed Woodrow's results. It follows that the subject in a choice-reaction experiment collects information from the blank display while he is waiting for the signal to appear, and this information must necessarily be irrelevant to the decision he ultimately has to make. There is no way of distinguishing the irrelevant information from the relevant and there are just two ways in which the subject might deal with it.

(i) The subject might sample information from the display until he is sure there is a signal present and then begin the random walk process of §3.2 afresh, discarding all information previously collected. Each response will then be the outcome of two independent decisions corresponding to the components of choice-reaction time T_i and T_d respectively (see p. 60). But there will be information collected during the first "input" stage which is relevant to the second "decision" stage; this information is nonetheless thrown away.

(ii) The alternative strategy is to begin the random walk process in advance of the presentation of the signal and distinguish between *three* possibilities: S_A, S_B and "No Signal" (cf. Hick 1952). The behaviour of the model will then depend not only upon the perceptual relation between the two signals but also on the relation of the signals to the background which the subject sees during the intertrial interval. Provided the background is qualitatively different from both of the signals and much less like either of them than they (the signals) are like each other (this condition seems to be satisfied by the signals and background used here; see §4.2), then by the time sufficient information has been collected to discriminate adequately between the two signals, the *a posteriori* probability of there being no signal present will invariably be negligible. This means that the fundamentally three-choice decision process can be approximated for practical purposes by a two-choice random walk. Now the information collected prior to the presentation of the signal, although it is relevant to the question whether a signal is present, is irrelevant to the question "which signal?". Yet there is no way of separating it from the relevant information collected subsequent to the presentation of the signal. So the modified two-choice random walk should begin with a section representing the irrelevant information collected prior to the presentation of the signal.

This second alternative strategy is investigated in §A.7. The assumption made there may be stated as a sixth axiom:

(6) *The subject begins sampling information from the blank display at some time (not necessarily fixed) before the signal is presented. The information so sampled is irrelevant to the discrimination between the signals.*

It seems reasonable in view of the perceptual relations between the signals and the background specified above that the irrelevant information in the random walk model should have zero mean[1] and a rate of increase of variance that is small compared with

---

[1] If the irrelevant information had a non-zero drift factor in the random walk representation, this would appear as a bias in the experimental results in favour of one response or the other and capable of representation as a constant displacement of the starting point of the random walk. Such a bias is not noticeable in the results of the two-choice experiments. The non-zero drift factor does not otherwise invalidate the theory of §A.7.

that of information collected from either signal. So that a short initial section of zero drift in the random walk may correspond to a disproportionately long period of sampling information prior to the presentation of the signal. It does not then matter how the subject determines when to begin sampling, and the variability of this instant is in no sense a lower bound for the variability of the subject's reaction time. No assumptions are made here about the amount of irrelevant information sampled by the subject or the length of time occupied by this part of the decision process. But obviously this amount ought to be invariant under most of the experimental variables studied here. Subjects might start sampling earlier under instructions to go fast and they must obviously collect less irrelevant information if the intertrial interval is short. These issues will be examined in §6.4.2.

The mathematical consequences of Axiom 6 are developed in §A.7. It is shown there that Predictions A and B on p. 44 remain approximately true, but that errors are now faster than the same response made correctly. The difference in mean between the distributions of error- and correct-reaction times,

i.e. $$E\{t \mid R_A S_A\} - E\{t \mid R_A S_B\}, \text{ etc.}$$

is shown to be approximately $2n_0 \, \delta t$ for both responses, where n_0 is the number of steps in the random walk which represent irrelevant information, and δt is the temporal length of a step representing relevant information.[2]

Since Prediction C applies equally to multi-choice as well as two-choice experiments, it might have been expected that it should also apply to the model in its modified form. It does not, however, because there is a sudden change in the statistical characteristics of the information stream at some point during the course of the decision process (i.e. when the signal is presented), and the subject does not know when this will take place. The essence of the modification is that the subject, as it were, assumes that the signal has already been presented, even at the beginning of the decision process, in that he treats all the information available as relevant to the discrimination. Under these circumstances the proof of Theorem B.6 is no longer valid (see p. 142). In fact the approximation of the modified model by a two-choice random walk is equivalent to the superposition of a certain random component on the starting point of the original model in §3.2, and Theorem B.6 implicitly assumes that the starting point is fixed.

6.4.2. An evaluation of the modified random walk model.

The modification of the random walk model in the preceding section leaves Predictions A and B unchanged, but replaces Prediction C with a new prediction:

PREDICTION C′: *In two-choice experiments errors are faster than the same response made correctly. The difference in mean between the distributions of error- and correct-reaction times is independent of most experimental conditions, but may be affected by excessive pressure on the subject to respond quickly, and will certainly decrease to zero with the intertrial interval.*

No corresponding prediction has yet been derived for multi-choice experiments.

---

[2] $n_0 \, \delta t$ is not necessarily equal to the time over which the irrelevant information is sampled, since in §A.7 a "step" is defined by a fixed increase in the variance of the random walk. The temporal length of an increment of irrelevant information may therefore be much greater than δt.

In view of the nature of the deviations from the original Prediction C summarized on p. 80 it seems *prima facie* likely that Prediction C′ will accord well with the data, but this needs to be tested. The observed differences in mean between errors and the corresponding correct reaction times are arranged in a 10×24 table (responses and series $\times$ subjects), which is evaluated by a Friedman two-way analysis of variance by ranks (see Siegel, 1956, pp. 166–172). If in any series a subject happens not to make any errors of a particular sort, the corresponding cell of the table is empty and is assigned a rank at random.

The median differences in mean between the distributions of error- and correct-reaction times in Experiments 1 and 2 are shown in Table 6.1. The scores are entered

TABLE 6.1.   MEDIAN DIFFERENCES IN MEAN (CORRECT R.T.—ERROR R.T.) BETWEEN THE DISTRIBUTIONS OF ERROR- AND CORRECT-REACTION TIMES FOR EACH RESPONSE IN EXPERIMENTS 1 AND 2.

Signal probability	*0·25*	*0·375*	*0·5*	*0·625*	*0·75*
Experiment 1: R_A	0·036	0·050	0·063	0·070	0·066
R_B	0·064	0·048	0·041	0·076	0·087
Experiment 2: R_A	0·025	0·028	0·035	0·062	0·053
R_B	0·052	0·041	0·066	0·066	0·080

under the *a priori* probability of the corresponding signal (so that the score for R_A in column 1 corresponds to $P(S_A) = 0{\cdot}25$, while the score for R_B in that column correspoinds to $P(S_B) = 0{\cdot}25$ and hence $P(S_A) = 0{\cdot}75$). The data from both these experiments conform to Prediction C′ (Experiment 1: $\chi_r^2 = 16{\cdot}54$ with 9 d.f., $p > 0{\cdot}05$; Experiment 2: $\chi_r^2 = 5{\cdot}70$ with 9 d.f., $p > 0{\cdot}70$). On the other hand the medians shown in Table 6.1 seem to increase with the *a priori* probability of the corresponding signal.

It is shown on p. 143 that $(E\{n\,|\,R_A\,S_A\}-E\{n\,|\,R_A\,S_B\})$ is a decreasing function of p, and hence an increasing function of $P(S_A)$, provided B is greater than about $\exp(1+K \coth K)$, where B is the distance from the starting point to the R_B-boundary and $K = n_0\,E\{\Delta I\,|\,S_B\}$, the amount the random walk would otherwise have drifted during the period occupied by irrelevant information. It is not possible to determine K in Experiments 1 and 2 accurately, but a very rough estimate may be made as follows: Take $\epsilon = 0{\cdot}025$, put $I_b = \log\{(1-\epsilon)/\epsilon\} = -I_a$ in equation (A.8) and differentiate with respect to I_0, giving $dE\{n\,|\,S_A\}/dI_0 \simeq 0{\cdot}812\,\delta t/|\,E\{\Delta I\,|\,S_A\}|$ at $p = \frac{1}{2}$. This differential coefficient may be roughly estimated by the change in $E\{n\,|\,S_A\}$ as p changes from 0·25 to 0·75 (cf. Figure 3.6); this change (cf. Figures 7.1 and 7.2) is about 0·09 seconds, and the value of the differential coefficient about $0{\cdot}09/\log 9$. In Table 6.1 $2n_0\,\delta t$ is about 0.06 seconds, so that $K = n_0|\,E\{\Delta I\,|\,S_A\}|$ (in view of the assumed symmetry of the decision process) is about 0·6 and $\exp(1+K \coth K)$ about 8·3. Now $B = (1-\epsilon)(1-p)/\epsilon p$ and therefore varies from about 13 to 117 in Experiments 1 and 2. It follows that $(E\{n\,|\,R_A\,S_A\}-E\{n\,|\,R_A\,S_B\})$ should be an increasing function of $P(S_A)$ in those experiments, and by the same argument $(E\{n\,|\,R_B\,S_B\}-E\{n\,|\,R_B\,S_A\})$ should be an increasing function of $P(S_B)$. (Hence the particular arrangement of Table 6.1). The correlation of each row of Table 6.1 with signal probability may be assessed by Kendall's rank correlation method (Siegel, 1956, pp. 213–223); it gives $\tau = 0{\cdot}8, 0{\cdot}4, 0{\cdot}8, 0{\cdot}6$ respectively, and combining these four test scores by Fisher's method (1934, §21.1) gives $\chi^2 = 19\cdot79$ with 8 d.f., which is significant at the 0·02 level. Hence there is evidence in Table 6.1 of the effect of the second order term in the expansion of the difference in mean between error- and correct-reaction times with respect to bias in the signal sequence.

The data from Experiments 3 and 4 also conform to Prediction C'. It might have been expected that under pressure to respond quickly subjects in Experiment 3 might begin sampling earlier and sample more irrelevant information before the signal was presented (see remark on anticipations on p. 59); this effect did not show up in the data ($\chi_r^2 = 10\cdot64$ with 9 d.f., $p > 0\cdot30$). In Experiment 4 it is possible to compare the two responses of series 1 with R_A in series 2 and R_B in series 3; (this gives $\chi_r^2 = 2\cdot58$ with 3 d.f., $p. > 0\cdot30$).

Experiment 5 does not conform to Prediction C' ($\chi_r^2 = 30\cdot20$, with 9 d.f., $p < 0\cdot001$). The median values of the differences in mean between the distributions of error- and correct-reaction times in that experiment are shown in Table 6.2. It can be seen there

TABLE 6.2.   MEDIAN DIFFERENCES IN MEAN (CORRECT R.T.—ERROR R.T.)
BETWEEN THE DISTRIBUTIONS OF ERROR- AND CORRECT-REACTION
TIMES FOR EACH RESPONSE IN EXPERIMENT 5.

Intertrial interval (msecs.)	4096	512	64	8	1
R_A	0·055	0·058	0·014	−0·015	−0·006
R_B	0·071	0·066	0·016	−0·004	0·011

that when the intertrial interval is 4096 or 512 milliseconds these differences are comparable in value to those found in Experiments 1 and 2; they are much reduced at 64 milliseconds and virtually zero at the two shortest intervals. Such a trend is to be expected in Experiment 5. While the intertrial interval is relatively long it is reasonable that the difference in mean between the distributions of error- and correct-reaction times should be independent of it; but if the intertrial interval is reduced sufficiently far, there must be a reduction in the difference between error- and correct-reaction times, because there is an upper limit to the amount of irrelevant information available to the subject; and if the intertrial interval is effectively zero, the difference in mean must also be zero. In fact, failure to find such a trend in Experiment 5 would count severely against this modification of the random walk model.

One consequence of the way in which temporal uncertainty has been represented in the random walk model is a reinterpretation of the components of reaction time (input time, T_i, decision time, T_d, and movement time, T_m) on p. 60. Since, in the representation of the process here, the detection that a signal is present and the discrimination of which signal it is are incorporated into one unitary decision process, T_i represents only the time taken by the information from the signal display to reach the relevant part of the subject's brain; this depends only on the physiological properties of the subject's perceptual system and will be independent of the signal presented. T_i does *not* include the time taken to detect that a signal is there; this is properly a part of T_d. T_d is never zero, not even in a simple reaction task. A simple reaction properly involves a decision between two alternatives, "signal" and "no signal", of which only one leads to a response (cf. McGill, 1963, pp. 329–331). It is now understandable that the variance of A-reaction time should be comparable to those of B- and C-reaction time in Experiment 4 (cf. Table 5.4.3, p. 62; but see Snodgrass, Luce and Galanter, 1967).

The second alternative on p. 81 is thus found to fit the data of the two-choice experiments, in so far as it has been possible to test it. The first alternative, the two-stage decision process, does not. It appears *prima facie* to represent an inefficient use of the available information; it leaves Prediction C on p. 44 unchanged; and it fails to explain why the variance of A-reaction times is as large as those of B- and C- reaction times. Alternative (i) must therefore be rejected as a possible interpretation of the role of a temporal uncertainty.

6.4.3. Relation to other work on temporal uncertainty.

Previous studies of temporal uncertainty have employed a simple reaction task with an objectively varied foreperiod (e.g. Karlin, 1959; Drazin, 1961). The experimenter-determined variance of the foreperiod has usually been large relative to the subject's inaccuracy of time estimation, so that where the foreperiod has been restricted to a set of discrete possible values, at least, the subject's strategy may be formulated as a sequence of C-reactions. At each time when a signal might be presented the subject decides between "signal" and "no signal". Thomas (1967) has recently reviewed both experiments and theories relating to temporal uncertainty.

The problem that has been considered here is rather different. The foreperiod (or intertrial interval) is fixed and the uncertainty arises solely because of subjective inaccuracies in time estimation. The appropriate strategy seems to be a generalization of the random walk model and not a chain of C-reactions. This idea is somewhat complementary to the studies cited above.

6.4.4. The limit to discrimination.

The modification of the random walk model in §6.4.1 explains why in two-choice experiments errors are faster than the same response made correctly. At short intertrial intervals in Experiment 5 error-reaction times showed a greater variance than correct-reaction times; this is probably because sequential relations increase in strength under these conditions. Sequential relations will be discussed in Chapter 8. It remains here to explain why in Experiments 6 and 7 errors should sometimes take longer than correct reactions and sometimes show a greater variance.

There must obviously be some limit to human ability to discriminate the signals used in these experiments. It seems reasonable that this should take the form of an effective limit to the time over which a subject can integrate information to reach any one decision. If a subject on any trial fails to collect sufficient information to satisfy any of the response criteria of Axiom 4 (p. 38) his best strategy is to make that response which has the greatest *a posteriori* probability. On such a trial the reaction time will be long and the probability of error greater than the average. In this way it is possible for the distribution of error-reaction times to have a greater mean than that of correct-reaction times. At present this seems the most plausible explanation of why errors should sometimes take longer than correct responses in Experiments 6 and 7. Some of the reaction times in the four- and five-choice series exceeded two and even three seconds, and it was found in Experiment 7 that the sign of the Kolmogorov-Smirnov statistic was correlated with the difficulty of discrimination (p. 77). The temporal limit to the integration of information would have to be about one second or perhaps a little longer.

Because the decision process takes longer in multi-choice experiments, and there is a lower limit to the decision latency leading to an interior response (see p. 156), temporal uncertainty will not play so obvious a part in Experiments 6 and 7. But it may nonetheless encourage a few hasty responses which are more likely than the average to be errors. The result in the testing of Prediction C will be that the distribution of error reaction times will be found to have a greater variance than the distribution of correct reaction times.

6.5. The multi-choice model.

The clustering of responses around the leading diagonal of the signal-response matrix suggests that the construction of Theorem B.1 might be achieved with a univariate random variable. This conclusion is supported by the way in which the shape of the mean reaction time relation was manipulated in Experiment 7 (see §5.7.2) by altering the ratios between the lengths of adjacent signals. But it is equally clear from that experiment that the important determinant of reaction time is the number of alternative signals, that is, the number of terms under the summation sign in the inequalities (B.8) which, as it were, reduce the *a posteriori* probabilities for a given sequence, $x_1, x_2 \ldots x_n$. Certainly the marked increase in the mean reaction time in Experiment 6 over the two-choice reaction time is due to this cause, since the ratio between any two adjacent signals there was the same as in the two-choice experiments.

Mean reaction time and the proportion of errors are both greater for interior than for exterior responses. Table 5.7.3 shows a refinement of the interior–exterior distinction, although the rank order relation with mean reaction time is not entirely maintained there. On p. 158 it is conjectured that the set of mean reaction times and decision

FIGURE 6.1

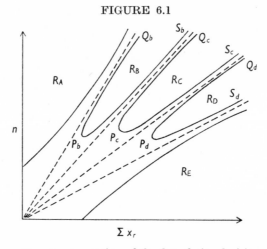

The $n - \Sigma\, x_r$ representation of the five-choice decision process

parameters is a compromise between constant accuracy of response and constant speed of response, made in order to optimise performance. The compromises observed in Experiment 6 and Series 5 of Experiment 7 seem to be approximately what one would expect in view of the unidimensional ordering of the signals.

Johnson (1955, pp. 353–359) argues that a central tendency of judgment is inevitable if there is a unidimensional ordering of the signals and some inaccuracy in response. But in Experiment 6 the effect is principally due to the way in which the λ_i vary through the response set, and this, as was shown above, is a product of the unidimensional ordering of the signals and the optimisation of performance in the sense of the fastest average speed of response compatible with a given overall accuracy. Exterior signals yield information at a faster rate than do interior signals, and so exterior responses are both faster and more accurate.

6.5.1. The structure of the decision problem in Experiment 6.

Figure 6.1 is a schematic map of the response boundaries in Experiment 6 referred to $\Sigma\, x_r$ and n as coordinates; Figure 6.2 shows a conjectural set of distributions of the observations.

From the result that responses tend towards signals of smaller physical size, provided such factors as *a priori* signal probability and accuracy of response do not obscure the issue, it seems likely that the distributions of the observations have a positive third moment. In Figure 6.1 an error response to S_C will occur much more frequently on $P_b\, S_b$ or $P_d\, Q_d$ than on $P_b\, Q_b$ or $P_d\, S_d$. Therefore the result implies that a majority of error responses to S_C will fall on $P_b\, S_b$, since this represents a downward movement of the response. That is, more errors will occur on the PS boundaries in general, and these must be balanced by a proportionate number of correct responses. Since most responses are correct, it follows that a majority of random walks, representing realisations of the decision process, pass to the right of their respective nodal points, P_b, P_c, P_d, in Figure 6.1. Such would be the case if the distributions of the X_r

FIGURE 6.2

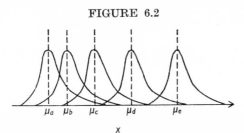

μ_a μ_b μ_c μ_d μ_e

x

Conjectured probability distributions corresponding to the five signals in Experiment 6.

conditional on each signal were positively skewed, as in Figure 6.2. There are, of course, other ways of choosing this set of distributions, but if it is required that they should differ only in location, they will, in general, have a positive third moment.

It appears from §5.7.4 that signals at the larger end of the signal set in Experiment 6 are easier to distinguish than the corresponding signals at the smaller end. Consequently the separation between the means in Figure 6.2 should be greater at the top end of the scale of signal magnitude. Since the physical sizes of the signals in Experiment 6 were chosen to lie in a geometric series, the Weber-Fechner Law predicts complete symmetry within the signal set, and the result actually obtained agrees with with the evidence on which Stevens (1957) based his argument for a power law, rather than a logarithmic one, relating subjective to objective magnitude. This result is also compatible with that obtained by Laming (1962, Experiment 1), which was interpreted in §3.5.(d) in terms of asymmetry in the decision process.

CHAPTER 7

A CRITICAL EXAMINATION OF CERTAIN ALTERNATIVE MODELS FOR CHOICE-REACTION TIME

7.1. Introduction.

In this chapter each of the models reviewed in Chapter 2 will be examined in turn in the light of the experimental results presented so far. In general none of them will appear compatible with the data. But the examination of them will not go very deep and no consideration will be given to how they might be modified to accommodate these results. It is left to the authors of these models to argue alternative points of view.

7.2. The relation between response latencies and probabilities proposed by Luce.

Equations (2.1) and (2.2) from Luce (1960) predict a linear relation between the mean reaction time for a given response and the response entropy. In practice this implies a functional relation between two sets of random variables, and a rigorous statistical test of such a prediction involves more labour than is justified here. Graphical plots of the mean reaction times from Experiments 1, 2 and 6 will be sufficient, and these are shown in Figures 7.1, 7.2 and 7.3 respectively. It is obvious from these figures that the mean reaction time for a given response is not linearly related to response entropy, and since the process of averaging over the performance of many subjects is usually kind to linear predictions, this judgment can be made with confidence. The relevant data from Experiment 3 are shown in Table 7.1, where the mean reaction time varies over a range of 0·06 seconds[1] with but a negligible change (0·0014) in the mean response

TABLE 7.1. Mean reaction times from Experiment 3 compared with response entropy and proportion of errors ($\hat{e}$) (cf. Luce, 1960). (Entropy calculated by taking logs. to base 10.)

| | Groups K, K', M, M' | | | Groups L, L', N, N' | | |
Series	Response entropy	Mean reaction time in secs.	$\hat{e}$	Response entropy	Mean reaction time in secs.	
1	0·3010	0·429	0·028	0·3010	0·396	0·035
2	0·3010	0·395	0·058	0·3010	0·374	0·055
3	0·3007	0·373	0·066	0·3009	0·365	0·066
4	0·2996	0·369	0·078	0·3001	0·366	0·073
5	0·3010	0·374	0·101	0·3009	0·364	0·082

[1] It might be thought that the differences in mean reaction time in Table 7.1 are not statistically significant. However a Friedman Analysis of Variance gives: Groups K,K', M,M': $\chi_r^2 = 23\cdot2$ with 4 d.f., $p < 0\cdot001$; Groups L,L', N,N': $\chi_r^2 = 9\cdot87$ with 4 d.f., $p < 0\cdot05$.

FIGURE 7.1

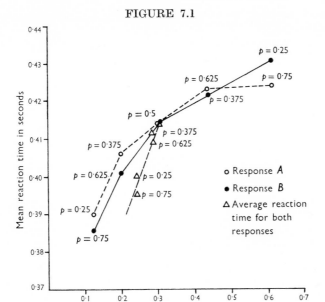

Mean reaction times from Experiment 1 plotted against response entropy (cf. Luce, 1960).

FIGURE 7.2

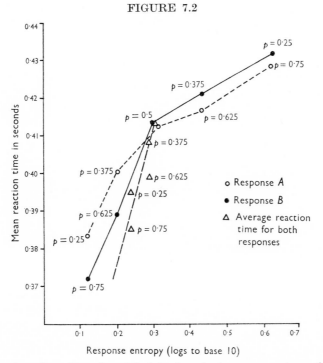

Mean reaction times from Experiment 2 plotted against response entropy (cf. Luce, 1960)

entropy. It appears that the proportion of errors is a more important correlate of mean reaction time.

In Figures 7.1 and 7.2 it happens that the average reaction time for both responses shows an approximately linear relation to response entropy, but with a slope substantially steeper than that of the curvilinear relation existing for the mean reaction time conditional on a given response. Since in Experiments 1 and 2 there were but

FIGURE 7.3

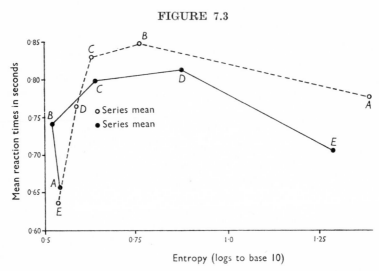

Mean reaction times for each response in Experiment 6 plotted against response entropy (cf. Luce, 1960). Open circles, Group K; filled circles, Group L.

few errors, this is essentially Hyman's (1953) finding concerning mean reaction times to individual signals (see §3.5.2). The pattern of Figures 7.1 and 7.2 is similar to that of Figure 3.6 (p. 42), which represents a theoretical relation derived from the random walk model.

There is an asymmetry between the responses (or signals) in Figures 7.1 and 7.2 in that the mean reaction times for the series $p = 0.25$ and 0.375, which have more long signals than short, are respectively greater than the means for the series $p = 0.75$ and 0.625. This repeats the result of Laming (1962). (See § 3.5.4).

7.2.1. Luce's choice axiom.

Since equation (2.1) does not hold in the experiments reported here, it is pertinent to enquire which of its underlying assumptions are at fault. The most important of these is Luce's (1959) Axiom 1 (see p. 18). Table 7.2 presents some data from Experiment 7 relevant to this axiom, showing the total response frequencies for one common response subset from each group. Since in that experiment the signals in each series were equiprobable and were always paired with the same finger, the axiom implies that for each group the relative response frequencies should be the same in each series. This is equivalent to homogeneity in each part of Table 7.1, and a significant χ^2 statistic is obtained in each case.

TABLE 7.2. RESPONSE FREQUENCIES FOR CERTAIN RESPONSE SUBSETS IN EXPERIMENT 7.

Group	Series	R_A	R_B	R_C	R_D	R_E	Test of homogeneity
K	3	573	—	728	—	699	$\chi^2 = 28\cdot42$
	4	768	—	756	—	684	with 4 d.f.,
	5	491	—	574	—	625	$p < 0\cdot001$
L	2	—	990	1010	—	—	$\chi^2 = 100\cdot39$
	3	—	487	811	—	—	with 3 d.f.,
	4	—	518	999	—	—	$p < 0\cdot001$
	5	—	465	755	—	—	
M	4	723	787	—	806	684	$\chi^2 = 13\cdot05$
	5	499	573	—	632	618	with 3 d.f.,
							$p < 0\cdot01$

This result, like the evidence from Experiment 6 shown in Figure 7.3, is due primarily to the perceptual relations between the signals used. This factor has found no place in Luce's model.

7.3. The explanation of choice-reaction phenomena in terms of sequential interactions proposed by Falmagne.

Falmagne (1965) has derived an asymptotic relation between the mean reaction time conditional on a given signal and signal probability (equation 2.6)

$$E\{t|S_i\} = \{p_i\,c\mu + (1-p_i)c'\bar{\mu}\}/\{p_i\,c + (1-p_i)c'\}, \qquad (7.1)$$

where c, c', μ, $\bar{\mu}$ are positive constants such that $\bar{\mu} > \mu$. $E\{t|S_i\}$ should therefore be a monotonic decreasing function of p_i. However the mean reaction times from Experiment 6, which may be found in the right hand column of Table 5.6.2, p. 69, do not preserve the correct rank order. The responses to the signals of probability 1/15 are much faster than equation (7.1) would predict, even when three parameters have been fitted to five points.

There are other, more exacting, criticisms of Falmagne's Markov model, which depend on a sequential analysis of the two-choice data. These criticisms will be deferred until §8.3.3. (p. 111). However, Falmagne's (1963) extension of his Markov model to deal with the making of mistakes may be discussed here in the light of the results already presented.

In the two-choice experiments equation (2.7), which Falmagne derives from his axioms, is equivalent to

$$(No.\ of\ errors|S_A) = (No.\ of\ errors|S_B), \qquad (7.2)$$

since, as is shown on p. 22, L in (2.7) must be 1. Equation (7.2) should be compared with the corresponding equation derived from the random walk model, (5.1) on p. 49. Equation (7.2) was tested by a similar method to that used for (5.1). The index

$$D' = (No.\ of\ errors|S_A) - (No.\ of\ errors|S_B)$$

should have a mean value of zero in each series of Experiments 1 and 2, and this null hypothesis was examined by a t-test. The results of this examination in the form of 5 per cent confidence intervals, values of t (with 23 d.f.) and two-tailed probability levels are shown in Table 7.3. The probability levels may be combined by the method suggested by Fisher (1934, §21.1) to give: Experiment 1: $\chi^2 = 19\cdot01$ with 10 d.f., $p < 0\cdot05$; Experiment 2: $\chi^2 = 36\cdot67$ with 10 d.f., $p < 0\cdot001$. It is clear from Table 7.3 that D' varies systematically with the bias in the signal series.

TABLE 7.3.   A SUMMARY OF THE T-TESTS APPLIED TO THE INDEX
$D' = \{(No.\ of\ errors\,|\,S_A) - (No.\ of\ errors\,|\,S_B)\}$ IN EXPERIMENTS 1 AND 2.

$P(S_A)$	0·25	0·375	0·5	0·625	0·75
Experiment 1:					
5% Confidence interval	1·99 −0·33	3·42 −0·84	0·83 −2·25	−0·21 −3·71	0·58 −2·24
t, (23 d.f.)	1·48	1·26	−0·95	−2·32	−1·23
p, (2-tailed)	0·139	0·221	0·352	0·030	0·231
Experiment 2:					
5% Confidence interval	3·26 0·58	2·12 −0·04	1·88 −0·96	2·37 −0·29	3·44 1·14
t, (23 d.f.)	2·96	2·01	0·67	−1·63	−4·12
p, (2-tailed)	0·007	0·056	0·510	0·117	0·001

The contention here is that equation (5.1) is approximately correct, while (7.2) is not. If this is so, the effect of the order of the test series in Experiment 1 (see pp. 50–2) will be to create a deviation in the error scores from equation (5.1), and to reduce, though not necessarily to extinguish, their deviation from equation (7.2).

Equation (2.7), may also be written in the form

$$P(R_i\,|\,\tilde{S}_i)P(\tilde{S}_i) = P(\tilde{R}_i\,|\,S_i)P(S_i),$$

putting $L = 1$, and hence

$$E\{No.\ of\ errors\,|\,R_i\} = E\{No.\ of\ errors\,|\,S_i\}. \tag{7.3}$$

Equation (7.3) implies that the frequency of each response in a choice reaction experiment should match the frequency of its corresponding signal, and this is incompatible with the highly significant central tendency of judgment found in Experiment 6 (see §5.7.2). The difference in this respect between Experiment 6 and Falmagne's (1963) experiment appears to be due to the strongly defined unidimensional structure of the signal set in the former experiment.

Falmagne's third error axiom (p. 21) requires that the distribution of reaction time when an error is made shall be independent of most, at least, of the experimental variables studied here. It is clear from Figures 5.1 and 5.2 (pp. 52 and 57) that the mean reaction time when an error is made is a function of the response (or signal) and the *a priori* signal probabilities at the least.

7.4. Fixed sample-size models.

In §2.4 it was argued by citing a result due to Hyman (1953) that a fixed sample-size model is incompatible with what is already known about choice-reaction times. The results of Experiments 1 and 2, shown in Figures 5.1 and 5.2, do but confirm Hyman's finding, in that within any given series the response to the signal of greater *a priori* probability is faster.

There are other features of the data which also bear on this issue. A fixed-sample model requires that all the variation in reaction time must be due to variation in T_i and T_m. The statistics in Tables 5.1.7 and 5.2.7 represent comparisons between reaction times for the same response made to different signals. The top row of these tables implies $T_i(S_A) > T_i(S_B)$, while the second row implies the contrary. Similarly in Table 7.4 the comparisons between the mean reaction times for S_A imply $T_m(R_A) > T_m(R_B)$, while the comparisons between the mean reaction times for S_B nearly all imply the contrary.

In Experiment 6, Table 5.6.2, the mean reaction times to particular signals do not preserve the same rank order in the two groups; so that differences between them cannot be attributed to differences in input time. Neither can the variation in mean reaction time amongst the responses be due to differences in movement time, since this leads to the ridiculous conclusion that the little finger is about 168 milliseconds faster than the index finger and 96 milliseconds faster than the thumb.

7.5. The recruitment model of La Berge.

In its present state of development the recruitment model of La Berge (1962) does not afford many opportunities for an experimental test. But it was shown in §2.5 that the reaction time when an error is made should be stochastically greater than that for the same response made correctly. Although some results in Tables 5.6.5 and 5.7.6 do show this relation, the two-choice experiments (Nos. 1–5) show nearly everywhere that errors are faster than correct responses (see p. 80).

This result was equally damaging to the random walk model proposed in §3.2, but it was successfully explained in §6.4.1 in terms of the subject's temporal uncertainty. The idea there was that the subject began sampling information before the signal was actually presented and that information so sampled was irrelevant to the decision. The corresponding idea in terms of La Berge's recruitment model seems to be that at the moment of presentation of the signal the quotas, $r_1, r_2 \ldots$ are already partially filled. But even if this is the case, the qualitative nature of the prediction derived in §2.5 is unchanged.

7.6. Partial memory models.

The zero memory model of p. 25 gives unequivocally the prediction that the distribution of reaction time for a given signal is independent of the response. The outcome of a test of this prediction is presented in Table 7.4, which shows the mean reaction times for every signal-response combination in Experiments 1 and 2 with significant differences underlined. This prediction was tested in the same way as Prediction C, (see p. 53 and Appendix C), except that here the combination $S_A R_A$ was compared with $S_A R_B$ etc. In these two experiments the distribution of reaction time for a given signal is not independent of the response. Further, it is clear from the graphical presentation of these data in Figures 5.1 and 5.2 that, while there might be a simple relation between the two mean reaction times conditional on a given response, there is no such relation existing between the two means conditional on a given signal.

There remains the possibility that the choice-reaction process is some sort of compromise between the zero-memory model of p. 25 and the complete memory or random walk model of §3.2. Such a partial memory model might be capable of representation as a moving average over a series of independent and identically distributed random variables, and in one special case considered in §2.6 it was shown that the distribution of reaction time when an error was made was a compromise between the distribution for the same response made correctly and that for a correct response to the same signal. It was conjectured there that this result held for a wide variety of partial memory models which are characterized by the fact that they select the most recent information as a basis for decision. If this result were true it would follow by reference

TABLE 7.4.   MEAN REACTION TIMES FOR EVERY SIGNAL-RESPONSE COMBINATION IN EXPERIMENTS 1 AND 2. (The means for the error combinations are underlined where they are significantly different from the means for correct responses to the same signal. A double underlining indicates significance at the 0·01 level, a single underlining at the 0·05 level.)

$P(S_A)$		0·25	0·375	0·5	0·625	0·75
Experiment 1:						
S_A	R_A	0·427	0·425	0·416	0·409	0·392
	R_B	0·289	0·307	0·368	0·364	0·358
S_B	R_B	0·388	0·404	0·416	0·424	0·435
	R_A	0·368	0·370	0·364	0·324	0·307
Experiment 2:						
S_A	R_A	0·430	0·417	0·414	0·402	0·385
	R_B	0·286	0·327	0·351	0·375	0·371
S_B	R_B	0·373	0·391	0·415	0·422	0·433
	R_A	0·381	0·380	0·364	0·349	0·329

to Figures 5.1 and 5.2 that the difference between the two means conditional on a given response (say R_A) should *decrease* as the *a priori* probability of the corresponding signal (S_A) increases. But on p. 83 precisely the contrary was found, namely, that the difference between the two means conditional on a given response *increased* with the probability of the corresponding signal, and this was explained as a second order effect of the modified random walk model in §A.7. It seems that partial memory schemes are contra-indicated by the data, although this conclusion must be regarded with caution at present since it is based partly on conjecture.

CHAPTER 8

SEQUENTIAL ANALYSIS

8.1. Introduction.

The model presented in Chapter 3 concerns only measures of performance averaged over long series of choice-reactions—proportions of errors, mean reaction times, distributions of reaction times—and the analysis of the experimental data has hitherto been confined to such measures as these. But a choice-reaction experiment also has a microstructure. Human performance is not steady but fluctuates in a way that is related to the signals and responses occurring in the experiment. This microstructure ought also to be studied because it affords additional insights into the nature of the decision process. At present very little is known, factually, about the sequential relations within a choice-reaction experiment. So instead of proposing a hypothetical model with which to compare the data, as Falmagne has done (see §2.3), it seemed better to undertake, in the first place, a comprehensive analysis of the data, without any theoretical bias, in order to discover the pattern of sequential relations that actually exists. This chapter is therefore principally descriptive.

8.1.1. The regression equations.

In the first place the response and the reaction time to a given signal in the series presented to the subject can be shown to be related to certain recent events (signals, responses, etc.) in the experiment. The influence of each event can be measured by a multiple regression analysis in which the events are represented by Boolean variables.[1] It is natural to use the signal and response at the ith trial, which will be denoted by S_i and R_i respectively, as the fundamental variables in terms of which the regression equation is expressed; if the signal at the ith trial is an S_A, $S_i = 0$, if it is an S_B, $S_i = 1$, and R_i is scored in similar manner.

It may be considered, however, that the response to S_i is related, not so much to the preceding response, R_{i-1}, but to whether that response was right or wrong. This latter event may be represented in the regression equation by the function

$$\mathscr{E}_{i-1} = [S_{i-1} + R_{i-1}],$$

where the square brackets indicate that the sum is to be taken modulo 2. If R_{i-1} is an error, $\mathscr{E}_{i-1} = 1$; if R_{i-1} is correct, $\mathscr{E}_{i-1} = 0$. For a similar reason $Q_{i,j}$ will be used to denote the function $[S_i + S_{i-j}]$. In this way complicated combinations of signals and responses may be represented as events in the regression equation. In order that the interpretation of the equation shall be unambiguous it is necessary that all the events so represented shall be mutually orthogonal. But there are many sets of events satisfying this condition, and the choice between the many alternative regression

---

[1] I am indebted to Mr. D. G. Champernowne for suggesting the use of multiple regression analysis in this context.

equations is made on purely psychological grounds. The sets of events represented in equations (8.1–3) were chosen because, in the light of the evidence available prior to carrying out this analysis, they seemed to be the most directly related to the response and reaction time to S_i. The problem of choosing between different sets of orthogonal events may be compared to that of reducing the equation of an ellipsoid to its principal axes: the correct choice of events is that choice which yields the simplest complete specification of the sequential pattern in terms of regression coefficients.

Although this method of multiple regression can, in principle, be used for the analysis of multi-choice experiments, so far only the two-choice experiments (Nos. 1–5) have been analysed. Three equations have been used, two for the response and one for the reaction time. The sets of events represented in these equations were chosen in the light of prior evidence which has already been presented elsewhere,[2] and no attempt will be made here to justify these choices. The equations will merely be stated in turn, together with the meaning of their coefficients. The regression coefficients were estimated by the conventional method of least squares.

For analyzing the occurrence of errors the following equation was used:

$$\mathscr{E}_i = e + a_0(S_i - \tfrac{1}{2}) + \sum_{j=1}^{n_1} a_j(Q_{i,j} - \tfrac{1}{2}) +$$

$$+ \sum_{k=1}^{n_2} a_{0k}(S_i - \tfrac{1}{2})(Q_{i,k} - \tfrac{1}{2}) + \sum_{j=1}^{n_2-1} \sum_{k=j+1}^{n_2} a_{jk}(Q_{i,j} - \tfrac{1}{2})(Q_{i,k} - \tfrac{1}{2}) +$$

$$+ \sum_{j=1}^{n_3} b_j \mathscr{E}_{i-j}[Q_{i,j} + 1] + \sum_{j=1}^{n_4} c_j \mathscr{E}_{i-j} Q_{i,j} + \epsilon_i, \tag{8.1}$$

where ϵ_i is an error term with zero expectation. The meaning of the coefficients in this equation may easily be discovered by taking conditional expectations on both sides, thus:

$e = E\{\mathscr{E}_i\}$, with, of course, the other effects represented in the equation partialled out; that is, e is the mean proportion of errors, being an equally weighted average over all the events represented in the equation.

For the coefficient a_0,
$$E\{\mathscr{E}_i | S_i = 1\} = e + \tfrac{1}{2}a_0$$
and
$$E\{\mathscr{E}_i | S_i = 0\} = e - \tfrac{1}{2}a_0.$$

Hence $a_0 = $ *(proportion of errors* $|S_B) - $ *(proportion of errors* $|S_A)$.

By similar arguments it can be seen that $a_j, 1 \leqslant j \leqslant n$, is the difference in proportion of errors between the events $S_{i-j} \neq S_i$, and $S_{i-j} = S_i$.

The $a_{jk}, 0 \leqslant j \leqslant n_2-1, j < k \leqslant n_2$, are second order terms. If the proportion of errors can be accurately represented as a moving average over S_i and the preceding events $Q_{i,j}, 1 \leqslant j \leqslant n_1$, these second order terms will be approximately zero.

The $b_j, 1 \leqslant j \leqslant n_3$, and $c_j, 1 \leqslant j \leqslant n_4$, represent the effect of making a mistake on subsequent performance. If R_{i-j} is an error, then either the b_j or the c_j term will

---

[2] The regression analysis of the two-choice data has in fact been carried out twice. The equations used here were constructed in the light of the results of the first analysis, which is reported in Laming (1963).

be non-zero. b_j represents the increase in the proportion of errors of the same sort, c_j the increase in the proportion of errors of the opposite sort.[3]

In Experiments 1 and 2 the total proportion of errors remains relatively constant from one experimental condition to another, but the relative numbers of errors of each sort change. The equation

$$(R_i-\tfrac{1}{2}) = r + \sum_{j=0}^{n_5} d_j(S_{i-j}-\tfrac{1}{2}) + \sum_{j=0}^{n_6-1}\sum_{k=j+1}^{n_6} d_{jk}(S_{i-j}-\tfrac{1}{2})(S_{i-k}-\tfrac{1}{2}) +$$

$$+ \sum_{j=1}^{n_7} b_j \mathscr{E}_{i-j}\,[Q_{i,j}+1](S_i-\tfrac{1}{2}) +$$

$$+ \sum_{j=1}^{n_8} c_j \mathscr{E}_{i-j}\, Q_{i,j}(S_i-\tfrac{1}{2}) + \rho_i, \qquad (8.2)$$

where ρ_i is an error term with zero expectation, is more sensitive than (8.1) to changes in the distribution of errors, because it analyses the variable $(R_i-\tfrac{1}{2})$ (i.e. proportion of R_B responses) rather than $\mathscr{E}_i$ (proportion of errors). The regression coefficients have the following interpretations:

r is half the mean difference in the proportions of each sort of error

i.e. $\qquad\qquad\qquad \tfrac{1}{2}\{P(R_B|S_A) - P(R_A|S_B)\},$

being an equally weighted average over all those events represented in the equation.

$d_j,\ 0 \leqslant j \leqslant n_5$, is the difference in the proportion of R_B responses between the events $S_{i-j} \equiv S_B$ and $S_{i-j} \equiv S_A$.

The $d_{jk},\ 0 \leqslant j \leqslant n_6-1, j < k \leqslant n_6$, are second order terms comparable to the a_{jk} of equation (8.1).

The b_j and c_j have the same interpretation here as in equation (8.1).

For analysing the sequential relations influencing reaction time the following equation was used:

$$T_i = t + \sum_{j=1}^{n_9} h_j\, T_{i-j} +$$

$$+ \sum_{j=1}^{n_{10}} \{f_j([R_i+R_{i-j}]-\tfrac{1}{2})(T_{i-j}-\mu) + g_j(Q_{i,j}-\tfrac{1}{2})(T_{i-j}-\mu)\} +$$

$$+ s_0\, \mathscr{E}_i + s_1(S_i-\tfrac{1}{2}) + s_2(R_i-\tfrac{1}{2}) +$$

$$+ \sum_{j=1}^{n_{11}} u_j(Q_{i,j}-\tfrac{1}{2}) + \sum_{j=1}^{n_{12}-1}\sum_{k=j+1}^{n_{12}} u_{jk}(Q_{i,j}-\tfrac{1}{2})(Q_{i,k}-\tfrac{1}{2}) +$$

$$+ \sum_{j=1}^{n_{13}} v_j\, \mathscr{E}_{i-j}\, Q_{i,j} + \sum_{j=1}^{n_{14}} w_j\, \mathscr{E}_{i-j}\,[Q_{i,j}+1] + \tau_i, \qquad (8.3)$$

[3] For the experiments under consideration here the b_j and c_j terms as written are preferable to terms representing responses or signal-response interactions, which are non-zero irrespective of whether an error has been made or not, because relatively few errors are made. If equation (8.1) had included terms of the form $b_j[S_i+R_{i-j}]$, the equation would have appeared to show separate signal and response tendencies, comparable in magnitude and opposite in sign, which oppose each other for all but a small proportion of the experimental trials (see Laming, 1963, Table 5:5:10, p. 219). The resolution of the sequential pattern here into a primary "signal" effect and a secondary "error" effect is considered to be more fundamental.

where T_i is the reaction time to S_i, $\mu = E\{T_i\}$, the unconditional expectation, and τ_i is an error term with zero expectation. The regression coefficients have the following interpretation:

t and the h_j, $1 \leqslant j \leqslant n_9$, are the coefficients of an autoregressive scheme relating T_i to the series of preceding reaction times.

The f_j and g_j, $1 \leqslant j \leqslant n_{10}$, are interaction terms between the autoregressive scheme and the preceding signal sequence. f_j represents the difference in the jth auto-regression coefficient contingent on the events $R_{i-j} \neq R_i$ and $R_{i-j} = R_i$; g_i represents the difference in the same coefficient contingent on the events $S_{i-j} \neq S_i$ and $S_{i-j} = S_i$.

s_0 is the increment in reaction time when an error is made.

s_1 and s_2 are the differences in reaction time contingent on the signal and the response respectively.

u_j represents the difference in reaction time between the events $S_{i-j} \neq S_i$ and $S_{i-j} = S_i$.

The u_{jk}, $1 \leqslant j \leqslant n_{12}-1$, $j < k \leqslant n_{12}$, are second order terms similar to the a_{jk}. If reaction time can be accurately represented as a moving average over the preceding events $Q_{i,j}$, $1 \leqslant j \leqslant n_{12}$, these second order terms will be approximately zero.

The v_j, $1 \leqslant j \leqslant n_{13}$, and w_j, $1 \leqslant j \leqslant n_{14}$, terms represent the increments in reaction time subsequent to an error and correspond to the c_j and b_j terms respectively in equation (8.1).[3] If R_{i-j} is an error either the v_j or the w_j term will be non-zero. w_j represents the increase in reaction time when the signal involved in the error is re-presented, and v_j represents the increase in reaction time when the alternative signal is presented.

Equations (8.1–3) represent a method of measuring the pattern of sequential relations existing in a series of choice-reaction data. A rough description of the several ways in which this technique was used will be given here; complete details of this method of analysis and its application to the two-choice experiments are given in Appendix C.

If the constant terms in equations (8.1–3) are replaced as follows:

$$\mathscr{E}_i = e_1\delta_{1j}+e_2\delta_{2j}+e_3\delta_{3j}+e_4\delta_{4j}+e_5\delta_{5j}+a_0(S_i-\tfrac{1}{2})+ \ldots \tag{8.4}$$

$$(R_i-\tfrac{1}{2}) = r_1\delta_{1j}+r_2\delta_{2j}+r_3\delta_{3j}+r_4\delta_{4j}+r_5\delta_{5j}+d_0(S_i-\tfrac{1}{2})+ \ldots \tag{8.5}$$

$$T_i = t_1\delta_{1j}+t_2\delta_{2j}+t_3\delta_{3j}+t_4\delta_{4j}+t_5\delta_{5j}+h_1T_{i-1}+ \ldots, \tag{8.6}$$

where $\delta_{ij} = 1$, if $i = j$, and 0 otherwise, and the suffix j refers to the experimental conditions, it is possible to fit one set of sequential coefficients to each subject's complete performance, except that the constant term is allowed to vary with the experimental condition. If the sequential pattern is invariant throughout the experiment, then the e_j, r_j, and t_j will have distributions that are independent of the experimental condition, that is, independent of j, and this null hypothesis may be tested by a Friedman analysis of variance. If, on the other hand, the sequential pattern is found not to be invariant, it is possible to discover the nature of the change by estimating the entire set of sequential coefficients separately for each experimental condition. Each coefficient may then be tested for invariance in the same way that is used for the e_j, r_j and t_j.

Since there are 24 (or 25) subjects in each experiment yielding independent values of the sequential coefficients, it is also possible to assess the significance of each one

[3] See footnote overleaf on p. 97.

without making any specific assumptions about its distribution. If there is no effect in the experiment corresponding to a given coefficient, its median value should be approximately zero, and this forms the basis of a simple binomial test.

There are therefore two distinct ways in which equations (8.1–3) were used. The question, whether the several conditions studied in an experiment created any change in the pattern of sequential relations, is discussed in §8.2. The other question, whether the events represented in the regression equations exercised a demonstrable influence on the response and the reaction time, is considered in the rest of the chapter. The coefficients of the regression equations fall naturally into five groups:

(i) the a_j, a_{jk}, u_j and u_{jk}, $k > j \geqslant 1$, which represent the influence of the preceding sequence of signals;

(ii) a_0 and the a_{0k}, s_0, s_1 and s_2, which represent the influence of the signal presented and the response made in the current trial;

(iii) the b_j, c_j, v_j, and w_j, which represent the after-effects of making a mistake;

(iv) t and the h_j, which are the constants of an autoregressive scheme among the reaction times;

(v) The f_j and g_j, which represent the interaction of the autoregressive scheme with signal and response factors. These groups of coefficients will be discussed in turn in successive sections of the chapter.

8.2. The fit of the regression equations.

In extracting the pattern of sequential relations from a set of experimental data it is difficult to decide whether all the important sequential influences are represented in the regression equation or not. At present there is no unequivocal answer to this question, but there is a technique that goes partway towards an answer. If it is found that the pattern of sequential relations, in so far as it is represented in the regression equation, changes with the several conditions of the experiment, then it

TABLE 8.1. MEDIAN VALUES AND SIGNIFICANCE LEVELS OF THOSE COEFFICIENTS OF EQUATION (8.2) WHICH SHOW SIGNIFICANT VARIATION AMONGST THE SEVERAL CONDITIONS OF EXPERIMENT 2.

$P(S_A)$	0·25	0·375	0·5	0·625	0·75	p
d_0	0·967	0·946	0·948	0·930	0·985	<0·01
d_3	0·039	0·007	0·011	0·001	0·037	<0·01
d_{02}	−0·060	−0·005	−0·002	0·010	0·037	<0·025
d_{03}	−0·037	0·002	0·019	0·011	0·059	<0·01
b_6	0·015	0·101	0·090	0·086	0·131	<0·025
c_2	0·012	0·030	−0·013	0·083	0·021	<0·01

seems that either the representation of the sequential pattern is incomplete, or it is capable of resolution in a different set of directions such that the effect of the experimental conditions enters explicitly into the regression equation. In either case it is important to discover how, and ultimately why, the pattern changes, and the method by which all this was done has already been outlined in §8.1.1.

The results of this investigation are shown in Tables 8.1 to 8.4. Wherever any of the equations showed that the sequential pattern differed amongst the several conditions of an experiment, the corresponding equation amongst (8.1–3) for the analysis of a single series of data was used to discover which of the coefficients were affected.

Those coefficients which showed a significant variation amongst the experimental conditions are listed in the tables, which show the median values of these coefficients under each condition and their significance levels. In these tables, as in all the other tables and figures in this chapter, medians are shown in preference to means, because the binomial test used to assess the significance of each coefficient tested the median, not the mean.

The five conditions of Experiments 1 and 2 were fitted by all three equations (8.4–6); only (8.5) detected any difference and that only in Experiment 2. Those coefficients that were affected are shown in Table 8.1. d_0, d_{02} and d_{03} indicate some

TABLE 8.2. MEDIAN VALUES AND SIGNIFICANCE LEVELS OF THOSE COEFFICIENTS OF EQUATIONS (8.1) AND (8.3) WHICH SHOW SIGNIFICANT VARIATION AMONGST THE SEVERAL CONDITIONS OF EXPERIMENT 3.

Series	1	2	3	4	5	p
e	0·025	0·043	0·052	0·054	0·067	<0·001
a_0	0·004	0·002	0·010	0·009	−0·011	<0·05
a_{02}	0·002	0·032	0·015	0·028	−0·026	<0·025
a_{12}	−0·002	−0·018	0·039	0·035	0·009	<0·005
v_1	0·123	0·055	0·090	0·061	0·038	<0·05

TABLE 8.3. MEDIAN VALUES AND SIGNIFICANCE LEVELS OF THOSE COEFFICIENTS OF EQUATIONS (8.1) AND (8.3) WHICH SHOW SIGNIFICANT VARIATION AMONGST THE SEVERAL CONDITIONS OF EXPERIMENT 4.

Series	1 B-reaction	2 C-reaction	3	4 A-reaction	5	p A-, B- and C- reactions	p B- and C- reactions
e	0·040	0·014	0·016	—	—	—	<0·001
a_0	−0·007	0·031	−0·038	—	—	—	<0·025
a_1	−0·003	0·029	0·022	—	—	—	<0·005
a_{01}	−0·027	0·053	−0·038	—	—	—	<0·025
a_{02}	0·024	0·032	−0·057	—	—	—	<0·005
a_{03}	−0·016	0·046	−0·021	—	—	—	<0·025
a_{12}	0·017	0·018	0·036	—	—	—	<0·05
a_{23}	0·001	−0·015	0·026	—	—	—	<0·05
c_1	0·011	0·009	0·028	—	—	—	<0·025
c_2	−0·035	0·001	0·030	—	—	—	<0·001
t	0·312	0·330	0·360	0·161	0·164	<0·001	—
h_3	0·052	−0·035	0·096	0·009	−0·005	<0·05	—
u_1	−0·001	0·066	0·066	−0·013	−0·021	<0·001	<0·025
u_3	0·007	−0·008	0·043	0·005	0·002	<0·025	<0·05

interaction between the signal presented and the bias in the signal sequence, while the other coefficients appear somewhat arbitrary. However there is an adequate explanation for these results which will be discussed in §8.2.1 below.

Differences amongst the conditions of Experiments 3, 4 and 5 were detected by both (8.4) and (8.6). The coefficients affected are shown in Tables 8.2, 8.3 and 8.4 respectively. In Experiment 3 the coefficient e shows the sort of increase in the probability of error that one would expect from the instructions given with each series (see Table 5.3.3). The sequential pattern in Experiment 4 also reflects in certain ways the general conditions of the experiment: the coefficient e is similar in value to the mean probability of error $\acute{\epsilon}$ in Table 5.4.3. a_0 is constrained by the fact that in the C-reaction errors of only one sort occur in practice. t shows a significant difference because the A-reaction is inherently faster than either of the other two. Since u_1 and u_3 also show a significant variation when the comparison is restricted to Series 1, 2 and 3 in Table 8.3 (t and h_3 do not) an additional significance level is shown for these coefficients in the right-hand column. In Experiment 5, Table 8.4, the coefficients t and e show that responses become inherently slower and less accurate as the

TABLE 8.4.　MEDIAN VALUES AND SIGNIFICANCE LEVELS OF THOSE COEFFICIENTS OF EQUATIONS (8.1) AND (8.3) WHICH SHOW SIGNIFICANT VARIATION AMONGST THE SEVERAL CONDITIONS OF EXPERIMENT 5.

Intertrial interval (msecs.)	4096	512	64	8	1	p
e	0·019	0·036	0·042	0·048	0·050	$<0·025$
a_1	$-0·008$	0·008	$-0·003$	0·003	$-0·023$	$<0·025$
a_{12}	$-0·016$	$-0·019$	$-0·067$	$-0·073$	$-0·085$	$<0·01$
a_{23}	0·014	0·005	0·041	$-0·044$	$-0·038$	$<0·05$
b_2	$-0·017$	$-0·025$	$-0·056$	$-0·020$	$-0·184$	$<0·01$
c_1	$-0·025$	0·001	0·293	0·329	0·352	$<0·005$
t	0·289	0·308	0·402	0·366	0·424	$<0·001$
u_2	0·016	0·016	$-0·005$	$-0·004$	$-0·011$	$<0·001$
u_{12}	$-0·009$	$-0·008$	$-0·029$	$-0·035$	$-0·070$	$<0·001$
v_1	0·095	0·120	0·203	0·265	0·316	$<0·1$
v_2	0·015	0·022	0·074	0·054	0·137	$<0·01$
w_1	0·054	0·097	0·234	0·168	0·294	$<0·025$

intertrial interval is decreased; this might have been expected. There is much more to be said about these results, of course, but further comments will be kept until later in this chapter, when each group of coefficients will be discussed in turn.

8.2.1. The order effect in Experiment 2.

In §5.3.2 (p. 56) it was shown that the order in which the experimental conditions were presented to the subjects in Experiment 2 influenced the distribution of errors between the two alternative signals. The distribution actually observed appeared to be a compromise between that distribution which was optimal (in the sense of equation A.13, p. 128) for the current series, and that which had been optimal for the preceding series. This factor is not represented in equation (8.5.).

Now the coefficient r in equation (8.2) is an estimate of the difference $\frac{1}{2}\{P(R_B|S_A)-P(R_A|S_B)\}$, with all the other effects represented in the equation partialled out. Hence in the symmetric optimal decision process, which will be assumed here,

$$E\{r\} = \tfrac{1}{2}(\alpha-\beta) = \tfrac{1}{2}\{\epsilon(1-\epsilon)/(1-2\epsilon)\}\{(2p-1)/p(1-p)\},　(8.7)$$

from equation (A.10). It follows that if the order effect is big enough to exert a demonstrable influence on the regression coefficients estimated from Experiment 2, then groups K and M should show more negative values of r than groups L and N, because groups K and M experienced the conditions of Experiment 2 in ascending order of p-values, while groups L and N experienced them in descending order. This is indeed the case: Table 8.5 shows the frequencies of positive and negative r_j coefficients for the two groups in the analysis of Experiment 2 with equation (8.5); the difference is significant at the 0·001 level. It is therefore reasonable to add an extra term to equation (8.5) to represent the order effect.

TABLE 8.5.   SIGNS OF THE ESTIMATES OF THE r_j COEFFICIENTS OBTAINED FROM THE ANALYSIS OF EXPERIMENT 2 WITH EQUATION (8.5).

	$r_j > 0$	$r_j < 0$
Groups K, M	22	38
Groups L, N	42	18

The nature of the order effect is such that the observed value of $\frac{1}{2}(\alpha-\beta)$ is approximately

$$\tfrac{1}{2}(\alpha-\beta) = \tfrac{1}{2}\{\epsilon(1-\epsilon)/(1-2\epsilon)\}[(1-\theta)\{(2p-1)/p(1-p)\}_j+\theta\{(2p-1)/p(1-p)\}_{j-1}], \tag{8.8}$$

where the subscripts j and $j-1$ refer to the current and preceding experimental conditions, and θ is a bias parameter. The term

$$\tfrac{1}{2}\{\epsilon(1-\epsilon)/(1-2\epsilon)\}(1-\theta)\{(2p-1)/p(1-p)\}_j$$

is represented by equation (8.5) as it stands at present. The term

$$\tfrac{1}{2}\{\epsilon(1-\epsilon)/(1-2\epsilon)\}\theta\{(2p-1)/p(1-p)\}_{j-1},$$

which represents the order effect, needs to be added to that equation;

i.e. $(R_i-\tfrac{1}{2}) = r_1'\delta_{1j}+r_2'\delta_{2j}+r_3'\delta_{3j}+r_4'\delta_{4j}+r_5'\delta_{5j}+$
$$+\tfrac{1}{2}\theta\{\epsilon(1-\epsilon)/(1-2\epsilon)\}\{(2p-1)/p(1-p)\}_{j-1}+d_o(S_i-\tfrac{1}{2})+\ldots (8.9)$$

where the r_j and θ are subject to one constraint.[4]   When equation (8.9) was fitted to the data of Experiment 2 there was no longer any significant difference between the series constants, r_j'. The bias term θ was not quite significant; its median lay in the interval $(-0·004, 0·292)$ with probability 0·936, and had a point estimate of 0·151. It follows from this analysis that the way in which a subject adjusts his performance to a change in the relative signal frequencies in a two-choice experiment may be accounted for by an invariant system of sequential relations operating on the changed sequence of signals.

8.3. The influence of the preceding sequence of signals.

The nature of the influence of the preceding sequence of signals is illustrated in Figure 8.1, which shows the mean reaction times and proportions of errors in Experiment 3 for each length of run of each signal. During a run of S_A s the reaction time

---

[4] The term $r_j\delta_{ij}$ in equation (8.5) is equivalent to the term

$$[r_j' +\tfrac{1}{2}\theta\{\epsilon(1-\epsilon)/(1-2\epsilon)\}\{(2p-1)/p(1-p)\}_{j-1}]\delta_{ij}$$

in equation (8.9). In equation (8.9) there are therefore six coefficients corresponding to the five degrees of freedom represented by the r_j of equation (8.5), and the constraint may be written

$$r_j'+\tfrac{1}{2}\theta\{\epsilon(1-\epsilon)/(1-2\epsilon)\}\{(2p-1)/p(1-p)\}_{j-1} = r_j, \quad j = 1\ldots 5.$$

θ may be evaluated by treating this as a regression equation with $r_j' = r'+\rho_j'$, where ρ_j' is an error term with zero expectation. The r_j' may then be obtained from the residuals.

and the probability of error to S_A both decrease, while the probability of error if an S_B is presented, ending the run, increases. During a run of S_B s the converse relations hold. The interrelations between mean reaction times and proportions of errors shown here are comparable to those that resulted from the changes in *a priori* signal probabilities in Experiments 1 and 2. So it seems likely that the preceding sequence

FIGURE 8.1

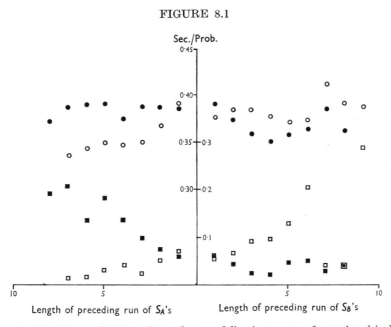

Mean reaction times and proportions of errors following a run of one signal in Experiment 3. Open circles, S_A, mean reaction times; filled circles, S_B, mean reaction times; open squares, S_A, proportions of errors; filled squares, S_B, proportions of errors.

of signals somehow determines the starting point of the random walk decision process (see p. 33). Indeed, insofar as the random walk model fits Experiments 1 and 2, the result in §8.2.1 implies this conclusion directly.

The influence of the preceding sequence of signals is represented by the a_j and a_{jk} coefficients in equation (8.4) and the u_j and u_{jk} coefficients in equation (8.6). The median values of the a_j and u_j coefficients from Experiments 1, 2 and 3 are shown in Figures 8.2 and 8.3; the a_{jk} and u_{jk} medians are shown in Tables 8.6 and 8.7. The three experiments are consistent in the values of these coefficients. Most of the a_j and u_j are significantly greater than zero, and both sets of coefficients show an approximately geometric decay with respect to position in the preceding sequence, except that a_1 and u_1 are both too small. The later values of these coefficients ($j > 5$) show a certain variation, which may be due to the particular sequences of signals used.[5]

[5] The same five sequences of signals were used for every subject in both Experiments 1 and 2; the two sets of coefficients are remarkably similar. Experiment 3 used different sequences of signals.

It will be easier to understand these results if a concept of subjective probability is introduced. Let q_i be the subjective probability at trial i that signal S_B will be presented. The starting point of the random walk at that trial will be $I_{0,i} = \log\{q_i/(1-q_i)\}$, and the two probabilities of error and the distributions of reaction time will be functions of q_i. The idea is that q_i is not necessarily equal to the objective probability of S_B, p, but is somehow determined by the sequence of signals presented up to S_{i-1}. In this way the response and reaction time at trial i are related to the preceding signals.

TABLE 8.6.   MEDIAN VALUES OF THE a_{jk} COEFFICIENTS FROM EXPERIMENTS 1, 2 AND 3. (Underlining indicates significance at the 0·064 level.)

Experiment	a_{12}	a_{13}	a_{14}	a_{23}	a_{24}	a_{34}
1	0·002	0·013	0·013	0·008	0·007	0·005
2	0·006	0·013	0·009	0·011	0·014	0·003
3	0·009	0·008	0·002	0·016	0·011	0·005

TABLE 8.7.   MEDIAN VALUES OF THE u_{jk} COEFFICIENTS FROM EXPERIMENTS 1, 2 AND 3. (A double underlining indicates significance at the 0·006 level, a single underlining at the 0·064 level. N.C. = not computed.)

Experiment	u_{12}	u_{13}	u_{14}	u_{23}	u_{24}	u_{34}
1	−0·019	−0·008	N.C.	−0·003	N.C.	N.C.
2	−0·012	−0·003	0·001	−0·004	0·001	0·001
3	−0·018	−0·009	N.C.	0·004	N.C.	N.C.

FIGURE 8.2

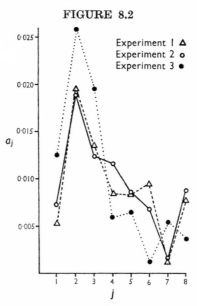

Experiment 1 △
Experiment 2 ○
Experiment 3 ●

Median values of the a_j regression coefficients in Experiments 1, 2 and 3.

Now the probabilities of error at trial i in a symmetric optimal decision process may be written (equation A.47)

$$\alpha_i = \epsilon\{(1-\epsilon)e^K q_i/(1-q_i)-\epsilon\}/(1-2\epsilon),$$
$$\beta_i = \epsilon\{(1-\epsilon)e^K(1-q_i)/q_i-\epsilon\}/(1-2\epsilon), \qquad (8.10)$$

where e^K is the correction for temporal uncertainty (see p. 141). The mean reaction time if S_A is presented at trial i may be written (equations A.8 and A.9)

$$E_i\{t|S_A\} = m^{-1}\,[\log\,\{q_i/(1-q_i)\}-$$
$$- \{2\epsilon(1-\epsilon)q_i e^K/(1-q_i)(1-2\epsilon)-(1-2\epsilon+2\epsilon^2)/(1-2\epsilon)\}\log\{(1-\epsilon)/\epsilon\}], \quad (8.11)$$

where $m = |E\{\delta I|S_A\}|/\delta t$, and there is a similar expression for $E_i\{t|S_B\}$. It follows from Tables 8.6 and 8.7 that $q_i/(1-q_i)$ is a positively accelerated function of the preceding signals (i.e. with positive second order terms) while (8.11) is negatively accelerated. This is consistent with the hypothesis that q_i or $I_{0,i}$ (or any similar variable)

FIGURE 8.3

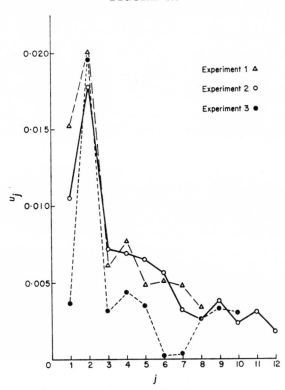

Median values of the u_j regression coefficients in Experiments 1, 2 and 3.

is a linear function of the preceding signals. The consistency may be shown by differentiating (8.10) and (8.11) twice with respect to q_i or $I_{0,i}$. For $d^2\alpha_i/dq_i^2$, $d^2\alpha_i/dI_{0,i}^2$, $d^2E\{t|S_A\}/dI_{0,i}^2$ the result follows immediately; $d^2E\{t|S_A\}/dq_i^2$ may be positive for certain values of q_i, but reference to the form of (8.11) in Figure 3.6

(p. 42, which shows $E_i\{t|S\}_A$ as a function of q_i with $k = 0$, $\epsilon = 0.025$) shows that the second order terms estimated from the data will generally be negative.

Further evidence comes from the analysis of Experiments 1, 2 and 3 with equation (8.5). This equation analyses the variable $(R_i - \frac{1}{2})$ and

$$E\{R_i - \tfrac{1}{2}\} = \tfrac{1}{2}(\alpha_i - \beta_i) = \tfrac{1}{2}\epsilon(1-\epsilon)\{q_i/(1-q_i) - (1-q_i)/q_i\}e^K/(1-2\epsilon) \qquad (8.12)$$

from equation (8.10). $E\{R_i - \tfrac{1}{2}\}$ is an antisymmetric function of q_i (or $I_{0,i}$) about the value of $q_i = \frac{1}{2}$. $E\{R_i - \tfrac{1}{2}\}$ also appears antisymmetric as a function of the preceding signals. In Experiments 1, 2 and 3, S_A and S_B appeared on average equally often and of the d_{jk} coefficients only one out of nine (d_{13} in Experiment 2 was negative and just significant at the 0.064 level) was significantly different from zero; this may be regarded as a chance result. The results of this analysis are therefore consistent with the hypothesis that q_i (or $I_{0,i}$) is an antisymmetric linear function of the preceding signals, i.e. q_i (or $I_{0,i}$) may be represented as a moving average over the variables $(S_{i-1} - \tfrac{1}{2})$, $(S_{i-2} - \tfrac{1}{2})$ . . . . Unfortunately it is not possible to discriminate between q_i and $I_{0,i}$ as a linear function of the preceding signals on the basis of the results presented here. Such a discrimination might be possible if third order terms were added to equations (8.4) and (8.6), but these terms would be unlikely to lead to a significant result.

It might have been expected that the mean reaction times in Figure 8.1 would have shown an increase following a run of the contrary signal. In fact the $E\{t|S_A\}$ following a run of S_B s and the $E\{t|S_B\}$ following a run of S_A s show no consistent change. In Figure 3.6 (p. 42) equation (8.11) reaches its maximum at $q_i = 0.84$. But if $\epsilon = 0.05$, as in Experiment 3, and $K = 0.6$, as on p. 83, the maximum occurs at $q_i = 0.59$. The failure of mean reaction times in Figure 8.1 to show a consistent increase following a run of the contrary signal now appears consistent with the other results presented here.

8.3.1. Alternations of the signal.

It would be particularly interesting if the influence of the preceding signals were mediated through a geometric moving average over the preceding sequence, because this system has the Markov property—its value at trial $i+1$ depends only on its value at trial i and the signal presented at that trial, S_i. It requires no memory for preceding signals. But this seems very unlikely because Figures 8.2 and 8.3 suggest that S_{i-2} exerts a greater influence on the response at trial i, R_i, than does S_{i-1}. There is also corresponding evidence from the reaction times. In Figure 8.1 the mean reaction time to S_A and the proportion of errors are both greater after the sequence of signals . . . $S_B S_A$ than after the sequence . . . $S_A S_B$.[6] The converse relation holds for the mean reaction times and proportion of errors to S_B, and this results holds not only for Experiment 3, but for Experiments 1 and 2 as well. This apparent anomaly requires some explanation.

The only plausible explanation seems to be that, although the subject is primarily concerned to estimate the relative frequencies of the two signals, he is also looking for alternating patterns of signals. Bertelson (1961, Figure 3) has already shown that two-choice reaction time decreases during an alternating sequence, albeit in a signal series that contained 75 per cent alternations. Figure 8.4 shows the mean reaction

---

[6] The organisation of Figure 8.1 is such that a preceding run of nS_A s implies the preceding sequences . . . $S_B S_A{}^n$, and so on.

times and proportions of errors in Experiment 3 for alternating preceding sequences of several different lengths. It looks there as though after one or more alternations the subject increasingly expects another alternation of the signal (cf. Figure 8.1), although this effect is small compared with that due to signal frequency in Figure 8.1, and is partially confounded with it. It seems likely, therefore, that the regression equations, (8.1–6), would have represented the influence of the preceding sequence of

FIGURE 8.4

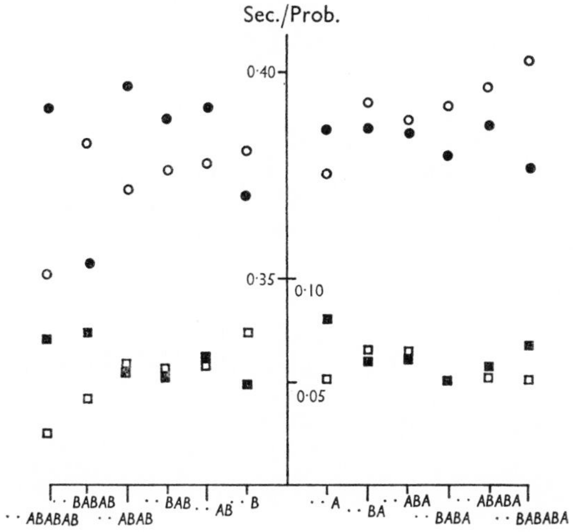

Mean reaction times and proportions of errors following certain alternating sequences of signals (denoted by $..BAB$ etc.) in Experiment 3. Open circles, S_A, mean reaction times; filled circles, S_B, mean reaction times; open squares, S_A, proportions of errors; filled squares, S_B, proportions of errors.

signals more accurately if they had contained two sets of terms, one set to represent the subjective estimate of signal frequency, the other to represent the subjective likelihood of an alternation of the signal.

The subjective probability of S_B at trial i may be represented as

$$q_i = \tfrac{1}{2} + \Sigma \, x_r(S_{i-r} - \tfrac{1}{2}) + \Sigma \, y_r([S_{i-1} + S_{i-r} + S_{i-r-1}] - \tfrac{1}{2}), \qquad (8.13)$$

where the x_r coefficients represent the subjective estimate of signal frequencies and the y_r coefficients represent the likelihood of an alternation;[7] as before, square brackets denote that the sum is to be taken modulo 2. The y_1 term in (8.13) simplifies to $y_1(S_{i-2} - \tfrac{1}{2})$; hence S_{i-2} may have a larger influence on the response and reaction time than S_{i-1}. In equations (8.4) and (8.6) interaction terms were included because $E\{\mathscr{E}_i\}$ and $E\{T_i\}$ are not linear functions of q_i (or $I_{0,i}$). Using $(x_r x_s)$, $(x_r y_s)$, $(y_r y_s)$

---

[7] $([S_{i-1} + S_{i-r} + S_{i-r-1}] - \tfrac{1}{2}) \equiv \{(\tfrac{1}{2} - S_{i-1})[S_{i-r} + S_{i-r-1}] + (S_{i-1} - \tfrac{1}{2})(1 - [S_{i-r} + S_{i-r-1}])\}$
and therefore corresponds to the combinations of events
$\{(S_{i-r} = alternation).(S_{i-1} = S_A)\}$ or $\{(S_{i-r} = repetition).(S_{i-1} = S_B)\}$,
under which circumstances the subject would expect S_i to be an S_B.

etc. to denote the second order coefficients in the expansion of $E\{\mathscr{E}_i\}$, it can be shown that

$$a_2 \longleftrightarrow x_2+y_1, \tag{8.14}$$

$$
\left.
\begin{aligned}
a_{12} &\longleftrightarrow (x_1 x_2)+(x_1 y_1), \\
a_{13} &\longleftrightarrow (x_1 x_3)+(x_2 y_2)+(x_4 y_3)+(y_1 y_2), \\
a_{14} &\longleftrightarrow (x_1 x_4)+(x_3 y_3)+(x_5 y_4), \\
a_{23} &\longleftrightarrow (x_2 x_3)+(x_1 y_2) \quad \text{etc.,}
\end{aligned}
\right\}
\tag{8.15}
$$

where $\longleftrightarrow$ indicates correspondence. Similar equations may be derived for the u_{jk} terms, while the y_r terms in (8.13) for $r \geqslant 2$ correspond to third order terms in (8.4) and (8.6)—these were not computed. The correspondences in (8.14) and (8.15) might well be sufficient to explain the pattern of u_j and u_{jk} values in Figure 8.3 and Table 8.7, but they do not appear adequate for the a_j and a_{jk} values. Two questions remain:

(i) Why is a_1 so small relative to a_2 and a_3?

(ii) Why is a_{12} not significantly greater than zero (cf. u_{12})?

The values of these coefficients might have been different had the third order terms corresponding to the y_r been computed; however, a conjectural answer to the second question will be given in the next section.

8.3.2. Changes in the sequential pattern.

In Experiments 1 and 2 an invariant pattern of sequential relations operating on the several signal series was found adequate to account for the changes in mean reaction times and error scores that occurred with changes in *a priori* signal probability. In the other experiments certain changes were detected in the sequential pattern with different experimental conditions. So far as these changes concern the influence of the preceding signals they will be discussed here.

In Experiment 3 the coefficient a_{12} was greater for Series 3 and 4 than for the other three series; the median values of this coefficient are shown in Table 8.2 (p. 100). In these two series the subject was instructed to respond faster to one signal than to the other, thereby producing more errors of one sort than of the other. Since in terms of the random walk model this is isomorphic to a change of starting point, it is not obvious why there should be any variation in a_{12}.

Certain changes in the influence of the preceding sequence were found amongst the B- and C-reaction conditions of Experiment 4; these changes are shown in Table 8.4 (coefficients a_1, a_{12}, a_{23}, u_1, u_3). In general the preceding signals exert a greater influence in the C-reaction than in the B-reaction. Superficially the C-reaction differs from the B-reaction only in the absence of one of the response boundaries, and this should have only a second order effect. In practice the difference seems to be more fundamental than this. In the A-reaction the influence of the preceding signals (represented by u_1, u_3 etc.) is negligible—this was to be expected.

As the intertrial interval is reduced from four seconds to near zero, some profound changes take place in the sequential pattern. The coefficients that were found to vary significantly in Experiment 5 are shown in Table 8.4. When the intertrial interval is long (4096 or 512 milliseconds) the pattern of sequential relations is similar to that found in Experiments 1, 2 and 3; the only noteworthy difference is that a_{12} here is significantly less than zero. But as the intertrial interval decreases to 1 millisecond the coefficients a_1, a_{23} and u_2 become negative, and a_{12} and u_{12}, which are negative throughout, increase in magnitude. Indeed, the interaction terms increase greatly in magnitude and come to dominate the sequential pattern. This implies that alternations of the signal *per se* become increasingly important as the intertrial interval is reduced.

The role played by alternating signal sequences is made clearer by Figures 8.5 and 8.6. For each intertrial interval in Experiment 5 these figures show the mean reaction times and proportions of errors for certain preceding signal sequences. The preceding signals are expressed relative to S_i; thus if $S_{i-j} = S_i$, it is represented by a 0; if

FIGURE 8.5

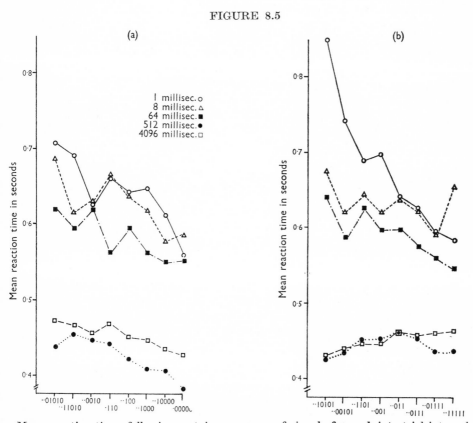

Mean reaction times following certain sequences of signals for each intertrial interval in Experiment 5. (For explanation see text).

$S_{i-j} \neq S_i$, it is represented by a 1. The sequential analyses of Experiments 1, 2 and 3 suggested that if the subject experiences a run of one signal or an alternating sequence, he expects these patterns to continue. On this basis the subjective expectation of S_i, the signal actually presented, increases from left to right in Figures 8.5(a) and 8.6(a) and from right to left in Figures 8.5(b) and 8.6(b). When the intertrial interval is long the mean reaction times and proportions of errors behave as one would expect; they both decrease as the subjective expectation of S_i increases. But when the intertrial interval is short they behave differently: after a run of either kind of signal the mean reaction times and proportions of errors all decrease, while after an alternating sequence they increase greatly, irrespective of which signal might have been most expected.

When the intertrial interval is short the interpretation of the influence of the preceding sequence in terms of q_i breaks down. In Experiments 1, 2 and 3 a change of the starting point gains speed and accuracy for one signal at the expense of the other. But here both signals show decrements in both speed and accuracy after an alternating sequence. The subject's decision process is then less efficient, and this all seems to imply that when the intertrial interval is short the mean rate of extraction of information from the signal presented is less after an alternating sequence of signals than it is after a run.

Several subjects in Experiment 5 commented, quite spontaneously, that in the short intertrial interval conditions they tended to build up an image of the signal.[8] When

FIGURE 8.6

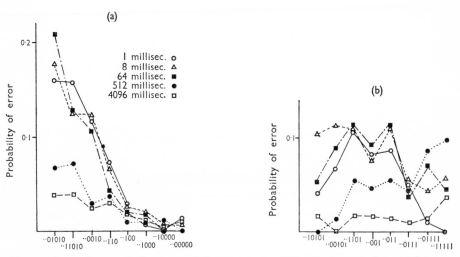

Proportions of errors following certain sequences of signals for each intertrial interval in Experiment 5. (For explanation see text).

the same signal was presented repeatedly the image became sharp and enabled the subject to detect either signal with relative ease. When the signals alternated the image became a blurred composite and the identification of the signal was more difficult. Now the stream of information in the random walk model might be thought of as a series of brief measurements of the signal, subject to error, and these measurements need to be interpreted on the basis of the possible alternative sizes of the signal, as subjectively remembered by the subjects (cf. §8.7). A memory image, such as was reported by some of the subjects in Experiment 5, is certainly not necessary for the process of interpretation, but it seems a reasonable conjecture that where it exists, it will dominate and maybe hinder the process.

[8] In the short intertrial interval conditions the signals were presented tachistoscopically in order to prevent interaction between successive signals on the retina. This image must therefore have been a mental image, existing at higher neural levels, and not a retinal image.

It is interesting that the coefficient a_{12} should have been negative, and significant too, at every intertrial interval in Experiment 5. It must be considered possible that the decrement in performance following an alternating sequence existed also in Experiments 1, 2 and 3, but was sufficiently small relative to other sequential effects that it was not readily detectable. This might explain why a_{12} in Table 8.6 was not significant while u_{12} in Table 8.7 was so unequivocally negative.

8.3.3. Falmagne's model for sequential interactions.

This model is contained in Falmagne's 1965 paper and has been described in §2.3 here. One criticism in §7.3 was based on its asymptotic prediction (equation 2.6); two further criticisms follow here based on sequential predictions.

The first criticism concerns the relative sizes of c and c'. It is possible to derive a theoretical expression from Falmagne's model for the interaction term u_{12} in equation (8.3). From equations (2.3), (2.4), and (2.5) on p. 20,

if S_A is presented at trial n,

$$J_{A,n+1}(t) = (1-c)J_{A,n}(t)+c\,K(t); \tag{8.16}$$

if S_B is presented at trial n,

$$J_{A,n+1}(t) = (1-c')J_{A,n}(t)+c'\,\bar{K}(t). \tag{8.17}$$

The coefficient

$$u_{12} = \tfrac{1}{2}[E_{A,n+2}\{t\,|\,S_{n+1} = S_A.S_n = S_A\}+E_{A,n+2}\{t\,|\,S_{n+1} = S_B.S_n = S_B\}-$$
$$-E_{A,n+2}\{t\,|\,S_{n+1} = S_A.S_n=S_B\}-E_{A,n+2}\{t\,|\,S_{n+1} = S_B.S_n = S_A\}+$$
$$+E_{B,n+2}\{t\,|\,S_{n+1} = S_A.S_n = S_A\}+E_{B,n+2}\{t\,|\,S_{n+1} = S_B.S_n = S_B\}-$$
$$-E_{B,n+2}\{t\,|\,S_{n+1} = S_A.S_n = S_B\}+E_{B,n+2}\{t\,|\,S_{n+1} = S_B.S_n = S_A\}]$$

(cf. equation 8.3). By using equations (8.16) and (8.17) twice and putting $E_{A,n}(t)$ and $E_{B,n}(t)$ equal to their asymptotic values (equation 2.6), it can be shown that

$$u_{12} = \tfrac{1}{2}cc'(c'-c)(\mu-\bar{\mu})[1/\{(1-p)c+pc'\}+1/\{pc+(1-p)c'\}], \tag{8.18}$$

where $p = P(S_B)$.

Estimates of u_{12} from the experiments here are all negative, so that, since $\bar{\mu} > \mu$ (see p. 20), $c' > c$. But Falmagne has always found $c > c'$ in his experiments. It is not necessary, as Falmagne (1965, p. 121) points out, for c and c' to be invariant under all conditions. But it does cast a little doubt on the value of the model when the two fundamental conditioning parameters are found to change their relative sizes.

The other criticism concerns the mean reaction time following an alternation of the signal. By the same method that was used in deriving (8.18) it can be shown that

$$E_{A,n+2}\{t\,|\,S_{n+1} = S_B.S_n = S_A\}-E_{A,n+2}\{t\,|\,S_{n+1} = S_A.S_n = S_B\} = cc'(\bar{\mu}-\mu) > 0. \tag{8.19}$$

So on the basis of Falmagne's model the ultimate signal in the preceding sequence should have a greater influence than the penultimate signal. But here the contrary has been found. In particular it was pointed out on p. 106 that the expression in equation (8.19) is, in practice, negative (see Figure 8.1), and this was taken to imply that the subject looked for alternating patterns in the signal sequence. Falmagne's model therefore fails at this point because his Markov chain is of only first order. The data presented here imply that a chain of at least second order is required.

8.4. Signal and response factors.

Differences in the probability of error and in mean reaction time associated with particular signals and responses are detected by the coefficients a_0 and a_{0k} in equation (8.4), r_j in (8.5) and s_1 and s_2 in (8.6).

The r_j are estimates of the mean difference in error probabilities, $\frac{1}{2}(\alpha-\beta)$. In Experiments 1 and 2 they do not differ significantly from zero, indicating no apparent response bias. This is confirmed by the a_0 coefficients, which have a similar interpretation (see p. 96); the a_0 coefficients are not significant anywhere except in the C-reaction conditions of Experiment 4. In those two conditions, however, not only a_0 but also a_{01}, a_{02} and a_{03} are significant. In Series 2 (Experiment 4), where R_A is the only response, these coefficients are all positive; in Series 3, where R_B is the only response, they are all negative. This is obviously due to the nature of the C-reaction condition, in which, in practice, errors of only one sort occur.

When there is no other evidence of a response bias, it is not clear how a significant a_{0k} coefficient should be interpreted. a_{01} and a_{02} in Experiment 1 and a_{01} in Experiment 5 are positive, while a_{01} in the B-reaction condition of Experiment 4 is negative. It is possible that the significant a_{0k} coefficients in Experiment 1 are associated with the asymmetry between the two signals found in that experiment (see p. 90).

s_1 and s_2 represent differences in mean reaction time peculiar to signals and responses respectively. s_1 in Experiment 1 is positive; otherwise s_1 and s_2 are not significant anywhere. This means that in Experiment 1 the mean reaction time conditional on S_B (2·83 in. high) was about 0.01 seconds longer than that conditional on S_A (4.00 in. high). It is unlikely that this is a chance result or artefact since it is confirmed by another analysis of the same data. In the course of testing Prediction C on p. 53 (see §C.1) it was possible to compare the distributions of $[E\{t \mid R_A.S_A\}-E\{t \mid R_A.S_B\}]$ and $[E\{t \mid R_B.S_B\}-E\{t \mid R_B.S_A\}]$. It was found that the difference conditional on R_B was greater than that conditional on R_A at the 0·025 level on a 2-tailed test, and a similar result has been obtained elsewhere for Experiment 3 (see Laming, 1963, pp. 136 and 179). Since in Experiment 1 $s_1 > 0$ while s_2 is not significant,[9] this result seems to imply a difference in reaction time peculiar to the signals rather than the responses, i.e. a difference in "input" time.

In the modification of the random walk model in §6.4.1 it is pointed out that in a two-choice experiment the subject actually has to distinguish between three possibilities: S_A, S_B and "No Signal". Because S_B is shorter than S_A and therefore more like "No Signal", it is effectively an interior signal in the sense of §B.3.3. Hence the mean rate of information when S_B is presented is less, at the beginning of the decision process at least, than that when S_A is presented, and so it takes longer to detect S_B than S_A. Such a result has been demonstrated for the area of a lighted patch in a simple reaction time experiment by Froeberg (1907). On the other hand it can be seen from equation (B.2) (p. 146) that the mean rate of information conditional on any signal at time $r\,\delta t$ is a function of the set of *a posteriori* probabilities at that time and is therefore not invariant with respect to time. In particular, in a two-choice experiment the mean rates of information will change as the *a posteriori* probability of "No Signal" tends to zero, and the information structure will then approximate that of a two-choice decision process, in which S_B may yield information at a *faster* rate than S_A. The

---

[9] In an earlier sequential analysis of these data reported in Laming (1963, Chapter 7) the coefficient there corresponding to s_1 here, e, was greater than zero in both Experiments 1 and 3.

above interpretation of the coefficient s_1 is therefore not inconsistent with the asymmetry of the decision process reported in §7.2.

It remains to consider why s_1 was not significant in Experiments 2 and 4, where a difference in "input" time was specifically looked for. These two experiments were done in darkness, while Experiments 1 and 3 were performed in daylight, under which condition the signals were harder to see. Evidently difficult conditions of viewing were necessary to make the small difference in reaction time between the two signals detectable.

8.5. After-effects of errors.

The making of an error is accompanied by certain effects on subsequent responses and reaction times, which are detected by the b_j, c_j, s_0, v_j and w_j coefficients in equations (8.4) and (8.6). s_0 is negative in every experiment, indicating that in the two-choice experiments errors are generally faster than correct responses. This confirms the finding in §6.4 and no more need be said here.

The median values of the b_j, c_j, w_j and v_j coefficients in Experiments 1, 2 and 3 are shown in Figures 8.7 to 8.10. The b_j and c_j coefficients are all negative and of similar

FIGURE 8.7 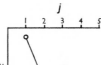 FIGURE 8.8

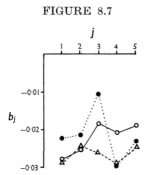

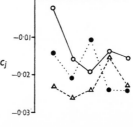

Median values of the b_j, regression coefficients in Experiments 1, 2 and 3. Triangles, Experiment 1; open circles, Experiment 2; filled circles, Experiment 3.

Median values of the c_j, regression coefficients in Experiments 1, 2 and 3. Triangles, Experiment 1; open circles, Experiment 2; filled circles, Experiment 3.

magnitude; most of them are significant. So that after making a mistake subjects are less likely than usual to make another one. The response immediately following an error takes longer than usual (v_1, w_1). If the signal presented is the alternative to that involved in the mistake (so that the response now required is the same as that which was made erroneously) the increase in reaction time is large (about 0·08 seconds) and persists for three signals following the error, decreasing sharply; this increase is represented by the v_j coefficients in Figure 8.10. If the signal involved in the mistake is repeated, the increase in reaction time is smaller and appears only on the signal immediately following the error (see the w_j coefficients in Figure 8.9).

These results are consistent with the following hypotheses: In two-choice experiments with an intertrial interval of 1500 milliseconds or more,

(i) Errors are caused principally by the irrelevant information which the subject inevitably samples prior to the presentation of the signal in a state of temporal uncertainty.

(ii) After an error has been made the time at which the subject begins to sample the information stream again to deal with the next signal is delayed, frequently until after that signal has been presented. The likelihood of another mistake is reduced because the subject now samples much less irrelevant information, and frequently none at all. If the subject does not begin sampling until after the signal has been presented there will also be a corresponding increase in reaction time.

(iii) The boundary at which the erroneous decision was made is adjusted outwards. Although this selectively reduces the probability of making the same response again, this reduction cannot be detected by itself because of (i) above. But the readjustment of the boundary selectively increases the reaction time following an error if the alternative signal is presented (compare v_j and w_j).

FIGURE 8.9   FIGURE 8.10

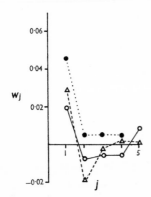

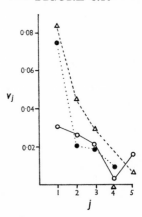

Median values of the w_j, regression coefficients in Experiments 1, 2 and 3. Triangles, Experiment 1; open circles, Experiment 2; filled circles, Experiment 3.

Median values of the v_j regression coefficients in Experiments 1, 2 and 3. Triangles, Experiment 1; open circles, Experiment 2; filled circles, Experiment 3.

(iv) After a correct response small contrary adjustments are made to the positions of the boundaries and to the time at which the sampling of information for the next decision begins. These parameters are thus determined by a stochastic process.

It follows that after a response has been initiated the subject continues sampling the information stream in order to check that the response was correct. It is certain that this does happen in practice, not least because in a two-choice experiment subjects invariably know when they have made a mistake without being told. This checking of the response must be regarded as an integral part of the decision process.

The differences between Experiments 1 and 3 on the one hand and Experiment 2 on the other are interesting. Experiments 1 and 3 were programmed by hand, so that the intertrial interval was variable and averaged about 2 seconds. Experiment 2 was programmed by machine with an intertrial interval of exactly 1500 milliseconds; the subject's temporal uncertainty would therefore have been less. In this experiment the increase in reaction time immediately after an error is less than in the other two experiments, and w_1 is not significantly different from zero. On the other hand v_2 and v_3, representing the increase in reaction time if the alternative signal is presented two and three places after an error, do not show any such difference from their values in Experiments 1 and 3, and are significantly greater than zero in all three experiments. It seems that when the intertrial interval is objectively constant the subject can adjust the time, relative to the appearance of the next signal, at which he begins sampling information, with greater accuracy, but that the adjustment of the boundary at which the error was made is unchanged.

8.5.1. Changes in the sequential pattern.

In the first three experiments, only the coefficient v_1 in Experiment 3 was found to change significantly between experimental conditions. Its median values are shown in Table 8.2. In general the value of v_1 is smaller, though always remaining significantly greater than zero, the more the subject is pressed to go fast. It seems that subjects save time, in part at least, by making smaller compensatory adjustments after they have made a mistake. It is possible that the size of such adjustments ultimately determines the error probabilities.

In Experiment 4, Table 8.3, the only difference in the after-effects of errors among the several series is that represented by the c_1 and c_2 coefficients. These coefficients represent the increase in probability of error after a mistake has been made given that the alternative signal is presented. But in the C-reaction conditions the probability of an error of this kind is, in practice, always zero, so that these coefficients do but reflect the constraints of the experiment.

In Experiment 5 there are several profound changes in the after effects of errors as the intertrial interval is reduced. They are represented by the coefficients b_2, c_1, v_1, v_2 and w_1 in Table 8.4. When the intertrial interval is short there is very little time during which the subject can sample irrelevant information, and temporal uncertainty can no longer be the principal cause of errors. It may be that the subject still delays the time at which he begins sampling information from the next signal, but this will no longer have the effect of reducing the probability of another error, as it does with an intertrial interval of, say, 1500 milliseconds. The decrease in the probability of error when the signal is repeated, represented by the coefficients b_j, is therefore due to an outward adjustment of the error boundary. Although only b_2 shows a significant variation with the intertrial interval, the other b_j coefficients are in each series comparable in magnitude to b_2. It therefore appears that as the intertrial interval is reduced, outward adjustments of the boundary at which an error is made become increasingly severe.

Another characteristic of short intertrial intervals is that the checking of the response after it has been initiated tends to last beyond the time at which the response is actually registered and overlap the presentation of the following signal. On first meeting a short intertrial interval condition subjects frequently reported that they were confused in that they tended to compare each response with the signal it triggered rather than the signal it followed. When the signal alternated they tended to question such knowledge of their mistakes as the machine afforded them. Even though in these conditions the signal was present for only 192 or 256 milliseconds, the subjects seem effectively to have had a source of information for as long as they needed it, in the form of a mental image. When a new signal was presented the fresh inflow of information was superimposed, it would seem, on the former image so that the subject could not readily (perhaps not at all) distinguish the new signal from the trace of the old. Under these conditions there is a direct interaction between successive signals. It may be that the checking of an erroneous response tended to result in a correction response, even though it was in practice not possible to register such a response, or it may be that the checking process takes longer after an error and coalesces into the decision about the subsequent signal. Either way, if an error is followed by the presentation of the alternative signal, there is an enormous increase in the probability of error (coefficient c_1). This increase affects only the signal immediately following an error; c_2 is not significantly different from zero.

There is a large increase in reaction time to the signal immediately following an error; this is shown by v_1 and w_1. This time is presumably taken up in appropriate adjustments to the decision process and in increased time spent checking the response —a sort of bookkeeping operation. It is likely that the checking of a response takes longer after an error, because confirmation that the response is correct (the most frequent outcome) would be accepted on slighter evidence than the conclusion that the response was wrong. It is probably peculiar to the immediately following signal, for w_2, although just significant, is much smaller in magnitude and shows no change with the intertrial interval. v_2 (see Table 8.4) shows an increase, but this may be accounted for by the adjustment of the error boundary. The general picture afforded by these results is that as the intertrial interval is reduced, so the adjustments of the decision process after an error become larger and less restrained, greatly increasing the variability of the subject's performance.

8.5.2. Comparisons with other work.

The data that were here analysed with equation (8.1) might alternatively have been analysed in terms of autocorrelation amongst the responses. A previous regression analysis of the same data revealed a tendency to alternate the response and a smaller negative autocorrelation amongst the sequence of errors.[10] Although response auto-correlation has not been studied in a choice-reaction task before, it has long been known to happen in psychophysical judgment experiments. It was first reported by Fernberger (1920) and Senders and Sowards (1952) reviewed the evidence as at that time. The several reports are not consistent with respect to the nature of the inter-dependence among the responses, but in all those experiments in which the response has been to some extent stimulus determined (as here), the subjects have tended to avoid repetition of preceding responses. This has usually been attributed to an innate preference to alternate or avoid repetition (e.g. Preston, 1936); equation (8.1) offers an alternative, more rational explanation.

The increase in reaction time with a short intertrial interval and particularly the increase after an error suggest a comparison with the notion of the psychological refractory period (cf. Welford, 1952, 1959). But the idea here is not that the sampling of information from the external environment is suspended while kinaesthetic feed-back from a peripheral response is monitored, but that the response is checked by continuing to sample information from the original signal, in so far as this can be

---

[10] The equation used was

$$R_i = r + \sum_{j=0}^{n_1} a_j S_{i-j} + \sum_{j=1}^{n_2} (b_j R_{i-j} + c_j [S_i + S_{i-j} + R_{i-j}]).$$

The b_j coefficients, which were negative, indicated an alternation tendency; the c_j co-efficients, also negative, autocorrelation amongst the errors. This analysis is reported in Laming (1963, Chapter 7).

distinguished from the following signal, and that the response to the following signal is delayed for this reason.

The idea of adjustments of the decision parameters after each decision is similar to Bertelson's (1961) concept of "preparation". But Bertelson was arguing from far fewer data than are available here and was primarily concerned with the increase in T_i in the case of $S_i \neq S_{i-1}$. It has been shown here that this is but one factor in a complex pattern, which involves interactions of higher order than the first between stimulus-response cycles. It is clear that the recorded reaction time represents only a part of the choice-reaction process.

Further work by Bertelson and Joffe (1962, 1963) led to a study of "blocking". They found in a serial responding task that unusually long response times became more frequent as time went on. These long reaction times were preceded by an increase in both reaction time and errors over the four or five preceding responses and were followed by a return of both variables to their normal level. This appears to be more or less the same phenomenon that was observed with a short intertrial interval in Experiment 5. Bertelson and Joffe considered that the long response times occurred in order that fatigue might be dissipated. A different explanation has been attempted here, in which all phenomena of this sort are considered to be products of a complex pattern of sequential relations. When the intertrial interval is short, the time available for adjustment of the decision process is restricted; such adjustments are therefore less accurate leading to greater variability of performance. Some "blocks" evidently arise from this process; another cause of long reaction times will be considered in §8.6.1.

8.6. Autocorrelation of reaction times.

Simple autocorrelation of the reaction times, independent of any signals or responses, is detected by the h_j coefficients in equation (8.6). Median values of these coefficients for the five two-choice experiments are shown in Figure 8.11; they decrease approximately exponentially with respect to position in the preceding sequence. Most of the coefficients up to six and even seven places back are significantly greater than zero. The results from the five experiments are very similar. The only coefficient to show any significant variation between experimental conditions is h_3 in Experiment 4 and this is probably a chance result.[11] This means that these autoregression coefficients detect some feature of reaction time that is independent of all the experimental variables that have been studied—in particular, it is independent of whether the subject has to use two different responses or make the same response to every signal. The most likely interpretation is that these coefficients indicate fluctuations in the subject's attention.

Kendall (1951, pp. 420–3) shows that an autoregressive scheme will admit a solution in which the time series is represented as a moving average of infinite extent over a series of independent random variables. He finds it very plausible that oscillations in times series should be generated in this way (§30.40). A hypothesis of this sort will therefore be considered here.

Let A_i be the level of attention that the subject gives to the experiment at the ith trial, and let $A_i = A + \alpha_i$, where $A = $ constant, $E\{\alpha_i\} = 0$ and A_i always positive.

---

[11] In the C-reaction conditions a reation time was measured to only one of the two signals. Where no reaction time existed the corresponding term was omitted from equation (8.3) (i.e. T_{i-j} was put equal to zero), and this may have helped to produce the apparent variation in h_3 in Experiment 4.

Suppose that $\alpha_i = \theta\alpha_{i-1}+\eta_i$, where $0 < \theta < 1$ and the η_i are a sequence of independent identically distributed random variables. Suppose also that reaction time is related to attention by an equation of the form

$$T_i = t+c/A_i, \tag{8.20}$$

where t and c are positive constants. Then, provided the η_i are small compared to A,

$$T_i = t+c/A\{1+(\sum_{r=0}^{\infty} \theta^r\eta_{i-r}/A)\}$$

$$\simeq t+c\{1-1/(1-\theta)\}/A+(c/A)\sum_{r=0}^{\infty} \theta^r(1-\eta_{i-r}/A)$$

$$\simeq t-c\theta/A(1-\theta)+\sum_{r=0}^{\infty} c\theta^r/(A+\eta_{i-r}) \tag{8.21}$$

plus some interaction terms, most of which have zero expectation, because the η_i are independent. Now $T_{i-r} = t+c/(A+\eta_{i-r}+\theta\alpha_{i-r-1})$ and is therefore positively correlated with $c/(A+\eta_{i-r})$. Hence when a regression equation of the form

$$T_i = t+\sum_{j=1}^{n_0} h_jT_{i-j}$$

is fitted to the data, the h_j coefficients will be approximately proportional to $c\theta^j/A$. It follows that the results in Figure 8.11 are consistent, so far as the present analysis goes, with a representation of attention as a geometric moving average over a sequence of independent random events.

FIGURE 8.11

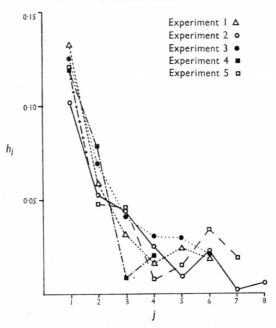

Median values of the h_j regression coefficients in Experiments 1–5.

The idea is that the subject's attention is attracted towards or deflected away from the experimental task by each of a series of discrete events, each of which exercises only a partial control of attention. These events are represented by the sequence of random variables, η_i, and the level of attention at trial i is the product of all the preceding events, each having an influence that decreases exponentially with respect to trials. η_i does not necessarily represent a single event, but rather all those events which have occurred since the previous signal was presented. However the events controlling attention seem to arise principally from the experimental task itself since the autoregression coefficients estimated from the data of Experiment 5 showed no variation with the intertrial interval.

On this view attention is not an all-or-nothing state (cf. Broadbent, 1957), but is continuously variable. It is likely that either concept of attention, continuous or discrete, could accommodate the results reported here. But there is no feature of the data which obviously suggests that attention is switched off and on.

8.6.1. Previous work on autocorrelation in reaction times.

Autocorrelation in reaction times has been reported twice before by Foley and Humphries (1962) and Leonard (private communication). Foley and Humphries used a simple reaction task with the stimuli presented at four-second intervals; they found significant serial correlation coefficients only for lags of one and two. Leonard used a five-choice reaction task with an intertrial interval of about 80 milliseconds. He found serial correlation coefficients of about 0·15 at lag one, and other indications of auto-correlation up to lags of eight. This is comparable to the results obtained here.

The interest in autocorrelation in reaction times arises from its relation to the phenomenon of "blocking". It will happen from time to time that the level of attention given to the task falls low producing, if equation (8.20) truly represents the relation, a disproportionately long reaction time. Foley and Humphries found blocks in their simple reaction task. There was only marginal evidence of an increase in reaction time before the block, and there was an almost immediate return to normal afterwards; but the autocorrelation among the reaction times was relatively weak.

It has been customary, following Bills (1931), to interpret blocks as rest pauses in human performance, which allow the dissipation of some cumulative state in the nervous system called "mental fatigue". There is no independent evidence for this hypothesis (see Bertelson and Joffe, 1963, p. 222), and here the view is preferred that that which is frequently called mental fatigue (by a spurious analogy with muscular fatigue) is in fact the decrement in performance which must inevitably recur on the view of attention above, particularly when the time series has reached a stationary state.

8.7. Interaction of the pattern of autocorrelation with signal and response factors.

Certain changes in the autoregressive scheme, depending on the preceding signals and responses, have been detected by the f_j and g_j coefficients in equation (8.6). The median values of these coefficients in Experiments 1, 2 and 3 are shown in Figures 8.12 and 8.13. f_2 is greater than zero in all three experiments and appears to be greater than f_1, which is significant only in Experiment 1. g_j is less than zero in all three Experiments for $j = 1, 2$ and 3 and decreases sharply in magnitude. In Experiment 5 none of these coefficients were significant.

The negative g_j coefficients imply that the autocorrelation between T_i and T_{i-j} is stronger when $S_i = S_{i-j}$ than when $S_i \neq S_{i-j}$. That is, long reactions to S_A are locally more closely associated with other long reactions to S_A than they are with long reactions to S_B, and conversely, reading "S_B" for "S_A" and "short" for "long".

FIGURE 8.12   FIGURE 8.13

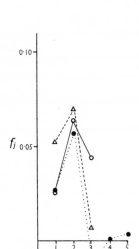

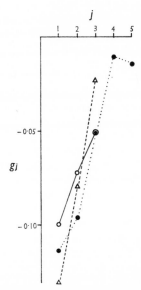

Median values of the f_j regression coefficients in Experiments 1, 2 and 3. Triangles, Experiment 1; open circles, Experiment 2; filled circles, Experiment 3.

Median values of the g_j regression coefficients in Experiments 1, 2 and 3. Triangles, Experiment 1; open circles, Experiment 2; filled circles, Experiment 3.

Since this effect is conditional on the signal rather than the response, it suggests local variations in the mean information rates conditional on each signal. For example, putting $\sigma_a = \sigma_b = \sigma$ and $(x+\delta)$ for x in equation (A.25),

$$\Delta' I_r = \{(\mu_b - \mu_a)/\sigma^2\}\{x_r + \delta - \tfrac{1}{2}(\mu_b + \mu_a)\}, \tag{8.22}$$

so that

$$\left. \begin{aligned} E\{\Delta' I_r | S_A\} &= -(\mu_b - \mu_a)(\mu_b - \mu_a - \delta)/2\sigma^2, \\ E\{\Delta' I_r | S_B\} &= (\mu_b - \mu_a)(\mu_b - \mu_a + \delta)/2\sigma^2. \end{aligned} \right\} \tag{8.23}$$

If $0 < \delta < \mu_b - \mu_a$, it can be seen by comparison with (A.26) that $|E\{\Delta' I_r | S_A\}|$ is decreased and $|E\{\Delta' I_r | S_B\}|$ is increased; if $0 > \delta > \mu_a - \mu_b$, the contrary is true. δ therefore introduces contrary changes in the absolute values of the mean information rates conditional on the two signals, and equation (8.22) appears to be a sufficient explanation of the negative g_j coefficients.

δ, as it appears in (8.22), represents a change in the zero of the subjective scale of length. The idea here is that the subject has to remember the two alternative lengths of stripe and to evaluate each observation, x_r, by reference to these subjective standards. It may happen that the two lengths, as they are remembered, differ from their objective values by an amount, δ, that is constant with respect to the signals;

then equation (8.22) represents the information subjectively contained in the observation, x_r. Alternatively, it may be that the subjective unit of length varies, so that the subjective standards suffer a multiplicative transformation. This could be represented by writing γx for x in equation (A.25), where γ is near 1. The data here are not capable of discriminating between these and other similar hypotheses. But the g_j coefficients seem to imply some change in the process of decision that selectively speeds up responses to one of the two signals, and the observations on Experiment 6 in §5.7.5 suggest a lateral shift in the subjective scale of length.

A comparison of Figures 8.11 and 8.13 shows that g_1, g_2 and g_3 are approximately equal in magnitude to h_1, h_2 and h_3 respectively and opposite in sign; this is probably coincidence. It seems reasonable that shifts in the subjective scale of length should be related to the sequence of signals in much the same way that the subject's attention is related to events in the performance of the experimental task, and hence g_j and h_j obey similar, approximately exponential laws. But it should be remembered that in equation (8.6) the total autoregression coefficient when $S_i \neq S_{i-j}$ is $(h_j + \frac{1}{2}g_j + \frac{1}{2}f_j)$, *not* $(h_j + g_j)$. If these interpretations of the coefficients are correct, then as the two signals are made more alike the g_j will increase in magnitude while the h_j remain invariant.

If the f_j coefficients had been negative they could readily have been interpreted, in a similar manner to the g_j, in terms of slow fluctuations of the starting point of the random walk, uncorrelated with the preceding signals. They were included in equation (8.6) specifically for this reason. But such an interpretation is not possible; not only are the f_j positive, but, most unexpected, f_2 appears to be greater than f_1.

The autoregressive terms in equation (8.6) may be rewritten in the form

$$d_j T_{i-j} + (f_j + g_j)(Q_{i,j} - \tfrac{1}{2})T_{i-j} + f_j[\mathscr{E}_i + \mathscr{E}_{i-j}](1 - 2Q_{i,j})T_{i-j}$$

This suggests an alternative interpretation, that $(f_j + g_j)$ is the true measure of shifts in the subjective scale of length, while f_j detects some after effect of making a mistake and is possibly confounded with v_j and w_j. The data at present available are not sufficient to discriminate between these alternative interpretations.

CHAPTER 9

FUTURE DEVELOPMENTS

The essence of the theory of choice-reaction times presented in this monograph may be expressed in just one proposition: At each instant of time the subject in a choice-reaction experiment makes optimal use of all the information that is available to him about the signal. By this time the reader will have made up his own mind how far this proposition agrees with the facts, as they are at present known, and it only remains to point out the directions in which the theory may be expected to develop.

The original random walk model in Chapter 3 is an ideal model for the behaviour of an ideal subject, who is assumed to know everything about the experiment except the identity of the signal that is about to be presented to him. The subject is assumed, in particular, to know exactly when the signal will be presented and the relative probabilities of the several alternatives. In practice, however, the human subject is not ideal and has this information only in part. He knows roughly when the signal will appear, but not exactly, and certain differences between the ideal model and the results of choice-reaction experiments may be explained in this and similar ways.

The treatment of temporal uncertainty in §6.4.1 is the best example of the limitations of human performance relative to the ideal due to lack of information about the experiment. At present the involvement of irrelevant information in the decision process is only conjecture and requires experimental confirmation. There are several ways this might be done, but the most efficient is an experiment in which the intertrial interval is varied at random within a sequence of signals. In §6.4.1. it was assumed implicitly that the sampling of information was an all-or-none affair. It may alternatively be that the subject pays increasing attention to the information stream as the time for the presentation of the next signal approaches, and these two alternative hypotheses may be distinguished by the same sort of experiment. It would also be interesting to know how the time at which the subject begins to sample information is related to the distribution of the intertrial interval, and the answers to these questions will lead naturally to a model for simple reaction times.

The sequential phenomena discussed in Chapter 8 indicate another respect in which human performance is non-ideal. In the ideal model successive decision processes are independent, but this is not so in any experiment here. It is clear that a human subject does not know the relative probabilities of the alternative signals and has therefore to estimate these probabilities from the sequence that is shown him. There are probably other respects in which the subject's knowledge is incomplete, and these will be known when the origin of the sequential relations is understood. The construction of a model for the sequential relations is principally an analytical problem, and its solution may confidently be expected to enlarge our understanding of the choice-reaction process.

One analysis of the data, which might have been expected in this monograph, is an estimation of the parameters of the mean reaction time equations (A.8) and (A.9).

But this is a technically difficult problem. Even for the ideal model of Chapter 3 it involves the estimation of a functional relation between two sets of random variables, the mean reaction times and the numbers of errors of each sort. The problem is further complicated by the sequential relations in the data. When these are well understood it may be possible to carry out this analysis.

The other direction in which further development of the theory may be looked for is in the mathematics of the multi-choice model of §B.3. An explicit solution of equation (B.8) comparable to that of equation (A.2) is clearly not possible, but it is reasonable to hope that the qualitative arguments used in the analysis of Experiment 6 may be improved on. It would help if further predictions capable of experimental testing were derived, but it is not yet possible to suggest what form these might take.

APPENDIX A

THE TWO-CHOICE THEORY

A.1. Introduction.

This appendix and the following one contain a mathematical development of the consequences of the axioms of §3.3. In this appendix discriminations between only two alternative signals will be considered; Appendix B is concerned with discriminations between an unspecified number, m, of alternatives. For the most part the mathematics is directed to the derivation of predictions that will be used in evaluating the experimental evidence, and the derivations have been made as rigorous and as general in their applicability as possible. But some of the mathematics, particularly §A.4, is frankly exploratory with a view to future experimental work.

Certain fundamental consequences of the axioms are proved once for all for a general m-choice discrimination, and these theorems have been placed in Appendix B. But their truth is assumed in establishing the two-choice model in §A.2, and reference is made to them there. The two-choice model is an elaboration of the sequential two-choice model due to Stone (1960), and this will be clear to any reader acquainted with Stone's paper. The model also depends much upon the theory of the sequential probability ratio test and several references are made to Wald (1947).

In subsequent sections the model is developed without assuming any particular distribution of information or of the "observations". But the "condition of symmetry" introduced by Stone (1960) leads to substantial simplifications in the mathematics and three theorems, generating empirically testable predictions, are proved for the symmetric decision process. The development of the symmetric process in §A.3 serves as a model for the more general asymmetric decision process in §A.5 and the C-reaction in §A.6. The three results, which are exact for the symmetric decision process, are found to be approximate for the asymmetric process.

Before the asymmetric process can reasonably be discussed, however, it is necessary to show that the equations derived from Wald's identity in §A.2 are exact. Their exact nature cannot be taken for granted because the asymmetry of the decision process implies that the information as a function of time contains a finite number of discontinuities and may jump over the boundary of the random walk. However, in §A.4 it is shown that the expressions of §A.2 are indeed exact, and four special cases of the decision process are examined from the point of view of the behaviour of the random walk.

Up to this point the development of the theory has proceeded on the implicit assumption that the random walk decision process is started at the exact instant that the signal is presented. This is very unlikely in any of the experiments reported in Chapter 5 since the subject there has no means of synchronizing the start of his decision process with the onset of the signal. In §A.7 some of the preceding results are modified to take account of the subject's uncertainty about when the signal will be presented, and thereby a quantitative explanation is found for an otherwise incompatible result.

A.1.1. Notation.

The principal notation to be used in this appendix is listed below in the order of its introduction:

S_A, S_B	alternative signals in two-choice theory.
$I(t)$	total information, including *a priori* information, available to the subject at time t in favour of S_B against S_A.
I_0	*a priori* information.
$f(x\|S_A), f(x\|S_B)$	probability density functions of "observations" conditional on S_A and S_B respectively.
I_a, I_b	values of information at boundaries.
R_A, R_B	alternative responses in two-choice theory corresponding to S_A and S_B respectively.
λ_a, λ_b	probabilities of error conditional on R_A and R_B respectively.
I_r	$= I(r\,\delta t)$.
δI_r	rth increment of information $(= I_r - I_{r-1})$.
α, β	probabilities of error conditional on S_A and S_B respectively.
p	*a priori* probability of S_B.
ϵ	average probability of error.
$g(\delta I\|S_A), g(\delta I\|S_B)$	probability density functions of increments of information conditional on S_A and S_B respectively.
n_0	number of increments of irrelevant information at the start of the decision process.
$\delta I^*, I_0^*$	irrelevant information.
K	$= n_0\,E\{\delta I\|S_B\}$.

A.2. The general two-choice model.

Fundamental notions. When there are only two alternative signals, they will be denoted by S_A and S_B. Axiom 1 of §3.3 postulates the existence of a stream of information emanating from the signal. The total information available to the subject at time t in favour of S against S_A is denoted by $I(S_B:S_A; t)$; here this will be abbreviated to $I(t)$. $I(S_A:S_B; t) = -I(t)$.

Axiom 2 places certain constraints on the distribution of $I(t)$. These constraints, together with the additional assumption that the distribution of $\{I(t_2)-I(t_1)\}$, $t_2 > t_1$, is infinitely divisible and a function of (t_2-t_1) only, ensure that for any $\delta t > 0$ there exist univariate density functions $f(x|S_A), f(x|S_B)$ such that

$$I(r\,\delta t) = I_0 + \sum_{s=1}^{r} \log\{f(x_s|S_B)/f(x_s|S_A)\}, \qquad (A.1)$$

where $I_0 = \log\{P(S_B)/P(S_A)\}$ is the *a priori* information: all this is shown in Theorems B.1, 2 and 3 and their corollaries.

Equation (A.1) implies that the random variable $\{I(t)-I_0\}$ may be represented as the sum of r independent and identically distributed random variables of the form $\log\{f(x|S_B)/f(x|S_A)\}$ and, further, that this division may be carried out to any degree of fineness. It seems intuitively reasonable that the flow of information should exist in continuous time[1] and that successive increments of information should be independent and have a stationary distribution. But nonetheless equation (A.1) represents a moderate restriction on the possible forms of the distributions of $I(t)$, $(x|S_A)$ and $(x|S_B)$. This question will be discussed in detail in §A.4; meanwhile the two-choice theory will be developed irrespective of the forms of these distributions.

Equation (A.1) also implies that $I(r\,\delta t)$ changes with respect to time by the accretion of further independent increments of information of the form $\log\{f(x|S_B)/f(x|S_A)\}$. $I(r\,\delta t)$ therefore describes a random walk. The starting point is I_0 and there are absorbing boundaries at $I_a = \log\{\lambda_a/(1-\lambda_a)\}$ and $I_b = \log\{(1-\lambda_b)/\lambda_b\}$, where λ_a and λ_b are parameters of the decision process. The walk continues so long as

$$I_a < I(r\,\delta t) < I_b.$$

Response R_A is made if $I(r\,\delta t) \leqslant I_a$, response R_B if $I(r\,\delta t) \geqslant I_b$. Axiom 3 imposes the condition $\lambda_a + \lambda_b < 1$; Theorem B.5 shows that this condition is necessary and sufficient that the response shall be unique.

It is now possible to give the reasons underlying the choice of axioms here. Axiom 1 makes the decision process analogous to a diffusion process in continuous time. On the other hand Axiom 2 and Theorems B.1, 2 and 3 permit the use of the mathematics of random walks in discrete time, and this leads to an easier development of the theory. But because the time scale is continuous, "fractional observations" (Wald, 1947, p. 47) are, as it were, possible, and there is no excess over the boundaries as in a sequential probability ratio test. It is therefore possible to find simple, yet exact, expressions for the characteristic functions of the decision latencies. At the same time the axioms are compatible with a concept of information flow that seems *prima facie* reasonable.

Wald's Identity. The following development follows Wald's methods closely. $I(r\,\delta t)$ will be abbreviated to I_r. δI will represent an increment of information; thus, $\delta I_r = \log\{f(x_r|S_A)/f(x_r|S_B)\}$. n is the number of increments δI required to reach a boundary and is a continuous (not an integral) variable.

THEOREM A.1. *Provided the variance of $\delta I > 0$ and $|I_b - I_a| < \infty$, the probability is 1 that the decision process will terminate.*
(For the proof, see Wald, 1947, Appendix 1).

In the notation used here Wald's identity becomes

$$E\{\exp[(I_n - I_0 - n\,\delta I)\theta]\} = 1, \tag{A.2}$$

and this is the characteristic function of n. By differentiating with respect to θ and putting $\theta = 0$,

$$E\{I_n - I_0\} = E\{n\}E\{\delta I\}. \tag{A.3}$$

This equation may be expressed in words as follows:

THEOREM A.2.

$$\textit{Average duration of decision process} = \frac{\textit{Average amount of information extracted}}{\textit{Average rate of extraction}}.$$

Expressions for the variance and higher moments of n may be obtained by differentiating equation (A.2) two or more times with respect to θ and putting $\theta = 0$.

Probabilities of error and mean reaction times. I_n is a random variable taking the values I_a and I_b; it is related to the two probabilities of error. Let $\alpha = P(R_B|S_A)$,

---

[1] The perceptual moment hypothesis, for example, postulates a discontinuous psychological time scale. See Shallice (1964).

$\beta = P(R_A|S_B)$, $p = P(S_B)$. The signal-response probabilities may be expressed in matrix form:

	R_A	R_B
S_A	$(1-p)(1-\alpha)$	$(1-p)\alpha$
S_B	$p\beta$	$p(1-\beta)$

Hence

$$\left.\begin{aligned}
I_0 &= \log\{p/(1-p)\}, \\
I_a &= \log\{p\beta/(1-p)(1-\alpha)\}, \\
I_b &= \log\{p(1-\beta)/(1-p)\alpha\};
\end{aligned}\right\} \tag{A.4}$$

$$\left.\begin{aligned}
\alpha &= (e^{I_0}-e^{I_a})/(e^{I_b}-e^{I_a}), \\
\beta &= (e^{-I_0}-e^{-I_b})/(e^{-I_a}-e^{-I_b});
\end{aligned}\right\} \tag{A.5}$$

$$E\{I_n-I_0|S_A\} = \alpha\log\{(1-\beta)/\alpha\}+(1-\alpha)\log\{\beta/(1-\alpha)\}. \tag{A.6}$$

This last expression is the average information for discrimination in favour of H_2 against H_1 in a single sample from the population of H_1, where H_1 and H_2 relate to binomial populations with parameters $(1-\alpha)$ and β respectively; $E\{I_n-I_0|S_B\}$ may be expressed similarly. Here H_1 and H_2 correspond to S_A and S_B and represent different probabilities of an R_A response. The decision process, as it were, consists of the drawing of a single sample from the binomial population presented, and each trial is thereby allocated to one of two response classes. A theorem of Wald (1947, Appendix 7) shows that this decision process is optimum in its use of information and the response is therefore a sufficient statistic for the information gathered prior to the making of the decision.

By substituting in equation (A.2) the characteristic function of n, conditional on each signal, can be obtained in the form

$$E\{e^{-I_0\theta}[P(R_A|S_A)E\{\exp(I_a-n\,\delta I)\theta|R_A.S_A\}+$$
$$+P(R_B|S_A)E\{\exp(I_b-n\,\delta I)\theta|R_B.S_A\}]\} = 1. \tag{A.7}$$

Moreover Theorem B.6 shows that if I_0 is constant the distribution of n conditional on a given response is independent of the signal.[2] But this is not true, if I_0 is variable, and such a case will be considered in §A.7.2.

Substituting in (A.3),

$$E\{n|S_A\} = [\{(I_a e^{I_b}-I_b e^{I_a})+(I_b-I_a)e^{I_0}\}/(e^{I_b}-e^{I_a})-I_0]/E\{\delta I|S_A\}, \tag{A.8}$$

and

$$E\{n|S_B\} = [\{(I_b e^{-I_a}-I_a e^{-I_b})-(I_b-I_a)e^{-I_0}\}/(e^{-I_a}-e^{-I_b})-I_0]/E\{\delta I|S_B\}, \tag{A.9}$$

give the mean decision latency conditional on each signal.

A.3. The symmetric decision process.

Condition of symmetry. If $E\{\delta I|S_A\}+E\{\delta I|S_B\} = 0$,[3] the mean information rate in favour of the signal presented is the same for both signals. The decision process then has a certain symmetry which leads to some simple results.

---

[2] Stone (1960, Appendix 2) gives another proof of this result for two-choice discriminations only.

[3] Stone's (1960, p. 254) condition of symmetry implied more than this, namely, that $g(\delta I|S_B) = g(-\delta I|S_A)$.

Theorem A.2 states that the mean decision latency is proportional to the average amount of information extracted. It will be interesting to find under what conditions the amount of information extracted becomes a minimum subject to a proportion of errors $\not> \epsilon$. The expression to be minimised is

$$p\,E\{I_n{-}I_0|S_B\}{-}(1{-}p)E\{I_n{-}I_0|S_A\}$$
$$= (p{-}y)I_b{+}(1{-}p{-}y)({-}I_a){+}(1{-}2p)I_0, \qquad (A.10)$$

where $y = (1{-}p)\alpha{+}p\beta$, the average probability of error, and, from Axiom 4,

$$-I_a = \log\{(1{-}\lambda_a)/\lambda_a\}, \qquad I_b = \log\{(1{-}\lambda_b)/\lambda_b\}.$$

Now consider a random variable X in the range $0 < x < \frac{1}{2}$. λ_a and λ_b are the probabilities of error conditional on responses R_A and R_B and x will be allowed to take these two values, subject to $E\{x\} = y$. $\log\{(1{-}x)/x\}$ is positively accelerated in the range of X and therefore $E\{\log[(1{-}x)/x]\}$ will be a minimum if X is constant. Hence the minimum value of the expression (A.10) is $(1{-}2y)\log\{(1{-}y)/y\}{+}(1{-}2p)I_0$ and this is a strictly monotonic decreasing function of y. This leads to

THEOREM A.3. *In a symmetric two-choice decision process the mean reaction time is a minimum subject to an error rate $\not> \epsilon$ if $\lambda_a = \lambda_b = \epsilon$. Conversely the error rate is a minimum subject to a given maximum mean reaction time if $\lambda_a = \lambda_b$.*

The optimal decision process. The symmetric decision process with $\lambda_a = \lambda_b = \epsilon$ will be called the optimal decision process for the error rate ϵ. Axiom 5 states that in the absence of experimental instructions or conditions to the contrary subjects will tend towards this optimum. For this optimum process

$$\left.\begin{array}{l} \alpha = \epsilon(p{-}\epsilon)/(1{-}p)(1{-}2\epsilon), \\ \beta = \epsilon(1{-}p{-}\epsilon)/p(1{-}2\epsilon). \end{array}\right\} \qquad (A.11)$$

The distance between the boundaries $I_b{-}I_a = 2\log\{(1{-}\epsilon)/\epsilon\}$, which is independent of p. The optimum value of the mean reaction time is

$$E\{n|p\} = [(1{-}2p)\log\{p/(1{-}p)\}{+}(1{-}2\epsilon)\log\{(1{-}\epsilon)/\epsilon\}]/|E\{\delta I\}|. \qquad (A.12)$$

Error Ratio. In evaluating the experiments the ratio

$$R_\epsilon\left(\frac{S_B}{S_A}\right) = \frac{\text{Expected no. of errors when } S_B \text{ is presented}}{\text{Expected no. of errors when } S_A \text{ is presented}},$$

for the error rate ϵ, will be useful. Its value for the optimal decision process is

$$R_\epsilon(S_B/S_A) = (1{-}p{-}\epsilon)/(p{-}\epsilon). \qquad (A.13)$$

A.3.1. A comparison with Communication Theory.

Figure 3.5 shows that equation (A.12) with the constants appropriately adjusted is similar to equation (1.3), which is derived from Communication Theory.

Let $H = -\{p\log p{+}(1{-}p)\log(1{-}p)\}$, Shannon's measure of entropy. Then $dE\{n|p\}/dH \geqslant 2/|E\{\delta I\}|$, with equality only at $p = \frac{1}{2}$. Hence, if data conforming to equation (A.12) were fitted by linear regression to equation (1.3), the estimate of b in that equation would not be less than $2/|E\{\delta I\}|$. Assuming the truth of (1.4),

$$E\{n|S_B\}{-}E\{n|S_A\} \geqslant 2\log\{(1{-}p)/p\}/|E\{\delta I\}|. \qquad (A.14)$$

But, by substitution for I_a and I_b in equations (A.8) and (A.9),

$$E\{n|S_B\}{-}E\{n|S_A\} < 2\log\{(1{-}p)/p\}/|E\{\delta I\}|. \qquad (A.15)$$

The comparison between (A.14) and (A.15) is interesting in the light of certain previous experimental results (see p. 41).

A.3.2. The qualitative relation between time and errors.

THEOREM A.4.   *Under the optimal decision process the expected reaction time and the probability of error are less when the more frequent signal is presented.*

Proof.   From equations (A.8) and (A.9)

$$E\{n|S_B\}-E\{n|S_A\} = \frac{2}{|E\{\delta I\}|}\left\{\log\frac{1-p}{p} - \frac{\epsilon(1-\epsilon)\,(1-2p)}{(1-2\epsilon)\,p(1-p)}\log\frac{1-\epsilon}{\epsilon}\right\}. \quad (A.16)$$

To show that $E\{n|S_B\} >$ or $< E\{n|S_A\}$ according as $p <$ or $> \frac{1}{2}$, the following lemma is needed:

LEMMA A.1. $f(x) = \{x/(x^2-1)\}\log x$ *is a positive monotonic decreasing function of* x *for* $x > 1$.

Proof.   For $x > 1, f(x)$ is clearly > 0 and $f'(x) = [1 - \{(x^2+1)/(x^2-1)\}\log x]/(x^2-1)$. Now $(t-1)/t < \log t$, for $t > 1$ (Hardy, 1955, p. 400).   Integrating from 1 to y and rearranging terms, $\frac{1}{2}\{(y+1)/(y-1)\}\log y > 1$, for $y > 1$.   Putting $y = x^2$ it can be seen that $f'(x) < 0$ for $x > 1$ and the result follows.   This completes the proof of the lemma.

Now (A.16) can be expressed in the form

$$E\{n|S_B\}-E\{n|S_A\} = [2(1-2p)/p(1-p)|E\{\delta I\}|]\,[f\{(1-p)/p\}-f\{(1-\epsilon)/\epsilon\}], \quad (A.17)$$

where $(1-p)/p < (1-\epsilon)/\epsilon$.   Hence $E\{n|S_B\} >$ or $< E\{n|S_A\}$ according as $p <$ or $> \frac{1}{2}$. Finally it is clear from an inspection of (A.11) that $\beta >$ or $< \alpha$ according as $p <$ or $> \frac{1}{2}$, and so the theorem is proved as well.

This correlation between the speed and the accuracy with which the two signals elicit responses is not peculiar to the optimal decision process.

THEOREM A.5.   *In a symmetrical two-choice decision process that signal with the smaller expected reaction time has the smaller probability of error and conversely.*

Proof. (i) It will be shown first that for any pair of error probabilities, $\alpha, \beta > 0$, $\alpha+\beta < 1$, there exist unique values of p_0 and ϵ_0, such that α and β are the error probabilities associated with the optimal decision process for the error rate ϵ_0 with $P(S_B) = p_0$.

From the equations (A.11) ϵ_0, p_0 must satisfy

$$\left.\begin{array}{l}\alpha(1-p)+\beta p = \epsilon, \\ \beta p(p-\epsilon) = \alpha(1-p)(1-p-\epsilon).\end{array}\right\} \quad (A.18)$$

Eliminating ϵ, $p_0 = P/(1+P)$ where $P = +\sqrt{\{\alpha(1-\alpha)/\beta(1-\beta)\}}$. p_0 and ϵ_0 are therefore unique.   Since $0 < P < \infty, 0 < p_0 < 1$ and $p_0 >$ or $< \frac{1}{2}$ according as $\alpha >$ or $< \beta$. It follows from equations (A.18) that $0 < \epsilon_0 < \min(p_0, 1-p_0)$, and so, from Theorem A.4,

$$E\{n|S_B\} > \text{ or } < E\{n|S_A\} \text{ according as } \beta > \text{ or } < \alpha.$$

(ii) The converse may be proved by showing that given any pair of values $E\{n|S_A\}$, $E\{n|S_B\} > 0$, there is an associated pair of error probabilities, $\alpha, \beta > 0$, such that $\alpha+\beta < 1$.   Putting $\exp(I_a-I_0) = A$, $\exp(I_b-I_0) = B$ in (A.8) and (A.9),

$$X = -E\{n|S_A\}E\{\delta I|S_A\} = \{(A-1)/(B-A)\}\log B + \{(1-B)/(B-A)\}\log A,$$

$$Y = E\{n|S_B\}E\{\delta I|S_B\} = \{A(B-1)/(B-A)\}\log A + \{B(1-A)/(B-A)\}\log B;$$

whence

$$(AX+Y)/(1-A) = \log B, \quad (A.19)$$

$$(BX+Y)/(B-1) = -\log A. \quad (A.20)$$

The form of these equations is shown in Figure A.1, from which it is evident that there is a solution such that $0 < A < 1 < B$. From equations (A.5) it follows that there exist values α and β, $\alpha + \beta < 1$, such that α and β are the probabilities of error associated with the given $E\{n|S_A\}$ and $E\{n|S_B\}$. Hence, in view of the first part of this theorem,

$$\beta > \text{or} < \alpha \text{ according as } E\{n|S_B\} > \text{or} < E\{n|S_A\}.$$

This completes the proof.

FIGURE A.1

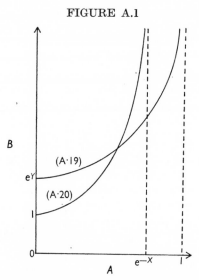

The form of equations (A.19) and (A.20)

A.4. The distribution of $I(t)$.

Infinitely divisible distributions. Equation (A.1) represents a restriction of the forms that the distributions of $I(t)$, $(X|S_A)$ and $(X|S_B)$ might take. This restriction was mentioned earlier, but discussion of it has been postponed until now.

$I(t)$ must have an infinitely divisible distribution, that is, it must be capable of representation as the sum of r independent and identically distributed random variables for any positive integral r. This condition is introduced explicitly in Theorem B.3, but it is inherent in the idea of an information flow with stationary increments defined in continuous time. The distribution of $I(t)$ depends on which signal, S_A or S_B, is presented and its two alternative distributions are related according to condition (iii) on p. 150. Since these distributions are both infinitely divisible,

$$g(\delta I|S_B) = g(\delta I|S_A)e^{\delta I}, \tag{A.21}$$

where $g(\delta I|S_A)$ and $g(\delta I|S_B)$ are the probability density functions of δI conditional on S_A and S_B respectively. They therefore belong to the same exponential family.

Although the distributions $f(x|S_A)$ and $f(x|S_B)$ may be represented in many different ways, there is one representation in which both distributions are infinitely divisible and their decomposition *generates the decomposition* of δI;[4] this representation

---

[4] See the definition on p. 150.

is unique up to a linear transformation of the variable: this is shown in Theorem B.4. In fact x must be linearly related to δI; this is shown in Lemma B.1.

The discussion that follows depends much on the comprehensive treatment of infinitely divisible distributions given by Gnedenko and Kolmogorov (1954). They show (pp. 71–5) that among common probability distributions the normal, Poisson, geometric and gamma are infinitely divisible. Four examples will be considered involving these common distributions.

A.4.1. The normal distribution.

Strong continuity. If $I(t)$ is stochastically strongly continuous, that is, if with probability one $I(t)$ is continuous as a function of t for all values of t, then the distribution of $I(t)$ is normal. Gnedenko and Kolmogorov (pp. 126–8) reproduce a theorem of Khintchine which states that the stochastic strong continuity of $I(t)$ is both necessary and sufficient that $I(t)$ should be normal. If $I(t)$ is normal, then so is δI, and it follows from equation (A.21) that the variance of δI is the same whichever signal is presented. Hence the variables $(X|S_A)$ and $(X|S_B)$ are normal and of equal variance, and the stochastic strong continuity of $I(t)$ implies the particular symmetric model presented as an illustration in §3.2.

If $I(t)$ is *not* stochastically strongly continuous (this includes all asymmetric decision processes), the results derived in §A.2 and §A.3 need further justification. Equation (A.6) is essential to the argument leading from Wald's Identity (A.2) to the subsequent results, and it assumes implicitly that when the decision process terminates I_n is exactly equal either to I_a or to I_b, according to which response is made. If $I(t)$ is stochastically strongly continuous this condition is obviously satisfied, but if the stochastic strong continuity of $I(t)$ is not made axiomatic, the most that can be said about the continuity of $I(t)$ is contained in the following lemma.

LEMMA A.2. *$I(t)$ is stochastically weakly continuous, that is, for each fixed t and each* $\epsilon > 0$, $\lim_{\delta t \to 0} P\{|I(t+\delta t)-I(t)| \geqslant \epsilon\} = 0$.

Proof. Let $\phi(\theta)$ be the characteristic function of $\{I(t+\Delta t)-I(t)\}$ for some fixed $\Delta t > 0$. Then $|\phi(\theta)| \leqslant 1$ for all θ. Further, because $I(t)$ is infinitely divisible,

(i) $\{I(t+\delta t)-I(t)\}$ has the characteristic function $\{\phi(\theta)\}^{\delta t/\Delta t}$,

and

(ii) $|\phi(\theta)| > 0$ for all θ (Gnedenko and Kolmogorov, Theorem 1, p. 72).

As $\delta t \to 0$, therefore, $\{\phi(\theta)\}^{\delta t/\Delta t} \to 1$, and this proves the lemma.

Weak continuity. The assertion of weak stochastic continuity admits the possibility that $I(t)$ may contain a finite or countably infinite number of discontinuities and, in particular, may *jump* over the decision boundary. In such a case, while the duration of the decision process and the boundary at which it terminates are both well-defined, the exact value of I_n at termination is indeterminate. It therefore needs to be shown that the expressions obtained from Wald's Identity by putting $I_n = I_a$ or I_b, as appropriate, are nonetheless exact.

THEOREM A.6. *The characteristic function for n obtained by inserting the boundary values for I_n in equation (A.2) (Wald's Identity) is exact.*

Proof. Figure A.2 shows a realisation of a continuous random walk with a jump from X to X' over the boundary. Consider the (discontinuous) random walk derived from $I(t)$ by connecting the points $I\{(r-1)\delta t\}$ and $I(r\delta t)$, $r = 1, 2 \ldots$, for some $\delta t > 0$, with straight lines. Let $I'(t)$ denote the derived random walk and suppose that it can terminate at any value of t (i.e. its duration is not restricted to be an integral multiple of δt; in terms of the sequential probability ratio test fractional observations are allowed). The derived path is continuous everywhere as a function of t and the characteristic function for n obtained from Wald's Identity is obviously

FIGURE A.2

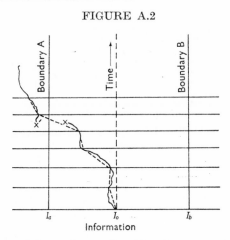

A realisation of the random walk with a jump over the boundary

exact. It will be shown that by choosing δt sufficiently small, the original process can be approximated arbitrarily closely by the derived process.

The discrepancy between the original and the derived path at time t is $\{I(t)-I'(t)\}$, and this is a random variable with period δt. It therefore has characteristic function, averaged over time,

$$\psi(\theta) = (\delta t)^{-1} \int_0^{\delta t}\int_{-\infty}^{\infty}\int_{-\infty}^{\infty} \exp[i\theta\{I(\tau)-\tau I(\delta t)/(\delta t)\}]g\{I(\tau)\,|\,\tau\}\,g\{I(\delta t)\,|\,\delta t\}\ dI(\tau)dI(\delta t)d\tau,$$

since $I'(\tau) = \tau I(\delta t)/(\delta t)$. By rearrangement of the variables

$$\psi(\theta) = (\delta t)^{-1} \int_0^{\delta t}\int_{-\infty}^{\infty}\int_{-\infty}^{\infty} \exp\{i\theta[(1-\tau/\delta t)I(\tau)-\tau I(\delta t-\tau)/\delta t]\}\ \times$$
$$\times\ g\{I(\tau)\,|\,\tau\}g\{I(\delta t-\tau)\,|\,\delta t-\tau\}\ dI(\tau)dI(\delta t-\tau)d\tau,$$

$$= \int_0^1\int_{-\infty}^{\infty} \exp\{i\theta(1-y)I(y\,\delta t)\}\ dG\{I(y\,\delta t)\,|\,y\,\delta t\}.\ \times$$

$$\times \int_{-\infty}^{\infty} \exp\{-i\theta y I(\delta t-y\,\delta t)\}\ dG\{I(\delta t-y\,\delta t)\,|\,\delta t-y\,\delta t\}dy,\ \text{putting}\ \tau = y\,\delta t,$$

$$= \int_0^1 \phi\{\theta(1-y);\,y\,\delta t\}\phi\{-\theta y;\,(1-y)\,\delta t\}\ dy,\ \text{writing}\ \phi(\theta;\,\delta t)\ \text{for the character-}$$

istic function of $I(\delta t)$,

$$= \int_0^1 [\phi\{\theta(1-y);\,\delta t\}]^y\ [\phi\{-\theta y;\,\delta t\}]^{1-y}\ dy.$$

But it was shown in the proof of Lemma A.2 that $\phi(\theta;\,\delta t) \to 1$ as $\delta t \to 0$.

Hence $\lim\limits_{\delta t \to 0} \psi(\theta) = \int_0^1 dy = 1$. It follows that $I(t)$ can be approximated arbitrarily closely by the derived process, $I'(t)$, and for the derived process the characteristic function of n obtained from Wald's Identity by inserting the boundary values for I_n is exact for every $\delta t > 0$. Hence the theorem is proved.

A.4.2. The gamma distribution.

If the distribution of δI given S_B is of the form

$$g(y|S_B) = c^{\nu\,\delta t}(y-d)^{\nu\,\delta t - 1}\, e^{-c(y-d)}/\Gamma(\nu\,\delta t), \quad \nu > 0, c > 0, y > d,$$

then it can be shown from equation (A.21) that

$$g(y|S_A) = (c+1)^{\nu\,\delta t}(y-d)^{\nu\,\delta t - 1}\, e^{-(c+1)(y-d)}/\Gamma(\nu\,\delta t)$$

The transformation $x = c(y-d)$ therefore gives

$$\left.\begin{aligned} f(x|S_A) &= \gamma^{\nu\,\delta t}\, x^{\nu\,\delta t - 1}\, e^{-\gamma x}/\Gamma(\nu\,\delta t), \\ f(x|S_B) &= x^{\nu\,\delta t - 1}\, e^{-x}/\Gamma(\nu\,\delta t), \end{aligned}\right\} \tag{A.22}$$

where $\gamma = (c+1)/c$, and

$$\delta I = x/c - \nu\,\delta t\,\log\gamma \tag{A.23}$$

It follows from the inequality

$$1 - 1/x \leqslant \log x \leqslant x - 1 \tag{A.24}$$

(Hardy, 1955, p. 401) that $E\{\delta I|S_A\} < 0 < E\{\delta I|S_B\}$. It can be seen that the random walk consists of a uniform negative drift with positive increments superimposed upon it. Although $P(\delta I > \epsilon) \to 0$ as $\delta t \to 0$ (i.e. $I(t)$ is stochastically weakly continuous), it can be shown that of the total measure of the positive increments superimposed on the negative drift a proportion $e^{-c\epsilon}$ when S_B is presented ($e^{-(c+1)\epsilon}$ when S_A is presented) is contributed by jumps of magnitude greater than ϵ. The random walk is therefore continuous across boundary A but will jump across boundary B with a non-negligible probability.

The normal model with unequal variances. The gamma distribution of $I(t)$ is important in constructing a normal model with unequal variances. Let X be normal $(\mu_a, \sigma_a{}^2)$ or $(\mu_b, \sigma_b{}^2)$ according as S_A or S_B is presented. Then

$$\delta I = \{(\sigma_b{}^2/\sigma_a{}^2 - 1)(x-\mu_b)^2/2\sigma_b{}^2 + \log(\sigma_a/\sigma_b)\} + \{x - \tfrac{1}{2}(\mu_a+\mu_b)\}(\mu_b-\mu_a)/\sigma_a{}^2 \tag{A.25}$$

and consists of a gamma component and a normal component, which are not independent.[5] Although the normal distribution is infinitely divisible, a normal model with unequal variances is not in canonical form (see p. 151), since the decomposition of X as a normal variable does not *generate the decomposition*[4] of the gamma component of δI. For a similar reason $(X|S_A)$, $(X|S_B)$ cannot properly be expressed as gamma random variables. However by constructing the characteristic function of δI it is possible to show that its distribution *is* infinitely divisible, and it is therefore meaningful to talk about a normal model with unequal variances, such that for a certain value of δt, δI is given by equation (A.25). If δt is decomposed into n independent and identically distributed variables $\delta I^{(n)}$ the distribution of $\delta I^{(n)}$ exists for all positive integral n and $E\{\delta I^{(n)}\} = E\{\delta I\}/n$. Because δI has a gamma component, $I(t)$ will be continuous across boundary A but may jump over boundary B.

---

[4] See the definition on p. 150.

[5] The decomposition of δI into gamma and normal components in equation (A.25) is correct if S_B is presented. If S_A is presented, the equation can be written

$$\delta I = \{(1 - \sigma_a{}^2/\sigma_b{}^2)(x - \mu_a)^2/2\sigma_a{}^2 + \log(\sigma_a/\sigma_b)\} + \{x - \tfrac{1}{2}(\mu_a+\mu_b)\}(\mu_b-\mu_a)/\sigma_b{}^2.$$

It will be interesting to compare the normal model with unequal variances with the equal variance model used as an illustration in §3.2.1.

THEOREM A.7.

(i) *A difference between the variances increases the mean information per unit time.*

(ii) $|E\{\delta I|S_A\}| >$ *or* $< |E\{\delta I|S_B\}|$ *according as* $\sigma_a >$ *or* $< \sigma_b$.

(iii) *The normal variate model is symmetric if, and only if,* $\sigma_a = \sigma_b$.

Proof. (i) From Equation (A.25),

$$E\{\delta I|S_B\} = \log(\sigma_a/\sigma_b) + \{\sigma_b{}^2 - \sigma_a{}^2 + (\mu_b - \mu_a)^2\}/2\sigma_a{}^2. \tag{A.26}$$

By putting $x = \sigma_a{}^2/\sigma_b{}^2$ in the inequality $\log x \geqslant 1 - 1/x$ it can be shown that $E\{\delta I|S_B\} \geqslant (\mu_b - \mu_a)^2/2\sigma_a{}^2$, with equality only if $\sigma_b = \sigma_a$; i.e. $E\{\delta I|S_B\}$ is a minimum when $\sigma_b = \sigma_a$. Under the same conditions $E\{\delta I|S_A\} \leqslant -(\mu_b - \mu_a)^2/2\sigma_b{}^2$, i.e. $|E\{\delta I|S_A\}|$ is a minimum when $\sigma_a = \sigma_b$.

(ii) LEMMA A.3. *For all* $x > 1$,

$$\log x < \tfrac{1}{2}(x - 1/x). \tag{A.27}$$

Proof. Equality holds at $x = 1$. Differentiating both sides,

$$d(\log x)/dx = 1/x < \tfrac{1}{2}(1 + 1/x^2) = d(\tfrac{1}{2}x - \tfrac{1}{2}/x)/dx.$$

Hence the lemma follows.

Now $E\{\delta I|S_A\} + E\{\delta I|S_B\} = 2\log(\sigma_a/\sigma_b) +$
$$+ \tfrac{1}{2}(\sigma_b{}^2/\sigma_a{}^2 - \sigma_a{}^2/\sigma_b{}^2) + \tfrac{1}{2}(\mu_b - \mu_a)^2(1/\sigma_a{}^2 - 1/\sigma_b{}^2).$$

By putting $x = \sigma_a{}^2/\sigma_b{}^2$ in (A.27), it follows that $E\{\delta I|S_A\} + E\{\delta I|S_B\} < 0$ if $\sigma_a/\sigma_b > 1$, and > 0 if $\sigma_a/\sigma_b < 1$. But $E\{\delta I|S_A\} < 0 < E\{\delta I|S_B\}$ from (i) above. Hence

$$|E\{\delta I|S_A\}| > \text{ or } < |E\{\delta I|S_B\}| \text{ according as } \sigma_a > \text{ or } < \sigma_b.$$

(iii) The condition of symmetry (p. 127) requires $|E\{\delta I|S_A\}| = |E\{\delta I|S_B\}|$, and by (ii) above this obviously occurs if, and only if, $\sigma_a = \sigma_b$. This completes the proof of the theorem.

Inequality of the variances increases the mean information rate because the scatter of the sample $(x_1 \ldots x_r)$ contributes to the value of I_r. It is intuitively reasonable that this rate should be greater when that signal associated with the greater variance is presented; e.g. if $\sigma_b > \sigma_a$, $f(x|S_B)/f(x|S_A) \to \infty$ as $x \to \pm \infty$.

A.4.3. The Poisson distribution.

It seems *prima facie* reasonable that the information afforded by the signal should be represented inside the subject's brain by a train of nerve impulses. The simplest probabilitistic structure for such a train of pulses is a Poisson process and this leads naturally to a consideration of information with a Poisson distribution.

Suppose when S_B is presented that $I(t)$ has a distribution of the form

$$P\{I(t) = y|S_B\} = (\mu_b t)^k \exp(-\mu_b t)/k!,$$

where $k = (y - c)/d$ is an integer and c and d are constants. Then it can be shown from equation (A.24) that

$$P\{I(t) = y|S_A\} = (\mu_a t)^k \exp(-\mu_a t)/k!,$$

and $c = I_0 + (\mu_a - \mu_b)t,$

where $\log(\mu_b/\mu_a) = d.$

δI therefore has a Poisson distribution with parameter $(\mu_a \, \delta t)$ or $(\mu_b \, \delta t)$, and by means of the transformation $k = \{y - I_0 - (\mu_a - \mu_b)t\} / \log(\mu_b / \mu_a)$,

$$p(k|S_A) = (\mu_a \, \delta t)^k \exp(-\mu_a \, \delta t)/k!, \left.\begin{matrix} \\ \\ \end{matrix}\right\}$$
$$p(k|S_B) = (\mu_b \, \delta t)^k \exp(-\mu_b \, \delta t)/k!, \qquad (A.28)$$

where k is a positive interger, and

$$\delta I = k \log(\mu_b / \mu_a) - (\mu_b - \mu_a) \, \delta t, \qquad (A.29)$$

where k has the distribution $p(k|S_A)$ or $p(k|S_B)$. If $\mu_b > \mu_a$, the random walk consists of a uniform negative drift with positive jumps of constant magnitude randomly distributed in time superimposed on it. The random walk will be continuous across boundary A, but will jump over boundary B with probability one. Since, obviously, $\mu_a \neq \mu_b$ the decision process cannot be symmetric.

A.4.4. The negative binomial distribution.

It is also possible to construct a decision process based on the negative binomial distribution. Let

$$p(k|S_A) = \binom{k+u-1}{u-1}(1-a)^u a^k, \left.\begin{matrix} \\ \\ \\ \\ \end{matrix}\right\}$$
$$p(k|S_B) = \binom{k+u-1}{u-1}(1-b)^u b^k, \qquad (A.30)$$

where $k = 0, 1, 2 \ldots$, and $b > a$. Then

$$I_u - I_0 = u \, \log\{(1-b)/(1-a)\} + k \, \log(b/a),$$

and, putting $u = 1/n$, $(I_u - I_0)$ has the decomposition

$$\delta I = (1/n)\log\{(1-b)/(1-a)\} + k \, \log(b/a), \qquad (A.31)$$

where k has the generating function $\{(1-a)/(1-as)\}^{1/n}$ or $\{(1-b)/(1-bs)\}^{1/n}$ according as S_A or S_B is presented. As $n \to \infty$, $P(k = 0) \to 1$, while $P(k = r) = 0(1/n)$ for $r = 1, 2, \ldots$ Hence the random walk consists of positive jumps with magnitudes that are integral multiples of $\log(b/a)$ superimposed on a uniform negative drift. In common with the Poisson walk, the negative binomial walk is continuous across boundary A and jumps over boundary B with probability one. Since $a \neq b$, the negative binomial process is never symmetric.

A.5.   The asymmetric decision process.

If $E\{\delta I | S_A\} + E\{\delta I | S_B\} \neq 0$, the decision process is asymmetric; three examples of asymmetric processes have been given in § A.4. It is nonetheless possible to define an optimum in the sense of Axiom 5, but explicit expressions for the parameter values can no longer be obtained.

THEOREM A.8. (i) *In a general two-choice decision process there is a unique optimum such that the mean reaction time is a minimum for an error rate $\not> \epsilon$. (ii) Conversely there is a unique optimum such that the error rate is a minimum for a mean reaction time $\not> t$.*

Proof. (i) Let α_0, β_0 be the optimum error probabilities. Then $(1-p)\alpha_0 + p\beta_0 = \epsilon$. Otherwise there exists $\alpha_0' > \alpha_0$ such that $(1-p)\alpha_0' + p\beta_0 = \epsilon$, and it is clear from (A.6) and Theorem A.2 that the mean reaction time can be reduced by substituting α_0' for α_0.

It will be shown that, subject to $(1-p)\alpha+p\beta = \epsilon$, the mean reaction time, $E\{n\,|\,p\}$, has a unique minimum.

First, $E\{n\,|\,p\}$ is expressed in terms of the conditional mean reaction times,

$$E\{n\,|\,p\} = (1-p)E\{n\,|\,S_\mathrm{A}\}+pE\{n\,|\,S_\mathrm{B}\}. \tag{A.32}$$

Putting
$$1/E\{\delta I\,|\,S_\mathrm{B}\}-1/E\{\delta I\,|\,S_\mathrm{A}\} = 2X,$$
$$1/E\{\delta I\,|\,S_\mathrm{B}\}+1/E\{\delta I\,|\,S_\mathrm{A}\} = 2Y,$$

and substituting in equation (A.32) from (A.5), (A.8) and (A.9), we find

$$E\{n\,|\,p\} = X\{(p-\epsilon)(I_b-I_0)-(1-p-\epsilon)(I_a-I_0)\}+$$
$$+Y[\{(1-p)\alpha+p(1-\beta)\}(I_b-I_0)+\{(1-p)(1-\alpha)+p\beta\}(I_a-I_0)]. \tag{A.33}$$

$E\{n\,|\,p\}$ can be expressed as a function of α by writing

$$\left.\begin{aligned}
f(\alpha) &= (p-\epsilon)(I_b-I_0)-(1-p-\epsilon)(I_a-I_0), \\
g(\alpha) &= \alpha(I_b-I_0)+(1-\alpha)(I_a-I_0), \\
h(\alpha) &= (1-\beta)(I_b-I_0)+\beta(I_a-I_0),
\end{aligned}\right\} \tag{A.34}$$

where $\beta = \{\epsilon-(1-p)\alpha\}/p$ and I_a, I_b are related to α, β by equations (A.4). Then $f(\alpha) = p\,h(\alpha)-(1-p)g(\alpha)$ and

$$\left.\begin{aligned}
d^2f/d\alpha^2 &> 0, \\
d^2g/d\alpha^2 &< 0, \\
d^2h/d\alpha^2 &> 0,
\end{aligned}\right\} \tag{A.35}$$

in the interval $0 < \alpha < \epsilon/(1-p)$. Now $E\{n\,|\,p\} \to \infty$ both as $\alpha \to 0$ and as $\beta \to 0$, so there is at least one minimum in the interval $0 < \alpha < \epsilon/(1-p)$. But $dE\{n\,|\,p\}/d\alpha$ can be expressed as the sum of two monotonic increasing functions as follows:

if $Y > 0$, $dE\{n\,|\,p\}/d\alpha = (X-Y)\,df/d\alpha+2pY\,dh/d\alpha$;

if $Y < 0$, $dE\{n\,|\,p\}/d\alpha = (X+Y)\,df/d\alpha+2(1-p)Y\,dg/d\alpha$.

Since $X-Y = -1/E\{\delta I\,|\,S_\mathrm{A}\} > 0$, and $X+Y = 1/E\{\delta I\,|\,S_\mathrm{B}\} > 0$, $dE\{n\,|\,p\}/d\alpha$ is monotonic increasing in the interval $0 < \alpha < \epsilon/(1-p)$ and has only one zero, giving a unique optimum.

(ii) Let t_0 be the optimum mean reaction time. Then $t_0 = t$, the permitted maximum. Otherwise, if $t_0 < t$, new values for the error probabilities, say α_0', β_0', can be found such that

$$\alpha_0' < \alpha_0, \qquad \beta_0' < \beta_0$$

and $t_0' > t_0$, where t_0' is the new mean reaction time. From equation (A.6) it is evident that $(\alpha_0'-\alpha_0)$, $(\beta_0'-\beta_0)$ can be made sufficiently small such that $t_0' \leqslant t$. But $(1-p)\alpha_0'+p\beta_0' < (1-p)\alpha_0+p\beta_0$, so that the error rate is thereby reduced.

There is an infinity of pairs of values (t_a, t_b) such that $(1-p)t_a+pt_b = t_0$. Putting $t_a E\{\delta I\,|\,S_\mathrm{A}\}/\delta t = E\{I_n-I_0\,|\,S_\mathrm{A}\}$, $t_b E\{\delta I\,|\,S_\mathrm{B}\}/\delta t = E\{I_n-I_0\,|\,S_\mathrm{B}\}$, it follows from the proof of the converse to Theorem A.5 that there is at least one associated pair of error probabilities (α, β), and hence an error rate $\epsilon = (1-p)\alpha+p\beta$. Let ϵ_0 be the minimum error rate so obtained. Then there is only one pair (α, β) among those constructed above, such that $(1-p)\alpha+p\beta = \epsilon_0$.

For by part (i) of this theorem ϵ_0 determines a unique pair of error probabilities (α_0, β_0), such that $(1-p)\alpha_0+p\beta_0 = \epsilon_0$ and the mean reaction time is a minimum. The minimum value of the mean reaction time is necessarily t_0. If (α_1, β_1) is another pair of error probabilities such that $(1-p)\alpha_1+p\beta_1 = \epsilon_0$, then (α_1, β_1) does not determine an optimum process and $t(\alpha_1, \beta_1) > t_0$. This completes the proof.

Optimal parameter values. The optimal values of the parameters can be obtained by differentiating (A.33) with respect to α and solving the equation $dE\{n|p\}/d\alpha = 0$. It can be shown that

$$dE\{n|p\}/d\alpha = X\,df/d\alpha + Y\{(1-p)\,dg/d\alpha + p\,dh/d\alpha\}. \tag{A.36}$$

If $Y \neq 0$, the solution cannot be obtained explicitly, but it is possible to find limits for the optimal parameter values.

$df/d\alpha = 0$ determines the optimum parameters for the symmetric decision process; it is satisfied by $\alpha = \epsilon(p-\epsilon)/(1-p)(1-2\epsilon)$ and this root will be denoted by α_1. Now by Lemma A.2,

$$\left[(1-p)\frac{dg}{d\alpha} + p\frac{dh}{d\alpha}\right]_{\alpha_1} = 2(1-p)\left\{2\log\frac{1-\epsilon}{\epsilon} - \frac{1-\epsilon}{\epsilon} + \frac{\epsilon}{1-\epsilon}\right\} < 0,$$

so that α_1 is an upper or lower limit for the asymmetric optimum value according as $Y <$ or > 0, since $dE\{n|p\}/d\alpha$ is monotonic increasing in the interval $0 < \alpha < \epsilon/(1-p)$. If $Y > 0$, an upper limit α_2 may be obtained by substituting $\{1-\alpha\beta/(1-\alpha)(1-\beta)\}$ for $\log\{(1-\alpha)(1-\beta)/\alpha\beta\}$ in (A.36) thus:[6]

$$\frac{d}{d\alpha}E\{n|p\} \geqslant X\left\{\frac{(1-p-\epsilon)^2}{p\beta(1-\alpha)} - \frac{(p-\epsilon)}{p\alpha(1-\beta)}\right\} +$$

$$+ Y(1-p)(1-\alpha-\beta)\left\{\frac{2}{(1-\alpha)(1-\beta)} - \frac{p}{(1-p)\alpha(1-\alpha)} - \frac{(1-p)}{p\beta(1-\beta)}\right\}. \tag{A.37}$$

Putting the right hand side of (A.37) = 0,

$$\alpha_2 = \frac{p-\epsilon}{1-p} \cdot \frac{\epsilon(X+Y)}{(1-2\epsilon)X-(1-2p)Y}. \tag{A.38}$$

Writing $Y/X = \rho$, the following inequalities hold for $Y > 0$:

$$\frac{p-\epsilon}{1-p}\cdot\frac{\epsilon}{1-2\epsilon} \quad < \quad \alpha_0 \quad < \quad \frac{p-\epsilon}{1-p}\cdot\frac{\epsilon(1+\rho)}{(1-2\epsilon)-\rho(1-2p)}, \tag{A.39}$$

$$\frac{1-p-\epsilon}{p}\cdot\frac{\epsilon}{1-2\epsilon} \quad > \quad \beta_0 \quad > \quad \frac{1-p-\epsilon}{p}\cdot\frac{\epsilon(1-\rho)}{(1-2\epsilon)-\rho(1-2p)}, \tag{A.40}$$

$$\frac{1-p-\epsilon}{p-\epsilon} \quad > \quad R_\epsilon\left(\frac{S_B}{S_A}\right)_0 \quad > \quad \frac{1-p-\epsilon}{p-\epsilon}\cdot\frac{1-\rho}{1+\rho}, \tag{A.41}$$

$$\log\frac{\epsilon}{1-\epsilon} \quad > \quad I_{a,0} \quad > \quad \log\frac{\epsilon(1-\rho)}{(1-\epsilon)-\rho(1-2p+\epsilon)}, \tag{A.42}$$

$$\log\frac{1-\epsilon}{\epsilon} \quad > \quad I_{b,0} \quad > \quad \log\frac{(1-\epsilon)-\rho(1-2p-\epsilon)}{\epsilon(1+\rho)}. \tag{A.43}$$

If $Y < 0$, (A.38) is a lower limit; the limits in (A.39—43) take the same formal values with the inequality signs reversed.

---

[6] A closer limit may be obtained by substituting $(1-\alpha-\beta)\{1/(1-\beta)+1/(1-\alpha)\}$ for $\log\{(1-\alpha)(1-\beta)/\alpha\beta\}$, but the resultant expressions are more cumbersome.

A.5.1. A comparison with the symmetric decision process.

The inequalities (A.39–43) may be summarized by saying that the optimal parameter values differ from their values in the symmetric decision process in such a way that the effect of the difference in information rates is reduced. If

$$|E\{\delta I|S_A\}| > |E\{\delta I|S_B\}|,$$

then $|E\{I_n-I_0|S_A\}|$ is increased and $|E\{I_n-I_0|S_B\}|$ is decreased. That is, more information, relative to that required in the symmetric process, is now required to satisfy the criterion for response R_A, and this additional information is usually gathered at the faster rate conditional on S_A; conversely, less information is required to initiate R_B.

It seems *prima facie* that the minimum mean reaction time, $E_{\min}\{n|p\}$, will be less when the greater *a priori* signal probability is associated with the greater information rate than when the same signal probabilities are paired the other way about. But because the equation $dE\{n|p\}/d\alpha = 0$ does not have an explicit solution, it is not possible to obtain an explicit expression for $E_{\min}\{n|p\}$ as a function of p, corresponding to equation (A.12), and the following argument must therefore suffice:

Consider the two pairs of *a priori* signal probabilties determined by $p = x$ and $p = 1-x$, $0 < x < 1$. If $|E\{\delta I|S_A\}| > |E\{\delta I|S_B\}|$ and $x < \frac{1}{2}$, the decision problem with $p = x$ has a majority of the signals associated with the faster information rate and therefore will not take longer than the decision problem with $p = 1-x$. There remains the possibility that $E_{\min}\{n|p\}$ is a symmetric function of p.

It is possible to obtain expressions for $\partial E\{n|p\}/\partial p$, $\partial E\{n|p\}/\partial\alpha$, subject to the restriction $(1-p)\alpha+p\beta = \epsilon$, by Lagrange's method of undetermined multipliers. The optimal parameter values for $p = x$ are determined by the equations

$$(1-x)\alpha+x\beta = \epsilon,$$

$$\partial E\{n|x\}/\partial\alpha = 0,$$

and those for $p = 1-x$ by a similar pair of equations. If $E_{\min}\{n|p\}$ is a symmetric function of p about $p = \frac{1}{2}$, then also

$$\partial E\{n|x\}/\partial p+\partial E\{n|1-x\}/\partial p = 0,$$

when the corresponding optimal values for α and β are inserted. However, these five equations in the four unknowns $\alpha,\beta|p = x$ and $\alpha,\beta|p = 1-x$ are not dependent unless the decision process is symmetric, i.e. unless $E\{\delta I|S_A\}+E\{\delta I|S_B\} = 0$. For an asymmetric process $E_{\min}\{n|p\}$ is therefore an asymmetric function of p about $p = \frac{1}{2}$. If $|E\{\delta I|S_A\}| > |E\{\delta I|S_B\}|$ and $x < \frac{1}{2}$, $E_{\min}\{n|x\} < E_{\min}\{n|1-x\}$, and $E_{\min}\{n|p\}$ has a maximum for some value of $p > \frac{1}{2}$.

Theorems A.4 and A.5 in §A.3.2 now need to be modified for the asymmetric decision process. Provided the asymmetry is not too great, these results will still be approximately true. If $|E\{\delta I|S_A\}| > |E\{\delta I|S_B\}|$, there will be an interval, $p_1 < p < \frac{1}{2}$ for some p_1, such that in the optimal process the infrequent signal elicits a faster response, and another interval, $\frac{1}{2} < p < p_2$ for some p_2, such that the more frequent signal is more liable to error. There will also be a region of values of α and β such that $\alpha > \beta$ but $E\{R.T.|S_A\} < E\{R.T.|S_B\}$. The size of these regions is a function of the asymmetry of the decision process and they will be small if $E\{\delta I|S_A\}+E\{\delta I|S_B\}$ is near zero.

A.6. The C-reaction.

In the C-reaction a response is required to only one of the two signals, say R_B. Results for the C-reaction may be obtained from the corresponding results for the B-reaction by equating R_A with "do nothing" and letting $I_a \to -\infty$. In particular if $I_a \to -\infty$ in equations (A.5), $\alpha \to \exp\{-(I_b-I_0)\}$, and $1-\beta \to 1$. Hence

COROLLARY A.1. *If* $I_a = -\infty$, $I_b < \infty$, *and* $E\{\delta I | S_B\} > 0$, *the random walk will terminate on the boundary at* I_b *with probability* 1 *when* S_B *is presented.*

In fact it can be shown that Corollary A.1 is true even when $E\{\delta I\} = 0$, but it then follows from equation (A.3) that the mean decision latency is infinite.

The characteristic function and mean of the decision latency when S_B is presented may be obtained by letting $I_a \to -\infty$ in equations (A.2) and (A.9). Then

$$E\{n|S_B\} = (I_b-I_0)/E\{\delta I | S_B\}. \tag{A.44}$$

It follows from Theorem B.6 that these equations also give the characteristic function and mean decision latency of $(n|S_A.R_B)$. The mean duration of the decision process

FIGURE A.3

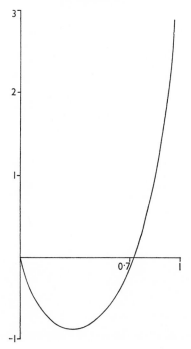

The function $G(x) = (1-2x)\log(1-x)+2x \log x$ in the interval $0 \leqslant x \leqslant 0\cdot96$.

when it leads to R_B is therefore directly proportional to the information required to make this response and is a little greater than it would be in an equivalent B-reaction, where I_a is finite. In the B-reaction some realisations of the random walk, which would otherwise reach I_b after a relatively long time, terminate prematurely at boundary I_a.

In any realisable C-reaction experiment the time taken to make R_A (no response) is not measureable, and so optimal performance consists in making R_B as quickly as possible consistent with a maximum probability of error. Although in practice an experimental trial is terminated by the experimenter after a finite time if no response is produced, $P(S_B.\,no\;response)$ may nonetheless be assumed zero. In the optimum decision process, then, $\alpha = \epsilon/(1-p)$ and $I_b = \log(p/\epsilon)$, so that

$$E_{\min}\{n\,|\,p\} = \{\log\,(1-p)-\log\,\epsilon\}/E\{\delta I\,|\,S_B\}.$$

Comparing this equation with (A.12),

$$E_{\min}\{n\,|\,B\text{-}reaction\}-E_{\min}\{n\,|\,C\text{-}reaction\} = g(\epsilon)-g(1-p), \qquad (A.45)$$

where $g(x) = (1-2x)\log(1-x)+2x\log x$. This function is plotted in Figure A.3 over the interval $0 \leqslant x \leqslant 0.96$. If $\epsilon = 0.03$, say, the C-reaction is faster than the B-reaction for $0.35 \leqslant p < 1-\epsilon$.

A.7. The two-choice model with temporal uncertainty.

Hitherto it has been supposed that the decision process begins at the exact moment that the signal is presented. But the subject has only approximate knowledge of when the signal will appear and has no other means of synchronizing his decision process with its onset. If the decision process were to begin reliably at some time after the onset of the signal, little modification to the theory would be required. But it seems more likely that the decision process frequently begins prior to the onset of the signal, and so at the start of the decision process the subject is sampling information from a blank display (see p. 81). This information is quite irrelevant to the decision which the subject is trying to make, but at the same time is inseperable from the subsequent relevant information. So the random walk representation of the decision process begins properly with a few steps due to the irrelevant information, and these steps have zero drift.

Wald's identity. It is not necessary that the distribution of the irrelevant information should bear any particular relation to the distribution of the relevant, but it seems reasonable that these two distributions should have the same form. It is then possible to represent the irrelevant information at the start of the decision process by n_0 increments of zero drift, denoted by δ^*I, where δ^*I has the distribution of $(\delta I-E\{\delta I\})$. Such a representation of the decision process is shown in Figure A.4. In retrospect it seems likely that the variance of the irrelevant information accumulates at a slower rate than that of the relevant. The foregoing representation of the irrelevant information is nonetheless admissible, although this information may in fact be gathered over a period of time greater than $n_0\,\delta t$.

Provided n_0 is small relative to $E\{n\}$, Wald's Identity (A.2) becomes[7]

$$E\{\exp[I_n-I_0^*-(n+n_0)\,\delta I]\theta\} = 1, \qquad (A.46)$$

where $I_0^* = I_0-n_0\,E\{\delta I\}$ and n is the number of increments subsequent to the onset of the signal to reach a decision. n can now be negative $(>-n_0)$, when the subject

---

[7] The approximation involved in the derivation of this generalisation of Wald's Identity is that of replacing

$$P(n \leqslant 0)E\{\exp[(I_n-I_0)\theta][E\{\exp(\delta^*I\,\theta)\}]^{-n}|n \leqslant 0\}$$

by

$$P(n \leqslant 0)E\{\exp[(I_n-I_0+n_0E\{\delta I\})\theta][E\{\exp\,(\delta I\,\theta)\}]^{-n}|n \leqslant 0\},$$

where

$$E\{\exp(\delta I\,\theta)\} = E\{\exp(\delta^*I\,\theta)\}\exp(E\{\delta I\,\theta\}).$$

anticipates a signal. Hence the effects of temporal uncertainty may be represented approximately by replacing the model of §3.2 with a random walk which starts from the point I_0^*, $\log\{\epsilon/(1-\epsilon)\} < I_0^* < \log\{(1-\epsilon)/\epsilon\}$, at time $-n_0\,\delta t$. Provided the probability of the decision process terminating before the onset of the signal (i.e. the

FIGURE A.4

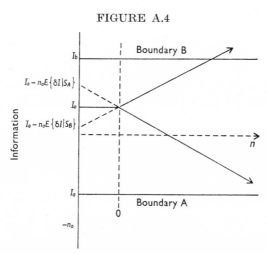

The two-choice process with irrelevant information.

probability of an anticipation in an experiment) is small, the accuracy of the approximation will be adequate for the analysis of empirical data.

A.7.1. The symmetric decision process with temporal uncertainty.

n_0 and I_0^* are functions of the signal presented. For the purposes of the analysis of the experiments in Chapter 5 it is sufficient to consider here only the simplest symmetric decision process in which $\mathrm{var}(\delta I\,|\,S_A) = \mathrm{var}(\delta I\,|\,S_B)$ and $E\{\delta I\,|\,S_A\} + E\{\delta I\,|\,S_B\} = 0$. Then n_0 is independent of the signal, and $(I_0^*\,|\,S_A) = I_0 + K$, $(I_0^*\,|\,S_B) = I_0 - K$, where $K = n_0\,E\{\delta I\,|\,S_B\}$.

Error probabilities. One immediate result of temporal uncertainty is an increase in both probabilities of error. Substituting in equation (A.5),

$$\left.\begin{aligned}\alpha &= \{\exp(I_0+K)-\exp(I_a)\}/\{\exp(I_b)-\exp(I_a)\},\\ \beta &= \{\exp(-I_0+K)-\exp(-I_b)\}/\{\exp(-I_a)-\exp(-I_b)\}.\end{aligned}\right\} \tag{A.47}$$

Provided I_0 is not near I_a or I_b (under those circumstances the approximation in §A.7 is poor), α and β are both increased by approximately the same multiplicative factor, e^K. So the optimal values of the boundaries may be obtained by writing ϵe^{-K} for ϵ in Theorem A.3. It follows by substitution in (A.47) that

$$R_\epsilon(S_B/S_A) = \{(1-p)(1-\epsilon)e^K-\epsilon p\}/\{p(1-\epsilon)e^K-\epsilon(1-p)\}. \tag{A.48}$$

Since $K > 0$, the value of $R_\epsilon(S_B/S_A)$ lies between $(1-p)/p$ and $(1-p-\epsilon)/(p-\epsilon)$, and is approximately that of (A.13).

Relative mean reaction times. Theorems A.4 and A.5 (p. 129) remain true when there is subjective uncertainty about the time of presentation of the signal. The differentiation of equation (A.46) leads to (A.3) as before, and the difference in expected duration of the decision process conditional on each signal is

$$E\{n|S_B\}-E\{n|S_A\} = \frac{2}{|E\{\delta I\}|}\left\{\log\frac{1-p}{p}-e^K\frac{\epsilon(1-\epsilon)(1-2p)}{(1-2\epsilon)p(1-p)}\log\frac{1-\epsilon}{\epsilon}\right\}. \quad (A.49)$$

Comparing this with (A.16) it follows that Theorem A.4 still holds provided $\eta < p < 1-\eta$, where

$$\{\eta(1-\eta)/(1-2\eta)\}\log\{(1-\eta)/\eta\} = e^K\{\epsilon(1-\epsilon)/(1-2\epsilon)\}\log\{(1-\epsilon)/\epsilon\}.$$

$\eta > \epsilon$, so that the range of values of p for which Theorem A.4 is true is a little restricted. However, the truth of Theorem A.4 may reasonably be assumed for all the *a priori* signal probabilities studied in Chapter 5.

The proof of Theorem A.5 follows a similar argument to that in §A.3.2:

(i) Given α, β, K, there are unique values, ϵ_0, p_0, such that α, β are the error probabilities associated with the optimal decision process for the error rate ϵ_0, with $P(S_B) = p_0$. For, substituting in (A.47), ϵ_0, p_0 must satisfy

$$\left.\begin{array}{l}\alpha = \epsilon\{p(1-\epsilon)\,e^K/(1-p)-\epsilon\}/(1-2\epsilon),\\[4pt]\beta = \epsilon\{(1-p)(1-\epsilon)e^K/p-\epsilon\}/(1-2\epsilon)\end{array}\right\} \quad (A.50)$$

Eliminating p between these two equations leads to a quadratic in $x = \{(1-\epsilon)/\epsilon\}^2$,

$$f(x) = \alpha\beta x^2+(\alpha+\beta-2\alpha\beta-e^{2K})x+(1-\alpha)(1-\beta) = 0.$$

Since $K \geqslant 0$, there is exactly one root of $f(x) = 0$ greater than 1. Hence there exist unique values ϵ_0, p_0, such that $0 < \epsilon_0 < \frac{1}{2}$, satisfying (A.50). Further,

$$p_0 > \text{ or } < \tfrac{1}{2} \text{ according as } \alpha > \text{ or } < \beta.$$

Hence from Theorem A.4

$$E\{n|S_B\} > \text{ or } < E\{n|S_A\} \text{ according as } \beta > \text{ or } < \alpha.$$

(ii) Conversely, if $E\{n|S_A\}$, $E\{n|S_B\}$ and K are given, there is an associated pair of error probabilities. As before, put $\exp(I_a-I_0) = A$, $\exp(I_b-I_0) = B$, $X = -E\{n|S_A\}E\{\delta I|S_A\}$, and $Y = E\{n|S_B\}E\{\delta I|S_B\}$.

Then, substituting in (A.3),

$$X = \{(A-e^K)/(B-A)\}\log B + \{(e^K-B)/(B-A)\}\log A$$

and
$$Y = \{A(Be^K-1)/(B-A)\}\log A + \{B(1-Ae^K)/(B-A)\}\log B,$$

whence
$$\log A = \frac{Y-XB(1-Ae^K)/(A-e^K)}{1+B(1-Ae^K)/(A-e^K)} \quad (A.51)$$

and
$$\log B = \frac{Y-XA(Be^K-1)/(e^K-B)}{1+A(Be^K-1)/(e^K-B)}. \quad (A.52)$$

These equations are continuous except where $ABe^K-(A+B)+e^K = 0$, and from a comparison with (A.19), (A.20) and Figure A.1, it is clear that there is at least one solution such that $0 < A < 1 < B$. It follows that $\beta > \text{ or } < \alpha$ according as $E\{n|S_B\} > \text{ or } < E\{n|S_A\}$, and this completes the proof.

A.7.2. The relation between error- and correct-reaction times.

Theorem B.6 shows that error- and correct-reaction times conditional on the same response are identically distributed. The proof of this theorem depends upon a "frequency of occurrence" interpretation of probability, and I_0 must therefore represent the objective *a priori* signal probabilities. Further, since both the distributions of reaction time and the probabilities of error are functions of the *a priori* signal probabilities (assuming the boundaries of the random walk fixed), I_0 must, with certain special exceptions, be constant for Theorem B.6 to be true. But it has just been shown that a two-choice decision process with temporal uncertainty may be represented approximately by replacing I_0 with I_0^*, which is a function of the signal presented, and it is therefore unlikely that Theorem B.6 will still be true. It will be shown that errors are, in the mean, faster than correct responses, and the difference in mean reaction time is, to a first order of approximation, constant and equal to $2n_0 \delta t$.

It is first necessary to express $E\{n|R_A\}$ and $E\{n|R_B\}$ as functions of I_0. From equation (A.7) and Theorem B.6

$$E\{n|S_A\} = P(R_A|S_A)E\{n|R_A\}+P(R_B|S_A)E\{n|R_B\}, \left.\begin{array}{c} \\ \end{array}\right\}$$
$$E\{n|S_B\} = P(R_A|S_B)E\{n|R_A\}+P(R_B|S_B)E\{n|R_B\}, \quad\quad (A.53)$$

for $I_0 =$ constant. Substituting from (A.8) and (A.9) into (A.53) and putting $E\{\delta I|S_B\} = -E\{\delta I|S_A\} = E\{\delta I\}$,

$$E\{n|R_A\} = \frac{1}{E\{\delta I\}}\left\{ (I_0-I_a)\frac{e^{I_a}+e^{I_b}}{e^{I_b}-e^{I_a}} - \frac{2e^{I_b}(I_b-I_0)\,(e^{I_0}-e^{I_a})}{(e^{I_b}-e^{I_0})\,(e^{I_b}-e^{I_a})} \right\} \quad (A.54)$$

and there is a similar expression for $E\{n|R_B\}$.

When there is temporal uncertainty in the decision process,

$$E\{n|R_A S_A\}-E\{n|R_A S_B\}$$
$$= E\{n|R_A . I_0^* = I_0+K\}-E\{n|R_A . I_0^* = I_0-K\}$$
$$= \{2K(B^2-1)-4B \log B \sinh K\}/\{B^2-2B \cosh K +1\}E\{\delta I\}, \quad (A.55)$$

where $B = \exp(I_b-I_0)$. Similarly

$$E\{n|R_B S_B\}-E\{n|R_B S_A\}$$
$$= \{2K(1-A^2)+4A \log A \sinh K\}/\{1-2A \cosh K+A^2\}E\{\delta I\}, \quad (A.56)$$

where $A = \exp(I_a-I_0)$. Hence the differences in mean reaction time are approximately $2K/E\{\delta I\} = 2n_0 \delta t$ to the first order. This first order approximation is good while the probabilities of error are small, and breaks down when the presence of a second boundary makes a detectable difference to the mean reaction time (cf. the C-reaction, p. 139).

On differentiating (A.55) with respect to I_0 it appears that

$$d[E\{n|R_A S_A\}-E\{n|R_A S_B\}]/dI_0 < 0$$

provided B is large enough, in particular, if $B >$ about $\exp(1+K \coth K)$. Hence, provided this condition is satisfied, $E\{n|R_A S_A\}-E\{n|R_A S_B\}$ will decrease as p increases; conversely $E\{n|R_B S_B\}-E\{n|R_B S_A\}$ will increase with p.

If $E\{\delta I|S_A\}+E\{\delta I|S_B\} \neq 0$, the difference in mean reaction time between error and correct responses is a function of the response made. Let

$$n_a \text{ var}(\delta I|S_A) = n_b \text{ var}(\delta I|S_B) = n_0 \text{ var}(\delta I|zero\ drift).$$

Then to a first approximation

$$E\{n|R_A S_A\}-E\{n|R_A S_B\} = [n_a E\{\delta I|S_A\}-n_b E\{\delta I|S_B\}]/E\{\delta I|S_A\}, \left.\begin{array}{c} \\ \end{array}\right\}$$
$$E\{n|R_B S_B\}-E\{n|R_B S_A\} = [n_b E\{\delta I|S_B\}-n_a E\{\delta I|S_A\}]/E\{\delta I|S_B\}. \quad (A.57)$$

APPENDIX B

THE MULTI-CHOICE THEORY

B.1. Introduction.

This appendix develops some of the implications of the axioms of §3.3 for a discrimination between the m alternative signals S_i, $i = 1 \ldots m$, $m \geqslant 2$. Some of the consequences established here are of fundamental importance to the mathematical and empirical theory; the normal multi-choice model developed in §B.3, on the other hand, is primarily an exploration with future experiments in view.

In the first part of this appendix certain important theorems are proved. It is shown that Axiom 2 specifies the necessary and sufficient conditions that a certain mathematical construction is possible; the entire mathematical development of Appendix A and §B.3 is built upon this construction. It is also shown that Axiom 4 specifies the necessary and sufficient condition that the response shall be unique. Another consequence of the axioms is that the distribution of reaction time for a given response is independent of whether the response is right or wrong; the significance of this result is considered in §B.2.1.

B.1.1. Notation.

The principal notation to be used in this appendix is listed below in the order of its introduction.

S_i, $i = 1 \ldots m$ alternative signals in m-choice theory.

$I(S_i : \underset{j \neq i}{\bigcup} S_j; t)$ total information, including *a priori* information, available to the

$I(S_i; t)$ subject at time t in favour of S_i against all the other signals.

$\mathbf{I}(t)$ the vector with components $I(S_i; t)$, $i = 1 \ldots m$.

$g(\mathbf{I} \,|\, S_i; t)$ probability density function of $\mathbf{I}(t)$ when S_i is presented.

p_i *a priori* probability of S_i.

$\pi_i(t)$ *a posteriori* probability of S_i at time t.

$\mathbf{Z}(t)$ the vector with components $\log\{\pi_i(t)/\pi_m(t)\}$, $i = 1 \ldots m-1$.

R_i, $i = 1 \ldots m$ alternative responses in m-choice theory.

λ_i probability of error conditional on R_i.

$F(t \,|\, R_i S_j)$ distribution function of reaction time conditional on R_i and S_j.

$P(n \,|\, R_i S_j)$ probability of a decision in the interval $\{(n-1)\,\delta t,\, n\,\delta t\}$ conditional on R_i and S_j.

μ_i, $i = 1 \ldots m$ expectation of X conditional on S_i.

z_i $= \log(\pi_i/\pi_m)$.

144

B.2. Fundamental theorems.

Approximation by means of a sequential probability ratio test. It is convenient in the development of the two-choice theory in Appendix A to follow the method of Wald (1947), which treats of a discrete series of random variables, $x_1, x_2, \ldots, x_n$. But if the sequential probability ratio test is used directly as the basis for a reaction time model two problems are met: firstly, how long does it take to make each "observation" and what is the experimental significance of this time? And, secondly, except in special circumstances the sequential probability ratio test terminates *after* the random walk has crossed the boundary, so that the characteristic functions derived from Wald's Identity are only approximate. These two problems may be evaded, however, by taking a continuous diffusion process with absorbing boundaries as the basis of the reaction time model. Then, in order to justify the use of Wald's method, it is necessary to show that the diffusion process may be approximated arbitrarily closely by a suitably constructed sequential probability ratio test.

Axiom 1 postulates the existence of a stream of information; Axiom 2 places certain constraints on the probability distribution of the information. Theorem B.1 and its corollaries show that the constraints of Axiom 2 are the necessary and sufficient conditions that the construction above is possible. $I(S_i: \underset{j \neq i}{\cup} S_j; t)$ has already been introduced as the total information available to the subject at time t in favour of S_i against all the other signals. Here this expression will be abbreviated to $I(S_i; t)$.

THEOREM B.1. *Let* $\mathbf{I}(t)$ *be the vector with components* $I(S_i; t)$, $i = 1 \ldots m$, *and let* $g(\mathbf{I} | S_i; t)$ *be the probability density function of* $\mathbf{I}(t)$ *when* S_i *is presented. Let* $\pi_i(t) = [1 + exp\{-I(S_i; t)\}]^{-1}$. *Then Axiom 3 and the three conditions specified in Axiom 2, namely:*

(i) *The* $g(\mathbf{I} | S_i; t)$ *are all distinct for sufficiently large* t;

(ii) $\sum_{i=1}^{m} \pi_i(t) = 1$, *for all* $t \geqslant 0$;

(iii) *For each fixed* $t \geqslant 0$ $p_i g(\mathbf{I} | S_i; t) [\pi_i(t)]^{-1}$ *is independent of* i, $i = 1 \ldots m$, *where* p_i *is the* a priori *probability of* S_i, $p_i > 0$;

(iv) *For all* $t_2 > t_1 \geqslant 0$, *the random variables* $\log \dfrac{\pi_i(t_2)\pi_j(t_1)}{\pi_j(t_2)\pi_i(t_1)}$ *and* $\log \dfrac{\pi_i(t_1)}{\pi_j(t_1)}$ *are independent;*

are the necessary and sufficient conditions that there exist for any $\delta t > 0$ *a series of independent random variables,* $X_1, X_2, \ldots$, *which may be vector random variables, and* m *sets of probability distribution functions* $F_s(x_s | S_i)$, $s = 1, 2, \ldots$, $i = 1 \ldots m$, *such that the products* $\prod_{s=1}^{r} F_s(x_s | S_i)$, $i = 1 \ldots m$, *are all distinct for sufficiently large* r *and*

$$I(S_i; r\,\delta t) = \log\{p_i \prod_{s=1}^{r} dF_s(x_s | S_i) \Big/ \sum_{j \neq i} p_j \prod_{s=1}^{r} dF_s(x_s | S_j)\} \tag{B.1}$$

for some $(x_1, \ldots, x_r)$.

Proof. (a) *Necessity.* Suppose that the construction is possible. Then $g(\mathbf{I} | S_i; r\,\delta t)$ is the distribution of the vector $\mathbf{I}$, with ith component $I(S_i; r\,\delta t)$ given by equation (B.1), when $(x_1, \ldots, x_r)$ has the distribution $\prod_{s=1}^{r} F_s(x_s | S_i)$. Hence for sufficiently large r the $g(\mathbf{I} | S_i; r\,\delta t)$ are all distinct.

From equation (B.1)

$$\pi_i(r\,\delta t) = p_i \prod_{s=1}^{r} dF_s(x_s|S_i) \Big/ \sum_{j=1}^{m} p_j \prod_{s=1}^{r} dF_s(x_s|S_j); \qquad (B.2)$$

hence $\sum_{j=1}^{m} \pi_i(r\,\delta t) = 1$.

Because of the relation between the distribution of $\mathbf{I}(r\,\delta t)$ and the distribution of $(x_1, \ldots, x_r)$ stated above,

$$g(\mathbf{I}|S_i; r\,\delta t)\,d\mathbf{I} = \int \prod_{s=1}^{r} dF_s(x_s|S_i),$$

where the integration takes place over the set $d\mathcal{X}$ containing all those sequences $(x_1, \ldots, x_r)$ which yield the vector $\mathbf{I}$ when inserted as the argument in equation (B.1). Therefore from equation (B.2)

$$p_i\, g(\mathbf{I}|S_i; r\,\delta t)\,[\pi_i(r\,\delta t)]^{-1} = \frac{d}{d\mathbf{I}} \int \sum_{j=1}^{m} p_j \prod_{s=1}^{r} dF_s(x_s|S_j),$$

where the integration takes place over the same set $d\mathcal{X}$, and the right hand side is independent of i.

From equation (B.2)

$$\log\{\pi_i(r_1\,\delta t)/\pi_j(r_1\,\delta t)\} = \log(p_i/p_j) + \sum_{s=1}^{r_1} \log\{dF_s(x_s|S_i)/dF_s(x_s|S_j)\}$$

and $\log\{\pi_i(r_2\,\delta t)\pi_j(r_1\,\delta t)/\pi_j(r_2\,\delta t)\pi_i(r_1\,\delta t)\} = \sum_{s=r_1+1}^{r_2} \log\{dF_s(x_s|S_i)/dF_s(x_s|S_j)\}$, for $r_2 > r_1$.

These variables are therefore independent.

When $t = 0$, $\mathbf{I}(0) = \{p_1, \ldots, p_m\}$ and conditions (ii) and (iii) are then trivially true. All four conditions have therefore been proved necessary for all positive integral r and all $\delta t > 0$, i.e. for all $t > 0$.

(b) *Sufficiency.* For any $\delta t > 0$ the distributions $g(\mathbf{I}|S_i; r\,\delta t)$ are given.

Let $\mathbf{Z}(r\,\delta t)$ be the vector with components $\log\{\pi_i(r\,\delta t)/\pi_m(r\,\delta t)\}$, $i = 1 \ldots m-1$, and consider the transformation $\mathbf{I}(r\,\delta t) \to \mathbf{Z}(r\,\delta t)$. In view of the definition of $\pi_i(t)$ on the one hand and condition (ii) on the other this transformation is one to one. Let the image of $g(\mathbf{I}|S_i; r\,\delta t)$ under this transformation be $h(\mathbf{Z}|S_i; r\,\delta t)$; then $h(\mathbf{Z}|S_i; r\,\delta t)$ is the probability density function of $\mathbf{Z}(r\,\delta t)$ when S_i is presented. Now let

$$\mathbf{X}_r = \mathbf{Z}(r\,\delta t) - \mathbf{Z}\{(r-1)\,\delta t\}.$$

Then it follows from condition (iv) that the $\mathbf{X}_r$ are mutually independent random variables and the distribution of $\{\mathbf{Z}(r\,\delta t) - \mathbf{Z}(0)|S_i\}$ can be expressed as the convolution of the distributions of $(\mathbf{X}_s|S_i)$, $s = 1 \ldots r$. Let $F_s(\mathbf{x}_s|S_i)$ be the probability distribution function of $(\mathbf{X}_s|S_i)$: it will be shown that the $F_s(\mathbf{x}_s|S_i)$ satisfy equation (B.1.).

Let $\mathbf{x}_1, \ldots, \mathbf{x}_r$ be a sequence of typical values of $\mathbf{X}_1, \ldots, \mathbf{X}_r$. The sequence $(\mathbf{x}_1, \ldots, \mathbf{x}_r)$ determines a unique value of $\mathbf{Z} = \sum_{s=1}^{r} \mathbf{x}_r$, and since the transformation $\mathbf{I} \longleftrightarrow \mathbf{Z}$ is one to one, $\mathbf{Z}$ is a sufficient statistic of the sample $(\mathbf{x}_1, \ldots, \mathbf{x}_r)$ for the discrimination between the S_i, $i = 1 \ldots m$, that is, for the information $\mathbf{I}$. Therefore the distribution of $(\mathbf{x}_1, \ldots, \mathbf{x}_r|\mathbf{Z})$ is independent of the signal presented and $\prod_{s=1}^{r} dF_s(\mathbf{x}_s|S_i)$ is of the form

$\psi_r(x_1, \ldots, x_r | \overset{r}{\underset{s=1}{\Sigma}} \mathbf{x}_r) h(\overset{r}{\underset{s=1}{\Sigma}} \mathbf{x}_r | S_i; r \, \delta t)$. Now $h(\mathbf{Z} | S_i; r \, \delta t) \, d\mathbf{Z} = g(\mathbf{I} | S_i; r \, \delta t) \, d\mathbf{I}$ and so from condition (iii) $p_i \, h(\mathbf{Z} | S_i; r \, \delta t) [\pi_i(r \, \delta t)]^{-1}$ is independent of i. So also must

$$p_i \prod_{s=1}^{r} dF_s(\mathbf{x}_s | S_i) [\pi_i(r \, \delta t)]^{-1}$$

be, and hence this function must have the form $\phi_r(\mathbf{x}_1, \ldots, \mathbf{x}_r)$ for some ϕ_r. It therefore follows from condition (ii) that

$$p_i \prod_{s=1}^{r} dF_s(\mathbf{x}_s | S_i) [\pi_i(r \, \delta t)]^{-1} = \sum_{j=1}^{m} p_j \prod_{s=1}^{r} dF_s(\mathbf{x}_s | S_j).$$

By substituting $[1 + \exp\{-I(S_i; r \, \delta t)\}]^{-1} = \pi_i(r \, \delta t)$ it can be seen that the functions $F_s(\mathbf{x}_s | S_i)$, $s = 1, 2, \ldots, i = 1 \ldots m$ satisfy equation (B.1). This completes the proof.

The $\mathbf{X}_r$ constructed in the course of the proof above are vector random variables with $(m-1)$ components; hence

COROLLARY B.1. *In order to represent a discrimination between m alternative signals a series of vector random variables is required with at most* $(m-1)$ *components.*

Independence from the experiment. Theorem B.1 shows that for a given set of signals and a given set of *a priori* probabilities it is possible to construct m distinct sets of distribution functions, $F_s(\mathbf{x}_s | S_i)$, $s = 1, 2, \ldots, i = 1 \ldots m$, satisfying equation (B.1). For this construction to be of any practical value it must be consistent between different sets of *a priori* probabilities and between different, but overlapping, sets of signals. Corollary B.2 and the following theorem show that such a consistent construction is possible.

COROLLARY B.2. *The* $F_s(\mathbf{x}_s | S_i)$, $s = 1, 2, \ldots, i = 1 \ldots m$, *constructed in the proof of Theorem B.1, are independent of* $\{p_i\}$.

Proof. Consider two sets of (non-zero) prior probabilities $\{p_i\}$ and $\{p_i'\}$. $\{p_i\}$ and $\{p_i'\}$ determine two different experiments with different distributions of information and posterior probabilities; these will be denoted by $\mathbf{I}(t)$ and $\pi(t)$ for one experiment and by $\mathbf{I}'(t)$ and $\pi'(t)$ for the other.

In the proof of the sufficiency of Theorem B.1 $\mathbf{Z}(r \, \delta t)$ is the vector with components $\log\{\pi_i(r \, \delta t) / \pi_m(r \, \delta t)\}$ and has probability density function $h(\mathbf{Z} | S_i; r \, \delta t)$, when S_i is presented. Let $\mathbf{Z}'(r \, \delta t)$ be the vector with components $\log\{\pi_i'(r \, \delta t) / \pi_m'(r \, \delta t)\}$ and let it have probability density function $h'(\mathbf{Z}' | S_i; r \, \delta t)$ when S_i is presented. In Axiom 2 (iii) put $t_2 = r \, \delta t$, $t_1 = 0$ and $j = m$; then $\log\{\pi_i(r \, \delta t) p_m / \pi_m(r \, \delta t) p_i\}$ is independent of $\log(p_i/p_m)$, that is, $\{\mathbf{Z}(r \, \delta t) - \mathbf{Z}(0)\}$ is independent of $\mathbf{Z}(0)$. The prior probabilities may be regarded as a vector variable that may take, *inter alia*, the values $\{p_i\}$ and $\{p_i'\}$. When the prior probabilities are $\{p_i'\}$, we write $\mathbf{Z}'(r \, \delta t)$ for $\mathbf{Z}(r \, \delta t)$ and $\mathbf{Z}'(0)$ for $\mathbf{Z}(0)$. Hence, because $\{\mathbf{Z}(r \, \delta t) - \mathbf{Z}(0)\}$ is independent of $\mathbf{Z}(0)$, $\{\mathbf{Z}(r \, \delta t) - \mathbf{Z}(0)\}$ and $\{\mathbf{Z}'(r \, \delta t) - \mathbf{Z}'(0)\}$ must be identically distributed;

i.e. if $\qquad\qquad \{\mathbf{Z}(r \, \delta t) - \mathbf{Z}(0)\} = \{\mathbf{Z}'(r \, \delta t) - \mathbf{Z}'(0)\},$

then $\qquad\qquad h(\mathbf{Z} | S_i; r \, \delta t) = h'(\mathbf{Z}' | S_i; r \, \delta t), \quad \text{for } i = 1 \ldots m.$

It is easy to see that the same $\mathbf{X}_r$ and $F_r(\mathbf{x}_r | S_i)$ are constructed in the proof of Theorem B.1 for both sets of prior probabilities. This proves the corollary.

THEOREM B.2. *The set $F_s(\mathbf{x}_s|S_i), s = 1, 2, \ldots,$ is independent of whether S_j, $1 \leqslant j \leqslant m, j \neq i,$ is a possible alternative to S_i.*

Let $p_1' \to 0$ in such a way that the $p_i', i = 2 \ldots m$ tend to non-zero limits.

Then
$$\lim_{p_1' \to 0} \pi_1'(r\,\delta t)/p_1' = \prod_{s=1}^{r} dF_s(\mathbf{x}_s|S_1)/\sum_{i=2}^{m} \lim_{p_1' \to 0} p_i' \prod_{s=1}^{r} dF_s(\mathbf{x}_s|S_i),$$

i.e.
$$\lim_{p_1' \to 0}\{\pi_1'(r\,\delta t)p_1/p_1'\pi_1(r\,\delta t)\} = \lim_{p_1' \to 0}\{\pi_i'(r\,\delta t)p_i/p_i'\pi_i(r\,\delta t)\}, \quad i = 2 \ldots m,$$

and hence
$$\lim_{p_1' \to 0}\{\mathbf{Z}'(r\,\delta t) - \mathbf{Z}'(0)\} = \{\mathbf{Z}(r\,\delta t) - \mathbf{Z}(0)\}.$$

If $p_1 = 0$, the first component of $\{\mathbf{Z}(r\,\delta t) - \mathbf{Z}(0)\}$ will be undefined, but the distribution of the other $(m-2)$ components will be identical to the marginal distribution of the last $(m-2)$ components of $\{\mathbf{Z}'(r\,\delta t) - \mathbf{Z}'(0)\}$. Hence the same $\mathbf{X}_r$ and $F_r(\mathbf{x}_s|S_i)$, $i = 2 \ldots m$, are constructed in the proof of Theorem B.1 for both $\{p_i\}$ and $\{p_i'\}$, where $p_1 = 0$; that is, $F_r(\mathbf{x}_s|S_i), i > 1$, is independent of whether p_1 is non-zero or not. The labelling of the signals is, of course, arbitrary, so that the theorem follows for any pair $(i, j), j \neq i$.

Probabilistic specification of the signals. Theorem B.2 has important implications. Let $\mathscr{S}$ be a finite set which contains, *inter alia,* all those signals S_i that might be employed in a given series of experiments. Then provided $p_1 \neq 0$ it is possible to choose the $F_s(\mathbf{x}_s|S_1)$ so that they do not depend on the particular S_i which are possible alternatives to S_1 in the experiment under consideration. But the $F_s(\mathbf{x}_s|S_1)$ will depend on $\mathscr{S}$, the *finite* universe of possible signals, because in the proof of sufficiency in Theorem B.1 these functions are constructed relative to a given set of signals. The information contained in the random variable, $\mathbf{X}_s$, defined in that proof, will serve only to discriminate between the members of $\mathscr{S}$. It will not necessarily help to distinguish a member of $\mathscr{S}$ from some other signal not included in $\mathscr{S}$. It is also essential that $\mathscr{S}$ be finite, because the proof of Theorem B.1 is valid only in this case.[1] The conclusion drawn from Theorem B.2 follows because in an experiment it makes no difference to include further members of $\mathscr{S}$ among the S_i provided they are assigned zero *a priori* probabilities.

The set of distributions $F_s(\mathbf{x}_s|S_i), s = 1, 2, \ldots,$ may therefore be regarded as a probabilistic specification of S_i relative to the set $\mathscr{S}$. Interest will naturally focus on those cases where the $F_s(\mathbf{x}_s|S_i)$ can be chosen independent of s,

i.e.
$$F_s(\mathbf{x}_s|S_i) \equiv F(\mathbf{x}_s|S_i).$$

$\mathbf{X}_1, \mathbf{X}_2, \ldots$ are then independent and identically distributed random variables, and the mathematical development of the theory can be pursued much further.

Time-stationary processes. Theorem B.3 gives a necessary and sufficient condition that the $F_s(\mathbf{x}_s|S_i)$ shall be independent of s. This condition has not been made a part

---

[1] With suitable modification the proof might be valid for a countable infinity of signals. It will certainly not hold for a non-countable infinity, because if $\sum_i p_i = 1$ and $p_i \geqslant 0$ for every i, at most a countable infinity of the p_i are non-zero. This is important because in some psychological experiments the subject is required to estimate the magnitude of a continuously variable stimulus or to choose from a continuous response set. In such experiments there is in effect a non-countable infinity of alternative signals and the particular development of the axioms given here will not apply.

of the axioms of §3.3 because it seems likely that it does not hold exactly in practice. The very existence of psychophysical thresholds when the subject can observe the stimulus for as long as he pleases suggests that there is some internal limit to the amount of information which a subject can process to reach any one decision. But a stationary series of distributions seems to provide an adequate account of the data from the two-choice experiments reported in Chapter 5. Appendix A and §B.3 assume throughout that $X_1, X_2, \ldots$ form a stationary time series.

THEOREM B.3. *For the $F_s(\mathbf{x}_s|S_i)$, $i = 1 \ldots m$, to be independent of s it is necessary and sufficient that the distributions of $\log\{\pi_i(t_2)\pi_j(t_1)/\pi_j(t_2)\pi_i(t_1)\}$ (all $j \neq i$) defined in condition (iii) of Axiom 2 shall be infinitely divisible[2] and depend on (t_2-t_1) only.*

(a) *Necessity.* It follows from the definition of $\pi_i(t)$ in Theorem (B.1) that for any $t_2 > t_1 \geqslant 0$

$$\log\{\pi_i(t_2)\pi_j(t_1)/\pi_j(t_2)\pi_i(t_1)\} = \log\{\prod_{s=1+t_1/\delta t}^{t_2/\delta t} dF_s(\mathbf{x}_s|S_i)/\prod_{s=1+t_1/\delta t}^{t_2/\delta t} dF_s(\mathbf{x}_s|S_j)\}.$$

If the $F_s(\mathbf{x}_s|S_i)$ are independent of s, this expression becomes

$$\sum_{s=1+t_1/\delta t}^{t_2/\delta t} \log\{dF(\mathbf{x}_s|S_i)/dF(\mathbf{x}_s|S_j)\},$$

and the condition is clearly necessary.

(b) *Sufficiency.* Renumber the signals so that S_i becomes S_m in the proof of sufficiency in Theorem B.1. Then $\{\mathbf{Z}(r_2\,\delta t)-\mathbf{Z}(r_1\,\delta t)\}$ is infinitely divisible and depends on (r_2-r_1) only. Hence the $\mathbf{X}_r$ defined in that proof are independent and identically distributed. This completes the proof of the theorem.

Now $\log\{\pi_i(t_2)\pi_j(t_1)/\pi_j(t_2)\pi_i(t_1)\} = I(S_i:S_j;t_2)-I(S_i:S_j;t_1)$, and the condition of Theorem B.3 is stated for a given i, paired with all $j \neq i$. But the following corollary obviously follows from the theorem:

COROLLARY B.3. *The information for discrimination between any pair of signals is infinitely divisible and its incremental distribution is stationary with respect to time.*

Recapitulation. To recapitulate the argument thus far: The constraints placed upon the information distributions by Axioms 2 and 3 are both necessary and sufficient that for any $\delta t > 0$ it should be possible to find a series of random variables, $X_1, X_2, \ldots$, and for each S_i, $i = 1 \ldots m$, a distinct set of distribution functions, $F_s(\mathbf{x}_s|S_i)$, $s = 1, 2, \ldots$, such that the information in favour of S_i at time $r\,\delta t$ should be related to the sequence $\mathbf{x}_1, \mathbf{x}_2, \mathbf{x}_3, \ldots$ by equation (B.1). The $F_s(\mathbf{x}_s|S_i)$ must be defined relative to a finite set of signals, $\mathcal{S}$, but they may be so chosen that they are independent of the *a priori* probabilities and of the other signals, belonging to $\mathcal{S}$, involved in the experiment. The $\mathbf{X}_r$ will generally be vector random variables and may have a separate component for each discriminable attribute of the signals in $\mathcal{S}$. But, for a discrimination between m signals only, the $\mathbf{X}_r$ need have at most $(m-1)$ components, and in Experiments 6 and 7, Chapter 5, for example, the $\mathbf{X}_r$ may be univariate, since the signals used there differed only in their length. Finally, Theorem B.3 states an additional condition that the $F_s(\mathbf{x}_s|S_i)$ shall be identical, $s = 1, 2 \ldots$.

Two-choice axioms. The conditions of Theorems B.1, 2 and 3 have been stated in a

---

[2] See Gnedenko and Kolmogorov (1954) for an account of the properties of infinitely divisible random variables.

form appropriate to multiple discriminations. When there are only two alternative signals, S_A and S_B, their statement can be simplified:

(i) $g(\mathbf{I}|S_A; t)$ and $g(\mathbf{I}|S_B; t)$ are distinct for sufficiently large t.

(ii) $I(S_B: S_A; t) = -I(S_A: S_B; t)$.

(iii) $g(\mathbf{I}|S_A; t) \exp\{I(S_B; t) - I(S_B; 0)\} = g(\mathbf{I}|S_B; t)$.

(iv) $\{I(S_B; t_2) - I(S_B; t_1)\}$ is independent of $I(S_B; t_1)$ for $t_2 > t_1$.

(v) $\{I(S_B; t_2) - I(S_B; t_1)\}$ is infinitely divisible and its distribution is a function of $(t_2 - t_1)$ only.

Canonical Representation. While it is certain that distribution functions $F(x|S_i)$, $i = 1 \ldots m$, exist under these conditions, their form is not unique. Any change of variable yields another set of distribution functions which also satisfies equation (B.1). However, there is one form of these distribution functions which remains the same, except for a single parameter, for all values of δt.

DEFINITION. *Let $F^{(n)}(x|S_i)$ be the distribution function of the n-th decomposition of the infinitely divisible random variable with distribution function $F(x|S_i)$, i.e. $\int e^{itx} dF^{(n)}(x|S_i) = [\int e^{itx} dF(x|S_i)]^{1/n}$. Then the decomposition of the $F(x|S_i)$, $i = 1 \ldots m$, is said to* generate the decomposition of $I(S_i: S_j; t)$ *if for every n*

$$I(S_i: S_j; t + \delta t/n) - I(S_i: S_j; t) = \log\{dF^{(n)}(x|S_i)/dF^{(n)}(x|S_j)\}.$$

THEOREM B.4. *The distributions $F(\mathbf{x}|S_i)$, $i = 1 \ldots m$, have a representation in which each distribution is infinitely divisible, and the decomposition of the $F(\mathbf{x}|S_i)$ generates the decomposition of the $I(S_i: S_j; t)$ for every $i \neq j$. Further this representation is unique up to a linear transformation of the variable.*

Proof. In the proof of Theorem B.3 $\{\mathbf{Z}(r_2 \delta t) - \mathbf{Z}(r_1 \delta t)\}$, $r_2 > r_1$, is infinitely divisible. It is the sum of $(r_2 - r_1)$ independent and identically distributed random variables, $\mathbf{X}$, which must themselves be infinitely divisible.[3] Now the ith component of $\mathbf{Z}(r \delta t)$ is

$$\log\{\pi_i(r \delta t)/\pi_m(r \delta t)\} = I(S_i: S_m; r \delta t)$$

and so for every i, j, $I(S_i: S_j; r \delta t) = I(S_i: S_m; r \delta t) - I(S_j: S_m; r \delta t)$. Hence the decomposition of $\mathbf{X}$ generates the decomposition of $I(S_i: S_j; t)$ for every $i \neq j$, and the $F(\mathbf{x}|S_i)$ can certainly be represented in the required way.

To show that this representation is unique up to a linear transformation of the variable, it is sufficient to consider a discrimination between any two signals, S_A and S_B. The following lemma will be needed:

LEMMA B.1. *Let the random variable X be such that $F(x|S_A)$ and $F(x|S_B)$ are both infinitely divisible distributions, whose decomposition generates the decomposition of $I(S_B: S_A; t)$. Let $x_1, x_2, \ldots$ be a typical sequence of values of X. Then $\sum_{s=1}^{r} x_s$ is a sufficient statistic for $I(S_B: S_A; r \delta t)$.*

Proof. Let $\delta I_r = I(S_B; r \delta t) - I(S_B; (r-1) \delta t)$. Then the lemma may alternatively be stated: $\delta I \equiv a + bx$, where a and b are constants. Suppose instead that $\delta I \equiv \psi(x)$ for some function ψ. Decompose x into two independent and identically distributed

---

[3] The random variable X is by definition infinitely divisible if and only if its characteristic function $\phi(t)$ is such that $[\phi(t)]^{1/n}$ is a characteristic function for every integral n. Obviously $[\phi(t)]^{1/n}$ is then itself the characteristic function of an infinitely divisible random variable.

parts, x' and x'', and let the decomposition generated on δI split that variable into $\delta I'$ and $\delta I''$.

Then $x'+x'' = x$, $\delta I'+\delta I'' = \delta I$ and there are functions ψ', ψ'' such that $\delta I \equiv \psi'(x')$, $\delta I'' \equiv \psi''(x'')$. Hence

$$\psi(x'+x'') \equiv \psi'(x')+\psi''(x''), \tag{B.3}$$

which implies that ψ, ψ' and ψ'' are linear.[4] This proves the lemma.

It is evident from this lemma that the random variable X must be linearly related to δI. It follows that the representation of the $F(x|S_i)$ is unique up to a linear transformation where there are two alternative signals; the theorem is therefore proved for m signals, $m \geqslant 2$.

The representation in which the $F(x|S_i)$, $i = 1 \ldots m$, are all infinitely divisible and their decomposition generates the decomposition of $I(S_i:S_j;t)$ for every (i,j) will be called the *canonical representation* of the decision process. Hitherto the $F(x|S_i)$ have been defined relative to a finite set, $\mathscr{S}$. If $\mathscr{S}^*$ is some other set of signals, which is added to $\mathscr{S}$, the functions defined relative to the combined set ($\mathscr{S} \cup \mathscr{S}^*$) will include those defined relative to the set $\mathscr{S}$. But the increase in the size of the set might make necessary some increase in the number of components of the vector random variable. In this case the original $F(x|S_i)$ will be marginal distribution functions of the corresponding new $F(x|S_i)$ for the combined set. Suppose $\mathscr{S}$ is a set of rectangles differing only in height and breadth; in the canonical representation $\mathbf{X}$ will have two components corresponding to these two discriminable attributes. Suppose now that $\mathscr{S}^*$ contains the same set of rectangles but in a different colour; then in the canonical representation for the combined set, $\mathbf{X}$ will have a third component corresponding to colour. But the marginal distributions of the first two components will be the canonically defined $F(x|S_i)$ for the set $\mathscr{S}$.

The condition of Theorem B.3 that the information for discrimination between any pair of signals is infinitely divisible restricts the range of possible decision processes that need be considered. Some particular examples have already been discussed in §A.4.

Response Criteria. Axiom 3, §3.3. states that response R_i is initiated as soon as

$$I(S_i;t) \geqslant \log\{(1-\lambda_i)/\lambda_i\} \quad (i = 1 \ldots m), \tag{B.4}$$

provided, of course, that no other response has previously been made. The axiom also places a condition on the λ_i, which ensures that the response shall be unique.

THEOREM B.5. *The necessary and sufficient condition that no two of the inequalities* (B.4) *may be simultaneously satisfied is that* $\lambda_i-\lambda_j < 1$ *for all* $i \neq j$.

Proof. If $I(S_i;t) \geqslant \log\{(1-\lambda_i)/\lambda_i\}$, then $\pi_i(t) \geqslant 1-\lambda_i$. If at the same time $I(S_j;t) \geqslant \log\{(1-\lambda_j)/\lambda_j\}$, $j \neq i$, then $1 \geqslant \pi_i(t)+\pi_j(t) \geqslant 2-\lambda_i-\lambda_j$; i.e. $\lambda_j+\lambda_j \geqslant 1$. Conversely, if $\lambda_i+\lambda_j < 1$, $\pi_i(t) \geqslant 1-\lambda_j$ implies $\pi_j(t) < 1-\lambda_j$, and this completes the proof.

---

[4] $\psi(x'+x''+\delta x) \equiv \psi'(x'+\delta x)+\psi''(x'') \equiv \psi'(x')+\psi''(x''+\delta x)$.
Hence $\psi'(x'+\delta x)-\psi'(x') \equiv \psi''(x''+\delta x)-\psi''(x'') \equiv f(\delta x)$, and within any neighbourhood of x, x' or x'', ψ, ψ' and ψ'' each have an infinity of values lying on a straight line. To prove the result there must also be some mild restriction on the class of functions to which ψ, ψ' and ψ'' belong: certainly, if they are continuous, then they must also be linear.

B.2.1. The relation between error- and correct-reaction times.

Stone (1960, Appendix 1) has shown that, for a decision between two alternatives made according to the criterion of Axiom 4, the distribution of decision latency for a given response is independent of the signal, that is, it is the same whether the response is right or wrong. This result is important because it affords a sensitive distribution-free test of the theory (see §6.4). Stone's proof is valid only for two-choice decisions and it assumes that both responses are made according to the criterion of Axiom 4 and that successive increments of information have a stationary distribution. An alternative proof of this result will be given here, valid under wider conditions.

THEOREM B.6. *If response R_i in any m-choice sequential decision process is initiated as soon as $I(S_i; t) \geqslant \log\{(1-\lambda_i)/\lambda_i\}$ for some λ_i, $0 < \lambda_i < 1$, then the distribution of the decision latency when R_i is made is independent of whether the response is right or wrong; this result is true irrespective of how the other responses, R_j, $j \neq i$, are determined.*

Proof. Consider those realisations of the decision process that lead to response R_i. If the random walk is continuous across the boundary, then at the point of decision $I(S_i; t) = \log\{(1-\lambda_i)/\lambda_i\}$. There is a possibility that the random walk may jump across the boundary (cf. §A.4). But $I(S_i; t)$ is stochastically weakly continuous and under this condition it is shown in the proof of Theorem A.6 that $I(S_i; t)$ may be approximated arbitrarily closely by a strongly continuous random walk. Hence exact results may be obtained by putting $I(S_i; t) = \log\{(1-\lambda_i)/\lambda_i\}$ at the point of decision even though the random walk jumps across the boundary.

Let $f_i(t)$ be the unconditional probability density function of response latency when the response is R_i. Then, since $I(S_i; t) = \log[\pi_i(t)/\{1-\pi_i(t)\}]$,

$$P\{S_i . \text{response in the interval } (t, t+\delta t) \,|\, R_i\} = (1-\lambda_i)f_i(t)\,\delta t$$

and $$P\{S_j, j \neq i \,.\text{response in the interval } (t, t+\delta t) \,|\, R_i\} = \lambda_i f_i(r)\,\delta t.$$

Since λ_i is constant, the distribution of decision latency conditional on R_i is the same whether that response is right or wrong. Hence the theorem is proved.

*Comments on Theorem B.*6. Implicit in the proof of this theorem is the requirement that the starting point of the decision process be fixed. $I(S_i; t)$ is interpreted in terms of signal-response frequencies and in this interpretation $I(S_i; 0) = \log\{p_i/(1-p_i)\}$, where p_i is the objective probability of S_i being presented. If the decision process could start from any of several positions, corresponding to different sets of *a priori* probabilities, so that, as it were, several otherwise distinct experiments were confounded, Theorem B.6 would no longer be true. This is demonstrated by the results of §A.7.

The theorem has been proved here for a given response, R_i, independently of the other responses, and for any number of alternative signals. In these respects this proof is more general than that given by Stone. When there are only two alternative signals, the distribution of decision latency for the given response is independent of the signal presented, but this is not true for more than two alternatives (cf. §B.3).

It is obvious from the way in which Theorem B.6 has been proved here that this result is intimately connected with the use of a probability ratio decision rule in Axiom 4. There arises therefore the possibility of arguing from experimental data to the truth of Axioms 1, 2 and 3. The question may be put as follows: If it is found empirically that the distribution of reaction time for a given response is the same whether that response is right or wrong, what additional conditions must be satisfied for it to be possible to construct a sequential decision procedure with a probability ratio decision rule to fit the experimental data? The answer is: It is always possible to construct a decision procedure to fit the data from any one experiment, and provided certain compatability conditions are satisfied the decision procedure can be so constructed to fit any finite number of experiments simultaneously. I do not know what additional conditions would be sufficient for the information to be capable of representation in terms of an infinitely divisible random variable.

The converse to Theorem B.6. Suppose Theorem B.6 is true for the response R_i in a given experiment. Let $P(S_j R_i)$ be the probability of the signal-response combination $S_j R_i$ and let $F(t|S_j R_i)$ be the distribution function of reaction time conditional on this combination. Then the condition on the distributions of reaction time may be written

$$F(t|S_i R_i) \sum_{j \neq i} P(S_j R_i) = \sum_{j \neq i} P(S_j R_i)F(t|S_j R_i). \tag{B.5}$$

Partition the time scale into intervals of length δt, for some $\delta t \geqslant 0$.

Let

$$P(n|S_j R_i) = F(n \, \delta t|S_j R_i) - F\{(n-1) \, \delta t|S_j R_i\},$$

$$Q(n|S_j) = 1 - \sum_{i=1}^{m} P(R_i|S_j)F(n \, \delta t|S_j R_i),$$

and consider the sequence $\mathbf{x} = (x_1, x_2, \dots)$. When signal S_j is presented, put

$x_r = 0, r = 1 \dots n$ *with probability* $Q(n|S_j)$,
$x_r = 0, r = 1 \dots (n-1), x_n = i$ *with probability* $P(n|S_j R_i)P(R_i|S_j)$,
$x_r = 0, r = 1 \dots (n-1), x_n = $ *some* $k \neq i$ *with probability* $\sum_{k \neq i} P(n|S_j R_k)P(R_k|S_j)$.

If $x_n \neq 0$, then $x_{n+1}, x_{n+2}, \dots$ are arbitrary. A response is made as soon as $x_n \neq 0$ for some n. If $x_n = i$, then response R_i is initiated. This criterion for R_i is equivalent to a likelihood ratio criterion, for

$$\frac{P(S_i|x_n = i)}{\sum_{j \neq i} P(S_j|x_n = i)} = \frac{P(n|S_i R_i)P(R_i|S_i)p_i}{\sum_{j \neq i} P(n|S_j R_i)P(R_i|S_j)p_j} = \text{constant}$$

by equation (B.5).

Now let $I(S_i; r \, \delta t)$ be defined in terms of $(x_1, x_2, \dots, x_r)$ by equation (B.1). In the construction above the experimental data may be approximated arbitrarily closely by further subdivision of the intervals δt. In the limit R_i is initiated according to the rule of Axiom 4. Since $I(S_i; t)$ has only a single discontinuity as a function of t, it is stochastically weakly continuous, and it must satisfy conditions (i) to (iv) of Axiom 2, since those conditions are necessary for the construction above to be possible.

The variable, x_r, introduced above can take only $(m+1)$ different values, that is, its probability distribution is defined only over $(m+1)$ disjoint and mutually exhaustive sets. Any other variable, y_r, with a distribution giving appropriate probability measures over these $(m+1)$ sets, might be substituted for x_r. Now if the experiment were repeated with the same set of signals and *a priori* signal probabilities, but different probabilities of error, the construction defined above would lead to a variable x_r' with a probability distribution defined over some other $(m+1)$ disjoint and mutually exclusive sets. The original question may now be stated: Under what additional conditions may the same y_r be substituted for both x_r and x_r', and indeed for any finite number of such variables?

Consider s replications of an experiment with the same set of signals and *a priori* signal probabilities. Let $\lambda_i = 1 - P(S_i|R_i)$ and let the probabilities and distribution functions associated with the uth replication be distinguished by the superscript (u). Let $\mathbf{y}_r = \{x_r^{(1)}, x_r^{(2)} \ldots x_r^{(5)}\}$ and consider the sequence $\{\mathbf{y}_1, \mathbf{y}_2, \ldots \}$. If $x_n^{(u)} = i$, then $I(S_i; n\,\delta t) \geqslant \log\{(1-\lambda_i^{(u)})/\lambda_i^{(u)}\}$ and $I(S_j; n\,\delta t) \leqslant \log\{\lambda_j^{(u)}/(1-\lambda_j^{(u)})\}, j \neq i$, and $x_{n+1}^{(u)}, x_{n+2}^{(u)}, \ldots$ are arbitrary and may be assigned any suitable values. The question now is: Is it possible so to correlate the $x_r^{(u)}$, $u = 1 \ldots s$, that the $\mathbf{y}_r$ are self-consistent?

Two conditions will be sufficient for the $\mathbf{y}_r$ to be self-consistent: If $x_n^{(u)} = i$,

(i) $x_n^{(v)} = 0$ or i, $v = 1 \ldots s$.

(ii) $x_n^{(v)} = i$, for all v such that $\lambda_i^{(u)} \leqslant \lambda_i^{(v)}$.

It does not affect the issue of self-consistency that the sequence $\mathbf{y}_1, \ldots, \mathbf{y}_n$ may contain a member, $\mathbf{y}_r$, $r < n$ with a component $x_r^{(v)} = j \neq i$.

In the construction for a single experiment $x_n^{(u)} = i$ with probability $P^{(u)}(n\,|\,S_j\,R_i)P^{(u)}(R_i\,|\,S_j)$. It is possible to satisfy condition (i) therefore if

$$\sum_i \underset{u}{\text{Max}}\; P^{(u)}(n\,|\,R_i\,S_j)P^{(u)}(R_i\,|\,S_j) < 1 \quad \text{for all } n \text{ and } j. \tag{B.6}$$

If the $F^{(u)}(t\,|\,R_i\,S_j)$ are continuous functions of time, inequality (B.6) may certainly be met by taking δt small enough.

Condition (ii) implies that if the sequence $\{\mathbf{y}_1, \mathbf{y}_2, \ldots, \mathbf{y}_n\}$ leads to response R_i at time $n\,\delta t$ in replication u, and v is such that $\lambda_i^{(u)} \leqslant \lambda_i^{(v)}$, then the same sequence must lead either to R_i at time $n\,\delta t$ in replication v or to some R_j, where $\lambda_j^{(u)} < \lambda_j^{(v)}$ at some time $\gg (n-1)\,\delta t$. If $\lambda_i^{(u)} \neq \lambda_i^{(v)}$ for some i and $\mathcal{I}(u, v)$ is the set of i such that $\lambda_i^{(u)} \leqslant \lambda_i^{(v)}$, then the distribution function of reaction time for responses in the set $\mathcal{I}(u, v)$ in replication u must be a lower limit for the corresponding function in replication v. A sufficient condition for compatibility of the $\mathbf{y}_r$ is

$$\sum P^{(u)}(R_i\,|\,S_j)F^{(u)}(t\,|\,R_i\,S_j) < \sum P^{(v)}(R_i\,|\,S_j)F^{(v)}(t\,|\,R_i\,S_j), \tag{B.7}$$

where the summation runs over the set $\mathcal{I}(u, v)$, for every t, j, u and v, except when both sides of the inequality are zero or unity. The approximate meaning of inequality (B.7) is that if a certain set of responses are made more accurately in one experiment than in another, those particular responses must take longer to make.

The $\mathbf{y}_r$ defined above may be contracted by writing

$$y_r \equiv 0 \text{ if } x_r^{(u)} = 0, u = 1 \ldots s$$
$$\equiv \log\{(1-\lambda_i^{(v)})/\lambda_i^{(v)}\} \text{ otherwise,}$$

where $\lambda_i^{(v)}$ has the smallest value of those $\lambda_i^{(u)}$ for which $x_r^{(u)} = i$. This variable may be substituted for the x_r in any finite number of replications of the experiment.

So far only compatibility between different experiments involving the same set of signals and *a priori* signal probabilities has been considered. However Theorem B.2 implies that replications u and v for which $\{p_i^{(u)}(1-\lambda_i^{(v)})/p_i^{(v)}(1-\lambda_i^{(u)})\} = \text{constant}$ are in a certain sense equivalent. If in this case $F^{(u)}(t\,|\,R_i\,S_j) \equiv F^{(v)}(t\,|\,R_i\,S_j)$ for all t, i and j, then y_r defined above will be compatible between these two experiments.

The foregoing results may be summarized as follows:

If for every response in an experiment the distribution of reaction time is the same whether the response is right or wrong, it is possible to construct a sequential decision procedure with a probability ratio decision rule satisfying Axioms 1, 2, 3 and 4 to fit the experimental data.

If in s replications of an experiment with the same set of signals and *a priori* signal probabilities,

(i) the $F^{(u)}(t\,|\,R_i\,S_j)$ are continuous functions of time,

(ii) for every t, j, u and v

$$\Sigma\, P^{(u)}(R_i\,|\,S_j)F^{(u)}(t\,|\,R_i\,S_j) < \Sigma\, P^{(v)}(R_i\,|\,S_j)F^{(v)}(t\,|\,R_i\,S_j),$$

where the summation runs over the set $\mathscr{I}(u, v)$ of i such that $\lambda_i^{(u)} \leqslant \lambda_i^{(v)}$, then it is possible to find a sequential decision procedure to fit all s replications simultaneously.

If in any two experiments involving the same signals but different *a priori* signal probabilities for which $\{p_i^{(u)}(1-\lambda_i^{(v)})/p_i^{(v)}(1-\lambda_i^{(u)})\} = \text{constant}$,

$$F^{(u)}(t\,|\,R_i\,S_j) \equiv F^{(v)}(t\,|\,R_i\,S_j),$$

then the sequential decision procedure defined above is compatible with both experiments.

B.3. The normal multi-choice model.

Consider an experiment with m signals, S_i, $i = 1 \ldots m$, and suppose that the X_r are independent and normal (μ_i, σ^2), with a different mean, but common variance, conditional on each signal. Let π_i be the *a posteriori* probability of S_i. Then R_i is initiated as soon as

$$\pi_i = \frac{p_i \exp\{-\tfrac{1}{2}\sum\limits_{r=1}^{n} (x_r-\mu_i)^2/\sigma^2\}}{\sum\limits_{j=1}^{m} p_j \exp\{-\tfrac{1}{2}\sum\limits_{r=1}^{n} (x_r-\mu_j)^2/\sigma^2\}} \geqslant 1-\lambda_i \tag{B.8}$$

for some $i = 1 \ldots m$.

If S_i and S_j are any two signals,

$$\pi_i/\pi_j = (p_i/p_j)\exp\{\Sigma\, x_r(\mu_i-\mu_j)/\sigma^2 - \tfrac{1}{2}n(\mu_i^2-\mu_j^2)/\sigma^2\}. \tag{B.9}$$

Hence $\sum\limits_{r=1}^{n} x_r$ and n are joint sufficient statistics, and if S_i, S_j and S_k are any three signals, it is possible to eliminate either $\Sigma\, x_r$ or n as follows:

$$(\mu_k-\mu_j)\log(\pi_i/p_i)+(\mu_i-\mu_k)\log(\pi_j/p_j)+(\mu_j-\mu_i)\log(\pi_k/p_k)$$
$$= \tfrac{1}{2}n(\mu_k-\mu_j)(\mu_i-\mu_k)(\mu_j-\mu_i)/\sigma^2, \tag{B.10}$$

$$(\mu_k^2-\mu_j^2)\log(\pi_i/p_i)+(\mu_i^2-\mu_k^2)\log(\pi_j/p_j)+(\mu_j^2-\mu_i^2)\log(\pi_k/p_k)$$
$$= \Sigma\, x_r(\mu_k-\mu_j)(\mu_i-\mu_k)(\mu_j-\mu_i)/\sigma^2. \tag{B.11}$$

So the ratios between any three posterior probabilities uniquely determine n, $\Sigma\, x_r$ and the entire set of π_i.

The most general solution of equation (B.10) is given by $\pi_i = \alpha p_i \exp(-n\mu_i^2/2\sigma^2)\zeta^{\mu_i}$, where $\zeta \geqslant 0$ is a parameter and $\alpha = \alpha(\zeta)$ is defined by the implicit equation $\Sigma\, \pi_i = 1$. Similarly that of equation (B.11) is given by $\pi_i = \beta p_i \exp(\Sigma\, x_r\mu_i/\sigma^2)\zeta^{\mu_i^2}$, where $\zeta \geqslant 0$ is a parameter, as before, and $\beta = \beta(\zeta)$ is defined by $\Sigma\, \pi_i = 1$. Alternatively $\pi_i = p_i \exp(-n\mu_i^2/2\sigma^2)\zeta^{\mu_i}$ and $\pi_i = p_i \exp(\Sigma\, x_r\mu_i/\sigma^2)\zeta^{\mu_i^2}$ may be regarded as coordinates in projective $(m-1)$ space, and equations (B.10) and (B.11) then become families of curves. Figure 3.3 (p. 34) shows these families for $m = 3$.

If S_i, S_j, S_k and S_l are any four signals it is possible to eliminate both $\Sigma\ x_r$ and n as follows:

$$(\mu_k-\mu_j)(\mu_j-\mu_l)(\mu_l-\mu_k)\log(\pi_i/p_i)+(\mu_k-\mu_i)(\mu_i-\mu_l)(\mu_l-\mu_k)\log(\pi_j/p_j)+$$
$$+(\mu_j-\mu_i)(\mu_i-\mu_l)(\mu_l-\mu_j)\log(\pi_k/p_k)+(\mu_j-\mu_i)(\mu_k-\mu_i)(\mu_k-\mu_j)\log(\pi_l/p_j)=0. \tag{B.12}$$

Hence if $m\geqslant 4$ the point $(\pi_1,\pi_2,\ldots,\pi_m)$ is constrained to lie on a two-dimensional surface, and a two-dimensional representation of the decision process is possible irrespective of the value of m.

B.3.1. The multi-choice model as a random walk.

The transformation

$$z_i=\log(\pi_i/\pi_m),\quad i=1\ldots m-1, \tag{B.13}$$

expresses the set of posterior probabilities as a point in $(m-1)$-dimensional Cartesian space. Each observation, x_r, changes the position reached by the decision by an increment $\delta z_i=\{(\mu_m-\mu_i)/\sigma^2\}\{x_r-\tfrac{1}{2}(\mu_m+\mu_i)\}$, $i=1\ldots m-1$. This may be resolved into a fixed step in the direction $\{(\mu_i{}^2-\mu_m{}^2)/2\sigma^2\}$, $i=1\ldots m-1$, and a variable step in the direction $\{(\mu_m-\mu_i)/\sigma^2\}$, $i=\ldots m-1$. This is therefore a one-dimensional random walk in $(m-1)$ space.

The random walk takes place in the plane whose parametric equation is

$$z_i=\{\log(p_i/p_m)+\Sigma\ x_r(\mu_i-\mu_m)/\sigma^2+\tfrac{1}{2}n(\mu_m{}^2-\mu_i{}^2)/\sigma^2\}, \tag{B.14}$$

where n and $\Sigma\ x_r$ are regarded as parameters. This is the transform of (B.12). The transforms of (B.10) and (B.11) now have solutions

$$\{\log(p_i/p_m)+\tfrac{1}{2}n(\mu_m{}^2-\mu_i{}^2)/\sigma^2+(\mu_i-\mu_m)\log\zeta\}$$

and

$$\{\log(p_i/p_m)+\Sigma\ x_r(\mu_i-\mu_m)/\sigma^2+(\mu_i{}^2-\mu_m{}^2)\log\zeta\},$$

and are therefore both families of parallel lines in the plane (B.14).

The boundary surfaces, $\pi_i=1-\lambda_i$, $i=1\ldots m$ are now,

$$R_i:\quad \exp(z_i)=(1-\lambda_i)\{\sum_{j=1}^{m-1}\exp(z_j)+1\},\ i=1\ldots m-1;$$

$$R_m:\quad \lambda_m=(1-\lambda_m)\sum_{j=1}^{m-1}\exp(z_j).$$

Figure 3.4 (p. 35) shows the form of the boundary curves in the plane and the two families of parallel straight lines when $m=3$. The intersection of the boundary R_i and the plane of the random walk (B.14), may be written in the form

$$p_i\exp\{\sum_{r=1}^{n}x_r\mu_i/\sigma^2-\tfrac{1}{2}n\mu_i{}^2/\sigma^2\}=(1-\lambda_i)\sum_{j=1}^{m}p_j\exp\{\sum_{r=1}^{n}x_r\mu_j/\sigma^2-\tfrac{1}{2}n\mu_j{}^2/\sigma^2\}, \tag{B.15}$$

where n and $\Sigma\ x_r$ are parameters specifying position in the plane.

If μ_i is neither the largest nor the smallest of the μ_j, $j=1\ldots m$, there is a value n_i, such that the n-contours do not cut the boundary R_i for $n<n_i$. This implies that the criterion for R_i cannot be satisfied with less than n_i observations, and $n_i\,\delta t$ is a lower limit to the decision time conditional on R_i. At the minimum the transform of

(B.10) is a tangent to (B.15) and $dn/d(\Sigma\,x_r) = 0$. Hence n_i is the joint solution of (B.15) and

$$\sum_{j=1}^{m} (\mu_i-\mu_j)p_j \exp\{\sum_{r=1}^{n} x_r\mu_j/\sigma^2-\tfrac{1}{2}n\mu_j^2/\sigma^2\} = 0. \tag{B.16}$$

(B.16) has no real root in $\Sigma\,x_r$ if μ_i is the largest or the smallest of the $\mu_j, j = 1 \ldots m$. In that case there is no minimum n_i, and it is possible to obtain sufficient information to satisfy the criterion R_i in any time interval, δt.

If $m = 3$, equations (B.15) and (B.16) have an explicit solution

$$n_b = \frac{2\sigma^2}{(\mu_b-\mu_a)} \left\{ \frac{1}{\mu_c-\mu_a} \log \frac{(\mu_b-\mu_a)p_a}{(\mu_c-\mu_a)p_c} - \frac{1}{\mu_c-\mu_b} \log \frac{(\mu_b-\mu_a)p_b\lambda_b}{(\mu_c-\mu_a)p_c(1-\lambda_b)} \right\}, \tag{B.17}$$

where $\mu_a < \mu_b < \mu_c$. If $m > 3$, there is no explicit solution for n_i, but it is possible to adapt (B.17) to give a lower limit for n_i by putting $S_B \equiv S_i$, S_A and $S_C \equiv$ the two adjacent signals. It is possible for n_b to be negative: this is so if the starting point is at, say, the point X in Figure 3.4. From X it is impossible to reach R_C without crossing the R_B boundary first; hence $P(R_C|\ starting\ point\ at\ X) = 0$.

B.3.2. The solution of equation (B.6) for the decision criteria.

Equation (B.8) does not admit any explicit solution, but it is possible to obtain a parametric solution for three alternative signals. Putting $\pi_i = 1-\lambda_i$, $\pi_j = t$, $\pi_k = \lambda_i-t$, $0 < t < \lambda_i$ in equations (B.10) and (B.11) gives the $(n, \Sigma\,x_r)$ coordinates of a point on the R_i boundary. As t traverses the interval $(0, \lambda_i)$, the entire boundary is covered. It is not possible to obtain the solution for any specified values of n or $\Sigma\,x_r$ directly by this means, but it is possible to locate a sufficient number of points on the boundary to plot a diagram such as Figure 6.1 (p. 86) or to construct a two-way table from which any derived values may be obtained by interpolation.

If $m \geqslant 4$ there is one additional problem to solve. The set of posterior probabilities is entirely determined by the ratios between any three π_i. So if π_i is put equal to $1-\lambda_i$ and arbitrary values are assigned to π_j and π_k in equations (B.10) and (B.11), only the proportionate values of these variables are in fact specified and the true value of π_i may be other than $1-\lambda_i$. In practice it will be possible to set $\pi_i = 1-\lambda_i$, $\pi_j = t < \lambda_i$, and then adjust π_k in the range $0 \leqslant \pi_k \leqslant t$ so that the set of posterior probabilities determined by equation (B.12) sum to unity; this will require some method of numerical approximation. The ultimate values $(1-\lambda_i, t, \pi_k)$ when substituted in equations (B.10) and (B.11) will give the $(n, \Sigma\,x_r)$ coordinates of a point on the R_i boundary, as above.

Since n and $\Sigma\,x_r$ are joint sufficient statistics for the sequence of observations, it is always possible to represent the solution of equation (B.8) in two dimensions (cf. Figure 6.1). The course of the decision is represented by the movement of the point $(n, \Sigma\,x_r)$ and the starting point of the decision process is the origin. The decision criteria are correct only for the particular set of *a priori* probabilities for which they were calculated. If $m = 3$, however, it is always possible to use the one set of decision criteria for any set of *a priori* probabilities by introducing a new origin; the position of the new origin is given by equations (B.10) and (B.11). Such use is only occasionally possible if $m \geqslant 4$.

B.3.3. "Interior" and "exterior" signals.

If μ_i is the largest or the smallest of the μ_j, $j = 1 \ldots m$, S_i is called an "exterior" signal and R_i an "exterior" response. Otherwise S_i is an "interior" signal and R_i an "interior" response. Interior responses cannot be made until a certain minimum number, n_i, of observations have been made; exterior responses are subject to no such constraint. The further significance of this distinction may best be illustrated by a three-choice decision.

Let S_A, S_B and S_C be three signals such that $\mu_a < \mu_b < \mu_c$. Suppose, for simplicity, that $p_a = p_b = p_c = \frac{1}{3}$. If S_A is presented and the first observation has value x_1, then

$$p(x_1|S_A) = (2\pi\sigma^2)^{-1/2} \exp\{-\tfrac{1}{2}(x_1-\mu_a)^2/\sigma^2\};$$
$$p(x_1|S_B) = (2\pi\sigma^2)^{-1/2} \exp\{-\tfrac{1}{2}[(x_1-\mu_a)^2+2(x_1-\mu_a)(\mu_a-\mu_b)+(\mu_a-\mu_b)^2]/\sigma^2\};$$
$$p(x_1|S_C) = (2\pi\sigma^2)^{-1/2} \exp\{-\tfrac{1}{2}[(x_1-\mu_a)^2+2(x_1-\mu_a)(\mu_a-\mu_c)+(\mu_a-\mu_c)^2]/\sigma^2\}.$$

$$\text{(B.18)}$$

Provided $(\mu_b-\mu_a)$ is comparable to $(\mu_c-\mu_b)$, $p(x_1|S_A)$, $p(x_1|S_B)$ and $p(x_1|S_C)$ will be in increasing orders of smallness. A similar result follows when S_C is presented. But when S_B is presented, $p(x_1|S_A)$ is of comparable order to $p(x_1|S_C)$, and both of these are comparable to $p(x_1|S_B)$ when S_A is presented. It follows from equation (B.8) that after n observations $E\{\pi_a|S_A\}$ and $E\{\pi_c|S_C\}$ are greater than $E\{\pi_b|S_B\}$, so that S_B, the interior signal, yields less information per observation than S_A and S_C, the exterior signals.

If $\lambda_a = \lambda_b = \lambda_c$, then $t_B > t_A, t_C$, writing t_i for the mean reaction time to S_i. Conversely if $t_A = t_B = t_C$, $\lambda_b < \lambda_a, \lambda_c$. Although I have not yet been able to prove this, I conjecture that the optimality postulate (Axiom 5, p. 38) will establish a subject's performance somewhere between the extremes of equal accuracy and equal speed of response. R_A and R_C should therefore be both faster and more accurate than R_B (cf. Theorems A.4 and 5).

APPENDIX C

TWO METHODS OF ANALYSIS

C.1. The relation between error- and correct-reaction times.

Theorem B. 6 (p. 152) predicts that the distribution of reaction time for a given response will be the same, whether the response is correct or an error. Although in a complete experiment a substantial number of errors are made, in any one test series there are a large number of correct reactions and only a very few errors. The distributions of reaction time vary from series to series and from subject to subject, and some special method is needed for combining the information afforded by the errors.

Suppose in a given test series n reaction times have been recorded with a given response. Let $x_1, \ldots, x_{n-k}$ be the correct reaction times, $y_1, \ldots, y_k$ the errors. If one of $y_1, \ldots, y_k$ is selected at random, say y_1, and $x_1, \ldots, x_{n-k}, y_1, \ldots, y_k$, are ranked, then under the hypothesis above y_1 will take any of the ranks $1 \ldots n$, with equal probability. Let this rank be r_1. If next one of $y_2, \ldots, y_k$ is selected at random, say y_2, and $x_1, \ldots, x_{n-k}, y_2, \ldots, y_k$, are ranked, then y_2 will take any of the ranks $1, \ldots, (n-1)$ with equal probability. Let this rank be r_2, and determine $r_3, \ldots, r_k$ in a similar manner. The particular values of $r_1, \ldots, r_k$ will depend on the order in which $y_1, \ldots, y_k$, have been selected, but provided this order is randomized, the $r_1, \ldots, r_k$ will be mutually independent.

Let z be a continuous rectangular random variable over the range $0 \leqslant z < 1$. Then $u_j = (r_j - z)/(n - j + 1)$ is a continuous rectangular random variable over the range $0 < u_j \leqslant 1$ and the $u_j, j = 1 \ldots k$, are mutually independent. The u_j for a given response and condition are collated from every subject, and the observed distribution of the u's is compared with the theoretical continuous rectangular distribution by a Kolmogorov-Smirnov one-sample test (Siegel, 1956, pp. 47–52), which is sensitive to any sort of discrepancy. The Kolmogorov-Smirnov test statistics, together with the number of u-variates in the sample, are quoted in Tables 5.1.7, 5.2.7, etc. It is also possible to combine the u_j from different responses or different experimental conditions to obtain the statistics in the margins of those tables.

Where a significant test result is obtained it is possible to determine the nature of the discrepancy (differences in location, dispersion, etc.), by examining the observed distribution of the u's. Where there is a difference in location, errors are faster than correct responses if the test statistic is positive, slower if it is negative.

C.2. The analysis of sequential relations in two-choice experiments by multiple regression.

Let S_i be the signal at the ith trial in the series presented to the subject and let R_i and T_i be the corresponding response and reaction time.

Let $S_i, R_i = 0$ if the signal, response at the ith trial is $S_A, R_A,$

$\qquad = 1$ if the signal, response at the ith trial is $S_B, R_B.$

Let $\mathscr{E}_i = [S_i + R_i]$, where the square brackets indicate that the sum is taken modulo 2, so that $\mathscr{E}_i = 1$ if R_i is an error and $\mathscr{E}_i = 0$ otherwise. Also let $Q_{i,j} = [S_i + S_{i-j}]$. Then the equation used for analyzing the occurrence of errors, (8.1), can be written

$$\mathscr{E}_i = e + a_0(S_i - \tfrac{1}{2}) + \sum_{j=1}^{n_1} a_j(Q_{i,j} - \tfrac{1}{2}) +$$

$$+ \sum_{k=1}^{n_2} a_{0k}(S_i - \tfrac{1}{2})(Q_{i,k} - \tfrac{1}{2}) + \sum_{j=1}^{n_3-1} \sum_{k=j+1}^{n_3} a_{jk}(Q_{i,j} - \tfrac{1}{2})(Q_{i,k} - \tfrac{1}{2}) +$$

$$+ \sum_{j=1}^{n_3} b_j \mathscr{E}_{i-j}[Q_{i,j} + 1] + \sum_{j=1}^{n_4} c_j \mathscr{E}_{i-j} Q_{i,j} + \epsilon_i, \qquad (C.1)$$

where ϵ_i is an error term with zero expectation.

The problem here is to determine the influence of certain events on the occurrence of errors. The events are represented by Boolean variables, taking the values 0 and 1 only, and formally the problem reduces to a multiple regression analysis; the procedure for solving this problem is well known. But the interpretation of the solution requires a little care. Normally in the analysis of a continuous variable the right hand side of the regression equation (without the error term) may be regarded as a predictor for the random variable on the left. But here $\mathscr{E}_i$ is restricted to the values 0 and 1 while the right hand side of equation (C.1) (again without the error term) may take any value in the interval $(0, 1)$. It is therefore natural to regard the right hand side of equation (C.1) as a predictor for the probability that $\mathscr{E}_i = 1$.

For the interpretation of the regression coefficients to be unambiguous it is necessary that the events represented in the regression equation shall be mutually independent. The events represented in equation (C.1) are equivalent to the Boolean variables $S_i, \mathscr{E}_{i-1}, Q_{i,1}, \mathscr{E}_{i-2}, Q_{i,2}, \ldots$ and provided there are no singularities in the data (see below p. 161) these variables are certainly independent. The variables $S_i, Q_{i,1}, Q_{i,2}, \ldots$ do not indicate the occurrence or non-occurence of an event, but rather the occurrence of an event of type A or an event of type B. The factors "$-\tfrac{1}{2}$" are introduced into equation (C.1) to make it symmetric between these two alternatives. Under these conditions each coefficient in that equation represents the difference in the frequency of errors contingent on the event to which it is attached. Specific interpretations of the several coefficients have already been given on p. 96. These coefficients will necessarily lie in the interval $(-1, +1)$ except possibly where there are singularities in the data. The a_j and a_{jk} are ordinary regression coefficients. The b_j and c_j are related to the autocorrelation coefficients of the $\mathscr{E}_i$, with the effect of the signal sequence partialled out. More specifically, $[\{p^2 + (1-p)^2\} b_j + 2p(1-p)c_j]$ is the partial autocorrelation coefficient of lag j, while $[\{p^2 + (1-p)^2\} b_j - 2p(1-p)c_j]$ is its interaction with the variable $Q_{i,j}$.

The other equation used for analysing the responses in Experiments 1 and 2 only, (8.2), is

$$(R_i - \tfrac{1}{2}) = r + \sum_{j=0}^{n_5} d_j(S_{i-j} - \tfrac{1}{2}) + \sum_{j=0}^{n_6-1} \sum_{k=j+1}^{n_6} d_{jk}(S_{i-j} - \tfrac{1}{2})(S_{i-k} - \tfrac{1}{2}) +$$

$$+ \sum_{j=1}^{n_7} b_j \mathscr{E}_{i-j}[Q_{i,j} + 1](S_i - \tfrac{1}{2}) + \sum_{j=1}^{n_8} c_j \mathscr{E}_{i-j} Q_{i,j}(S_i - \tfrac{1}{2}) + \rho_i, \qquad (C.2)$$

where ρ_i is an error term with zero expectation. The comments appended to equation (C.1) apply equally here.

For analyzing the sequential relations influencing reaction time equation (8.3) was used:

$$T_i = t + \sum_{j=1}^{n_9} h_j T_{i-j} + \sum_{j=1}^{n_{10}} \{f_j([R_i + R_{i-j}] - \tfrac{1}{2})(T_{i-j} - \mu) + g_j(Q_{i,j} - \tfrac{1}{2})(T_{i-j} - \mu)\} +$$
$$+ s_0 \mathscr{E}_i + s_1(S_i - \tfrac{1}{2}) + s_2(R_i - \tfrac{1}{2}) +$$
$$+ \sum_{j=1}^{n_{11}} u_j(Q_{i,j} - \tfrac{1}{2}) + \sum_{j=1}^{n_{12}-1} \sum_{k=j+1}^{n_{12}} u_{jk}(Q_{i,j} - \tfrac{1}{2})(Q_{i,k} - \tfrac{1}{2}) +$$
$$+ \sum_{j=1}^{n_{13}} v_j \mathscr{E}_{i-j} Q_{i,j} + \sum_{j=1}^{n_{14}} w_j \mathscr{E}_{i-j}[Q_{i,j} + 1] + \tau_i, \qquad (C.3)$$

where μ is the unconditional expected reaction time and τ_i is an error term with zero expectation. In estimating the coefficients μ was set equal to the average reaction time in the series of data being analysed. The interpretation of the several coefficients has already been given on p. 98 and only a few further comments are necessary here.

t and the h_j are the constants of an autoregressive scheme; the h_j are equal to the partial autocorrelation coefficients multiplied by the variance of T_i. The f_j and g_j are interaction terms between the autoregressive scheme and the sequence of signals and responses. Since the proportion of errors in the data was small, it was necessary to estimate both f_j and g_j simultaneously to obtain an unambiguous estimate of either. The remaining coefficients in equation (C.3) represent the increments in reaction time contingent on the events to which they are attached.

The numbers $n_1, \ldots, n_{14}$ in equations (C.1–3) are parameters specifying the lengths of the equations. The analysis was, of course, done on a computer, and the computer programme was so written that these parameters could be specified independently. In practice certain restrictions on the parameters had to be observed, as follows:

$$n_1 \leqslant n_2, n_3 \text{ or } n_4$$
$$n_5 \leqslant n_6, n_7 \text{ or } n_8$$
$$n_9 \leqslant n_{10}$$
and
$$n_{11} \leqslant n_9, n_{10}, n_{12}, n_{13} \text{ or } n_{14}.$$

At the beginning of a series of data it is not possible to evaluate all the terms in equations (C.1–3). Consequently the variable $\mathscr{E}_i$ was analysed only for $i > n_1$, R_i for $i > n_5$ and T_i for $i > n_{11}$.

Another difficulty occurred if there were only a very few errors in the series of data to be analysed. It was then possible that the least squares equations might be singular. In practice the data were examined prior to the compilation of the least squares equations and, if necessary, certain coefficients in the regression equations were omitted. If there were no errors at all, all the coefficients of (C.1) and (C.2) were omitted except a_0 and d_0, which then equalled 1, and all the terms in (C.3) involving response variables were also omitted. It was always possible for some of the b_j, c_j, v_j and w_j terms to be zero for all values of i, and the parameters n_3, n_4, n_7, n_8, n_{13} and n_{14} were reduced as necessary. Further singularities were possible in equation (C.3): if there were errors of only one kind, s_2 was omitted; and the f_j terms were omitted if there was only one error or if there were two errors and s_2, v_1 and w_1 were all included. Further abbreviations were required in analysing the C-reaction data of Experiment 4, since there, when no response was made, no reaction time could be measured. In particular the f_j terms were omitted and the g_j terms subjected to the same restrictions as the f_j terms in analysing Experiments 1, 2, 3 and 5.

In the two-choice experiments, each subject yielded five series of data. Suppose the e, r and t coefficients in (C.1–3) are replaced as follows:

$$\mathcal{E}_i = e_1\delta_{1j} + e_2\delta_{2j} + e_3\delta_{3j} + e_4\delta_{4j} + e_5\delta_{5j} + a_0(S_i - \tfrac{1}{2}) + \ldots \tag{C.4}$$

$$(R_i - \tfrac{1}{2}) = r_1\delta_{1j} + r_2\delta_{2j} + r_3\delta_{3j} + r_4\delta_{4j} + r_5\delta_{5j} + d_0(S_i - \tfrac{1}{2}) + \ldots \tag{C.5}$$

$$T_i = t_1\delta_{1j} + t_2\delta_{2j} + t_3\delta_{3j} + t_4\delta_{4j} + t_5\delta_{5j} + h_1 T_{i-j} + \ldots, \tag{C.6}$$

where δ_{ij} is the Kronecker delta and j ($= 1 \ldots 5$) refers to the experimental conditions. If the several experimental conditions create no change in the sequential pattern, then provided the regression equation contains all the necessary terms, there will be no systematic difference among the values of e_j, r_j and t_j obtained from a regression of each subject's data on (C.4), (C.5) and (C.6). This null hypothesis was tested by a Friedman two-way analysis of variance by ranks (Siegel, 1956, pp. 166–172).

In such an analysis one value of each of the other coefficients is obtained from each subject, 24 or 25 values in all. If there is no effect corresponding to a given coefficient its median value should be approximately zero, and this forms the basis of a two-tailed binomial test of significance. Alternatively it is possible to obtain a 0·936 confidence interval for the median by picking out the 8th and 17th coefficients in rank order (or 18th coefficient if there are 25 subjects in the experiment; the confidence interval then covers the median with probability 0·956).

If it is found that the sequential pattern does change between experimental conditions, it is possible to determine in what way it changes by analysing each series of data seperately by regression on (C.1) or (C.2) and (C.3). There are then five values of each coefficient from each subject, corresponding to the five experimental conditions. The complete set of values for each coefficient may then be tested by a Friedman analysis of variance to determine whether that coefficient is affected by the experimental conditions. In this way it is possible to discover the nature of changes in the sequential pattern.

REFERENCES

ALLUISI, E. A., MULLER, P. F., and FITTS, P. M. (1957). An information analysis of verbal and motor responses in a forced-pace serial task. *J. exp. Psychol.*, **53**, 153–8.

ATKINSON, R. C., BOWER, G. H. and CROTHERS, E. J. (1965). *An introduction to Mathematical Learning Theory.* New York: Wiley.

AUDLEY, R. J. (1960). A stochastic model for individual choice behaviour. *Psychol. Rev.*, **67**, 1–15.

AUDLEY, R. J. and PIKE, A. R. (1965). Some alternative stochastic models of choice. *Brit. J. math. statist. Psychol.*, **18**, 207–25.

BECKER, G. M. (1958). Sequential decision making: Wald's model and estimates of parameters. *J. exp. Psychol.*, **55**, 628–36.

BERTELSON, P. (1961). Sequential redundancy and speed in a serial two-choice responding task. *Quart. J. exp. Psychol.*, **13**, 90–102.

BERTELSON, P. (1963). S–R relationships and reaction times to new versus repeated signals in a serial task. *J. exp. Psychol.*, **65**, 478–84.

BERTELSON, P. and JOFFE, R. (1962). L'influence du méprobamate et de l'émylcamate sur la performance humain dans une tâche sériale prolongée. *Psychopharmacologia,* **3**, 242–53.

BERTELSON, P. and JOFFE, R. (1963). Blockings in prolonged serial responding. *Ergonomics*, **6**, 109–116.

BILLS, A. G. (1931). Blocking: a new principle of mental fatigue. *Amer. J. Psychol.*, **43**, 11, 240–45.

BIRREN, J. E. and BOTWINICK, J. (1955). Speed of response as a function of perceptual difficulty and age. *J. Geront.*, **10**, 433–6.

BLANK, G. (1934). Brauchbarkeit optischer Reactionsmessungen. *Industr. Psychotech.*, **11**, 140–50.

BOTWINICK, J., BRINLEY, J. F. and ROBBIN, J. S. (1958). The interaction effects of perceptual difficulty and stimulus exposure time on age differences in speed and accuracy of response. *Gerontologia*, **2**, 1–10.

BOWER, G. H. (1959). Choice-point behavior. In BUSH, R. R. and ESTES, W. K. (eds.), *Studies in Mathematical Learning Theory.* Stanford: Stanford University Press.

BRAINARD, R. W., IRBY, T. S., FITTS, P. M. and ALLUISI, E. A. (1962). Some variables influencing the rate of gain of information. *J. exp. Psychol.*, **63**, 105–10.

BRICKER, P. D. (1955). Information measurement and reaction time: a review. In QUASTLER, H. (ed.), *Information Theory in Psychology.* Glencoe, Illinois: The Free Press.

BROADBENT, D. E. (1957). A mechanical model for human attention and immediate memory. *Psychol. Rev.*, **64**, 205–15.

BROADBENT, D. E. and GREGORY, M. (1965). On the interaction of S–R compatibility with other variables affecting reaction time. *Brit. J. Psychol.*, **56**, 61–7.

BUSH, R. R. and MOSTELLER, F. (1955). *Stochastic Models for Learning.* New York: Wiley.

CARTERETTE, E. C. (1966). Random walk models for reaction times in signal detection and recognition. *Proc. XVIII Intern. Congr. Psychol.*, **16**, 84–95. Also in LOMOV, B. (ed.), *Detection and Recognition of Signals.*

CARTERETTE, E. C., FRIEDMAN, M. P. and COSMIDES, R. (1965). Reaction-time distributions in the detection of weak signals in noise. *J. Acoust. Soc. Amer.*, **38**, 531–42.

CHOCHOLLE, R. (1940). Variation des temps de réaction auditifs en fonction de l'intensité à diverses fréquences. *L'Année Psychol.*, **41**, 5–124.

CHRISTIE, L. S. and LUCE, R. D. (1956). Decision structure and time relations in simple choice behavior. *Bull. math. Biophys.*, **18**, 89–111.

CRONBACH, L. J. (1955). On the non-rational application of information measures in psychology. In QUASTLER, H. (ed.), *Information Theory in Psychology.* Glencoe, Illinois: The Free Press.

CROSSMAN, E. R. F. W. (1953). Entropy and choice time: the effect of frequency unbalance on choice response. *Quart. J. exp. Psychol.*, 5, 41–51.

CROSSMAN, E. R. F. W. (1955). The measurement of discriminability. *Quart. J. exp. Psychol.*, 7, 176–95.

CROSSMAN, E. R. F. W. (1956). The information capacity of the human operator in symbolic and non-symbolic control processes. In *Information Theory and the Human Operator*. London: Min. Supply.

DEININGER, R. L. and FITTS, P.M. (1955). Stimulus-response compatibility, information theory and perceptual-motor performance. In QUASTLER, H. (ed.), *Information Theory in Psychology*. Glencoe, Illinois: The Free Press.

DONDERS, F. C. (1868). Die Schnelligkeit psychischer Processe. *Arch. Anat. Physiol.*, 657–81.

DRAZIN, D. H. (1961). Effects of foreperiod, foreperiod variability, and probability of stimulus occurrence on simple reaction time. *J. exp. Psychol.*, 62, 43–50.

EDWARDS, W. (1965). Optimal strategies for seeking information: models for statistics, choice reaction times and human information processing. *J. math. Psychol.*, 2, 312–29.

ESTES, W. K. (1960). A random walk model for choice behavior. In ARROW, K. J., KARLIN, S. and SUPPES, P. (eds.), *Mathematical Methods in the Social Sciences*, 1959. Stanford: Stanford University Press.

FALMAGNE, J. C. (1963). Le conflit rapidité-précision dans les T.R. de choix. Une approche théorique. *Bull. Cent. Étud. Rech. Psychtoech.*, 12, 161–86.

FALMAGNE, J. C. (1965). Stochastic models for choice reaction time with applications to experimental results. *J. math. Psychol.*, 2, 77–124.

FANO, R. M. (1949). *The Transmission of Information*. Technical Report No. 65, Research Laboratory of Electronics, M.I.T.

FANO, R. M. (1961). *Transmission of Information: A Statistical Theory of Communications*. New York: Wiley.

FELLER, W. (1957). *An Introduction to Probability Theory and its Applications*, Vol. 1. New York: Wiley.

FERNBERGER, S. W. (1920). Interdependence of judgments within the series for the method of constant stimuli. *J. exp. Psychol.*, 3, 126–50.

FISHER, R. A. (1934). *Statistical Methods for Research Workers*, 5th ed. Edinburgh: Oliver and Boyd.

FITTS, P. M. (1966). Cognitive aspects of information processing: III set for speed versus accuracy. *J. exp. Psychol.*, 71, 849–57.

FITTS, P. M., PETERSON, J. R. and WOLPE, G. (1963). Cognitive aspects of information processing: II adjustments to stimulus redundancy. *J. exp. Psychol.*, 65, 423–32.

FITTS, P. M. and SEEGER, C. M. (1953). S–R compatibility: spatial characteristics of stimulus and response codes. *J. exp. Psychol.*, 46, 199–210.

FOLEY, P. J. and HUMPHRIES, M. (1962). Blocking in serial simple reaction tasks. *Canad. J. Psychol.*, 16, 128–37.

FROEBERG, S. (1907). The relation between magnitude of the stimulus and the time of the reaction. *Arch. Psychol. N.Y. No.* 8.

GNEDENKO, B. V. and KOLMOGOROV, A. N. (1954). *Limit Distributions for Sums of Independent Random Variables* (translated from the 1949 Russian edition by K. L. CHUNG; with an appendix by J. L. DOOB.) Reading, Mass.: Addison-Wesley.

HARDY, G. H. (1955). *A Course of Pure Mathematics*, 10th ed. London: Cambridge University Press.

HENMON, V. A. C. (1906). The time of perception as a measure of differences in sensation. *Arch. Phil. Psychol. sci. Meth. No.* 8.

HICK, W. E. (1950). Information theory in psychology. In JACKSON, W. (ed.), *Proceedings of a Symposium on Information Theory*. London: Min. Supply.

HICK, W. E. (1952). On the rate of gain of information. *Quart. J. exp. Psychol.* 4, 11–26.

HILGENDORF, L. (1966). Information input and response time. *Ergonomics*, 9, 31–7.

HOLLINGWORTH, H. L. (1910). The central tendency of judgment. *J. Phil. Psychol. sci. Meth.*, 7, 461–9.

HYMAN, R. (1953). Stimulus information as a determinant of reaction time. *J. exp. Psychol.*, 45, 188–96.

JOHNSON, D. M. (1955). *The Psychology of Thought and Judgment*. New York: Harper.

KARLIN, L. (1959). Reaction time as a function of foreperiod duration and variability. *J. exp. Psychol.*, **58**, 185–91.

KENDALL, M. G. (1951). *Advanced Theory of Statistics, Vol. 2, 3rd ed.* London: Griffin.

KINTSCH, W. (1963). A response time model for choice behavior. *Psychometrika*, **28**, 27–32.

KIRCHNER, W. K. (1958). Age differences in short-term retention of rapidly changing information. *J. exp. Psychol.*, **55**, 352–8.

KLEMMER, E. T. and MULLER, P. F. (1953). *The Rate of Handling Information: Key Pressing Responses to Light Patterns.* HFORL Memo. Report No. 34, ARDC, Washington, D.C.

KULLBACK, S. (1959). *Information Theory and Statistics.* New York: Wiley.

LABERGE, D. L. (1962). A recruitment theory of simple behavior. *Psychometrika*, **27**, 375–96.

LAMING, D. R. J. (1962). A statistical test of a prediction from information theory in a card-sorting situation. *Quart. J. exp. Psychol.*, **14**, 38–48.

LAMING, D. R. J. (1963). *Human Choice-reaction Times.* Unpublished Ph.D. thesis. Cambridge.

LAMING, D. R. J. (1966). A new interpretation of the relation between choice-reaction time and the number of equiprobable alternatives. *Brit. J. math. statist. Psychol.*, **19**, 139–49.

LEONARD, J. A. (1959). Tactual choice reactions: I. *Quart. J. exp. Psychol.*, **11**, 76–83.

LEONARD, J. A. (1961). Choice-reaction time experiments and information theory. In CHERRY, E. C. (ed.), *Information Theory.* London: Butterworths.

LINDSAY, R. K. and LINDSAY, J. M. (1966). Reaction time and serial versus parallel information processing. *J. exp. Psychol.*, **71**, 294–303.

LUCE, R. D. (1959). *Individual Choice Behaviour.* New York: Wiley.

LUCE, R. D. (1960). Response latencies and probabilities. In ARROW, K. J., KARLIN, S. and SUPPES, P. (eds.), *Mathematical Methods in the Social Sciences*, 1959. Stanford: Stanford University Press.

McGILL, W. J. (1963). Stochastic latency mechanisms. In LUCE, R. D., BUSH R. R. and GALANTER, E. (eds.), *Handbook of Mathematical Psychology, Vol. 1.* New York: Wiley.

McGILL, W. J. and GIBBON, J. (1965). The general-gamma distribution and reaction times. *J. math. Psychol.*, **2**, 1–18.

MERKEL, J. (1885). Die zeitlichen Verhältnisse der Willensthätigkeit. *Phil. Stud.*, **2**, 73–127.

MOOD, A. F. and GRAYBILL, F. A. (1963). *Introduction to the Theory of Statistics.* New York: McGraw-Hill.

MOWBRAY, G. H. (1960). Choice reaction times for skilled responses. *Quart. J. exp. Psychol.*, **12**, 193–202.

MOWBRAY, G. H. (1964). Subjective expectancy and choice reaction times. *Quart. J. exp. Psychol.*, **16**, 216–23.

MOWBRAY, G. H. and RHOADES, M. V. (1959). On the reduction of choice-reaction times with practice. *Quart. J. exp. Psychol.*, **11**, 16–23.

PAGE, E. S. (1954). Continuous inspection schemes. *Biometrika*, **41**, 100–15.

PICKETT, R. M. (1967). Response latency in a pattern perception situation. *Acta Psychol.*, **27**, 160–9; also known as SANDERS, A. F. (ed.), *Attention and Performance.* Amsterdam: North-Holland.

POWERS, K. H. (1956). *A Unified Theory of Information.* Technical Report No. 311, Research Laboratory of Electronics, M.I.T.

PRESTON, M. G. (1936). Contrast effects and the psychometric functions. *Amer. J. Psychol.*, **48**, 625–31.

QUASTLER, H. and WULFF, V. J. (1955). *Human Performance in Information Transmission, Part Two: Sequential Tasks.* Report No. 62, Control Systems Laboratory, University of Illinois, Urbana, Illinois.

RAPOPORT, A. (1959). A study of disjunctive reaction times. *Behav. Sci.*, **4**, 299–315.

RESTLE, F. (1961). *Psychology of Judgment and Choice.* New York: Wiley.

ROBERTS, S. W. (1959). Control chart tests. *Technometrics*, 1, 239–50.

SANDERS, A. F. (1967).   Some aspects of reaction processes.   *Acta Psychol.*, **27**, 115–30; also known as SANDERS, A. F. (ed.), *Attention and Performance*. Amsterdam: North-Holland.

SANDERS, A. F. and TER LINDEN, W. (1967).   Decision making during paced arrival of probabilistic information.   *Acta Psychol.*, **27**, 170–7; also known as SANDERS, A. F. (ed.), *Attention and Performance*. Amsterdam: North-Holland.

SCHOUTEN, J. F. and BEKKER, J. A. M. (1967).   Reaction time and accuracy.   *Acta Psychol.*, **27**, 143–53; also known as SANDERS, A. F. (ed.), *Attention and Performance*. Amsterdam: North-Holland.

SENDERS, V. and SOWARDS, A. (1952).   Analysis of response sequences in the setting of a psychophysical experiment. *Amer. J. Psychol.*, **65**, 358–74.

SHALLICE, T. (1964).   The detection of change and the perceptual moment hypothesis. *Brit. J. statist. Psychol.*, **17**, 113–35.

SHALLICE, T. and VICKERS, D. (1964).   Theories and experiments on discrimination times. *Ergonomics*, **7**, 37–49.

SHANNON, C. E. (1949).   The Mathematical theory of communication.   In SHANNON, C. E. and WEAVER, W. *The Mathematical Theory of Communication*.   Urbana, Illinois: University of Illinois Press.

SIEGEL, S. (1956).   *Non-parametric Statistics for the Behavioral Sciences*.   New York: McGraw-Hill.

SNODGRASS, J. G., LUCE, R. D. and GALANTER, E. (1967).   Some experiments on simple and choice reaction time.   *J. exp. Psychol.*, **75**, 1–17.

STEVENS, S. S. (1957).   On the psychophysical law. *Psychol. Rev.*, **64**, 153–81.

STONE, M. (1960).   Models for choice-reaction time. *Psychometrika*, **25**, 251–60.

SWETS, J. A. and GREEN, D. M. (1961).   Sequential observations by human observers of signals in noise.   In CHERRY, E. C. (ed.), *Information Theory*. London: Butterworths.

SWETS, J. A., TANNER, W. P. and BIRDSALL, T. G. (1961).   Decision processes in perception. *Psychol. Rev.*, **68**, 301–40.

TANNER, W. P. and SWETS, J. A. (1954).   A decision making theory of visual detection. *Psychol. Rev.*, **61**, 401–9.

TAYLOR, D. H. (1965).   Latency models for reaction time distributions.   *Psychometrika*, **30**, 157–63.

THOMAS, E. A. C. (1967).   Reaction-time studies: the anticipation and interaction of responses. *Brit. J. math. stat. Psychol.*, **20**, 1–29.

WALD, A. (1947).   *Sequential Analysis*. New York: Wiley.

WALD, A. and WOLFOWITZ, J. (1948).   Optimum character of the sequential probability ratio test. *Ann. math. Statist.*, **19**, 326–39.

WEAVER, W. (1949).   Recent contributions to the mathematical theory of communication. In SHANNON, C. E. and WEAVER, W., *The Mathematical Theory of Communication*. Urbana, Illinois: University of Illinois Press.

WELCH, B. L. (1947).   The generalisation of "Student's" problem when several different population variances are involved. *Biometrika*, **34**, 28–35.

WELFORD, A. T. (1952).   The "psychological refractory period" and the timing of high speed performance—a review and a theory. *Brit. J. Psychol.*, **43**, 2–19.

WELFORD, A. T. (1959).   Evidence of a single-channel decision mechanism limiting performance in a serial reaction task. *Quart. J. exp. Psychol.*, **11**, 193–210.

WELFORD, A. T. (1960).   The measurement of sensory-motor performance: survey and reappraisal of twelve years' progress. *Ergonomics*, **3**, 189–230.

WIENER, N. (1948).   *Cybernetics*. New York: Wiley.

WILKS, S. S. (1962).   *Mathematical Statistics*. New York: Wiley.

WOLFENDALE, G. L. (1967).   Decision times in signal detection. *Acta Psychol.*, **27**, 154–9; also known as SANDERS, A. F. (ed.), *Attention and Performance*. Amsterdam: North-Holland.

WOODROW, H. (1930).   The reproduction of temporal intervals. *J. exp. Psychol.*, **13**, 473–99.

WOODWORTH, R. S. (1938).   *Experimental Psychology*. New York: Holt.

AUTHOR INDEX

The numbers in *italics* refer to the pages on which the references are listed

A

Alluisi, E. A., 8, 14, *163*
Atkinson, R. C., 18, *163*
Audley, R. J., 18, 23, 24, 26, 28, 29, *163*

B

Becker, G. M., 29, 40, *163*
Bekker, J. A. M., 44, *166*
Bertelson, P., 19, 20, 64, 106, 117, 119, *163*
Bills, A. G., 119, *163*
Birdsall, T. G., 22, 40, *166*
Birren, J. E., 11, 12, *163*
Blank, G., 1, *163*
Botwinick, J., 11, 12, *163*
Bower, G. H., 18, 23, *163*
Brainard, R. W., 14, *163*
Bricker, P. D., 4, 13, *163*
Brinley, J. F., 12, *163*
Broadbent, D. E., 20, 119, *163*
Bush, R. R., 24, *163*

C

Carterette, E. C., 28, 29, *163*
Chocolle, R., 24, *163*
Christie, L. S., 24, *163*
Cosmides, R., 29, *163*
Cronbach, L. J., 6, *163*
Crossman, E. R. F. W., 1, 2, 4, 10, 11, 12, 13, 14, 19, 22, 43, 48, 68, 71, *164*
Crothers, E. J., 18, *163*

D

Deininger, R. L., 15, *164*
Donders, F. C., 1, 42, 62, *164*
Drazin, D. H., 85, *164*

E

Edwards, W., 28, 38, *164*
Estes, W. K., 23, *164*

F

Falmagne, J. C., 18, 20, 21, 22, 91, 92, 111, *164*
Fano, R. M., 18, 39, *164*
Feller, W., 26, *164*
Fernberger, S. W., 116, *164*
Fisher, R. A., 50, 84, 92, *164*
Fitts, P. M., 8, 14, 15, 28, 43, 44, *163, 164*
Foley, P. J., 119, *164*
Friedman, M. P., 29, *163*
Froeberg, S., 112, *164*

G

Galanter, E., 24, 62, 81, *166*
Gibbon, J., 24, *165*
Gnedenko, B. V., 131, 149, *164*
Graybill, F. A., 32, *165*
Green, D. M., 29, 40, *166*
Gregory, M., 20, *163*

H

Hardy, G. H., 133, *164*
Henmon, V. A. C., 1, 12, *164*
Hick, W. E., 1, 3, 7, 9, 10, 13, 15, 19, 73, 74, 75, 81, *164*
Hilgendorf, L., 13, *164*
Hollingworth, H. L., 70, *164*
Humphries, M., 119, *164*
Hyman, R., 1, 4, 5, 10, 13, 16, 19, 20, 22, 41, 48, 90, 92, *164*

I

Irby, T. S., 15, *163*

J

Joffe, R., 117, 119, *163*
Johnson, D. M., 86, *164*

167

SUBJECT INDEX

A

A-reaction, see *Reaction time, simple*
After effects of errors, 113–115
  comparison with other work, 116
  interaction with experimental conditions, 115
Anticipations, 59, 61
Apparatus, 46
Asymmetric decision process, 42, 79, 90
  optimal parameter values, 135–137
  compared with symmetric process, 138
Attention, 117–119
Autocorrelation of reaction times, 117–119
  previous work, 119
  interaction with signals and responses, 119–121
Autocorrelation of responses, 116
Axioms, 36–39
  Luce's choice, 18, 90
  Falmagne's error, 21

B

Bayesian model, 28
Binary classification models, 7, 15
Binomial trials, discrete presentation of, 29
Blocking, 117, 119
Boundaries, 32
  adjustment of, 114, 115
  exponential, 35, 156
  jumps across, 38, 131–133

C

C-reaction, see *Reaction time, C-reaction*
Card-sorting, 42, 45, 49
Cartesian sequential test, 25, 27
Central tendency of judgment, 70, 86
Channel capacity, 2, 3, 10, 13, 16
  theorem, 5
Choice axiom, 18, 90
Choice-point behaviour, 18, 22–25
Coding, 5, 7, 9, 15
  time, 7
  uncertainty, 15

Communication Model, 2–16, 40
  identification of elements, 5
Communication Theory, 2, 15, 18, 19, 40, 128
  relation to random walk model, 39
Condition of symmetry, 28, 127
Confusion function, 11
Continuous responding tasks, 7
Costs and pay-offs, 28

D

Decision latency, 32
  minimum value, 36, 157
Decision parameters, 71
Decision process
  as choice of parameters, 38
  asymmetric, see *Asymmetric decision process*
  binomial representation, 127
  canonical representation, 150
  multi-choice, 87, 123, 155–158
  optimal, see *Optimal decision process*
  parallel, 25
  serial, 24
  symmetric, 41, 127, 141
  two-stage, 81, 85
Decision time, see *Reaction time, decision component*
Delayed responding tasks, 9
Decomposition of information, 130, 133, 150
Difference count, 27, 29
Diffusion process, 126, 145
Discriminability, 16, 43, 73, 80
Discrimination
  experiments, 10–13
  limit to, 85
  simultaneous versus successive, 12
  time, 11

E

Entropy, 3, 9
  of a measurement, 11, 12
  relation to reaction time, 10
  response, 18, 88
  signal, 3, 14, 15

169